"In an era where our understanding of the universe is expanding at an unprecedented pace, this book serves as an indispensable guide for anyone seeking to comprehend the philosophical implications of our cosmic pursuits. *The Philosophy of Outer Space* is a timely and thought-provoking contribution to the New Space Age. One of the strengths of this volume is its ability to appeal to both experts and newcomers to the subject. The essays are written with intellectual rigor, in a manner accessible to a broad audience. Whether you are an astrophysicist, a philosopher, or simply a curious reader, *The Philosophy of Outer Space* provides a rich and rewarding exploration into the intellectual landscape where space science and philosophy converge."

Julian Savulescu, *Chen Su Lan Centennial Professor in Medical Ethics and Director of the Centre for Biomedical Ethics, Yong Loo Lin School of Medicine, National University of Singapore*

"Outer space and its exploration raise deeply fascinating and fundamental philosophical questions about the meaning of human life, our place in the larger cosmos, whether we should try to spread to other planets, and much more. In this New Space Age, what used to be science fiction can quickly become a live possibility, and there is a pressing need for philosophical reflection about these and other questions. This excellent and absorbing book is an absolute must-read for anybody interested in this new philosophical frontier."

Sven Nyholm, *Professor of the Ethics of Artificial Intelligence, Ludwig Maximilian University of Munich*

"Anticipation research sometimes shows us that what is furthest away can bring us closest to ourselves. For humanity, living together on our planet Earth in interdependence with everything else, the perspective of outer space and our exploration of it can bring us close to ourselves, to the world around and within us and to the expansive possibilities of peace and freedom. This is a book of cultural renewal."

Johan Siebers, *Professor of Philosophy of Language and Communication, Middlesex University London, UK*

"Garasic and Di Paola have assembled an excellent group of experts who navigate with unparalleled clarity and depth the complex terrain where advancements of the space age intersect with the timeless inquiries of philosophy. From the ethical implications of space exploration to the existential questions raised by our place in the cosmos, this collection allows anyone interested in these topics to explore this complex intersection. The interdisciplinary approach of this volume ensures a comprehensive exploration of the scientific and technological dimensions, as well as the profound implications for our understanding of humanity."

THE PHILOSOPHY OF OUTER SPACE

This volume provides a rigorous philosophical investigation of the rationales, challenges, and promises of the coming Space Age.

Over the past decade, space exploration has made significant and accelerating progress, and its potential has attracted growing attention from science, states, businesses, innovators, as well as the media and society more generally. Yet philosophical theorizing concerning the premises, values, meanings, and impacts of space exploration is still in its infancy, and this potentially immense field of study is far from mainstream yet. This book advances outer space philosophy by integrating key scientific and societal debates sparked by recent developments in space research and activities with conceptual, existential, ethical, aesthetic, and political themes and concerns. It maps various regions of philosophical exploration, reflection, and speculation regarding humanity's present and future emanations into outer space, to promote a broad, rich, and nuanced societal debate regarding this transformative enterprise, which is as stimulating as it can be disorienting.

This book will be a fascinating read for academics, researchers, and students interested in philosophy, space studies, science and technology studies, future studies, and sustainability.

Mirko Daniel Garasic is Assistant Professor of Moral Philosophy at the Department of Education Science, Roma Tre University, Italy. He has been Visiting Professor in Neuroethics at IMT School for Advanced Studies, Lucca, and Research Scholar at the UNESCO Chair in Bioethics and Human Rights in Rome. He is the author of *Guantanamo and Other Cases of Enforced Medical Treatment: A Biopolitical Analysis* (2015). His articles have been published in *BMC Medical Ethics*; *Medicine, Health Care, and Philosophy*; *Topoi*; and the *Journal of Medical Ethics*.

Marcello Di Paola is Assistant Professor of History of Philosophy at the Department of Humanities, University of Palermo, Italy. He works in environmental philosophy, particularly climate change, the Anthropocene, and the philosophy of plants. Among his publications are *Ethics and Politics of the Built Environment: Gardens of the Anthropocene* (2017), and the co-edited *Handbook of the Philosophy of Climate Change* (2023), *Plant Ethics: Concepts and Applications* (2018), and *Canned Heat: Ethics and Politics of Global Climate Change* (2014).

ROUTLEDGE RESEARCH IN ANTICIPATION AND FUTURES

Series editors: Keri Facer and Johan Siebers

For more information about this series, please visit: www.routledge.com/Routledge-Research-in-Anticipation-and-Futures/book-series/RRAF

THE PHILOSOPHY OF OUTER SPACE

Explorations, Controversies, Speculations

Edited by Mirko Daniel Garasic and Marcello Di Paola

LONDON AND NEW YORK

Designed cover image: magann © Getty Images

First published 2024
by Routledge
4 Park Square, Milton Park, Abingdon, Oxon OX14 4RN

and by Routledge
605 Third Avenue, New York, NY 10158

Routledge is an imprint of the Taylor & Francis Group, an informa business

British Library Cataloguing-in-Publication Data
A catalogue record for this book is available from the British Library

ISBN: 978-1-032-44892-3 (hbk)
ISBN: 978-1-032-44889-3 (pbk)
ISBN: 978-1-003-37438-1 (ebk)

DOI: 10.4324/9781003374381

Typeset in Sabon
by Taylor & Francis Books

CONTENTS

CONTRIBUTORS

Marta Benenti is Marie Skłodowska-Curie Postdoctoral Fellow at the University of Murcia, where she carries out the project LEAP – Learning to Appreciate Aesthetic Values. She has published on the topics of expressiveness, emotions, the aesthetics of tourism, and on the persuasive power of fictional narratives about climate change.

Vincent Blok is Professor at Wageningen University (The Netherlands) and scientific director of the 4TU Centre for Ethics of Technology. His articles have been published in *Environmental Values; Synthese; Philosophy & Technology; JBSF; Science; Journal of Cleaner Production; Public Understanding of Science*; and *Journal of Responsible Innovation*.

Matteo Cerri is an MD and an Associate Professor of Physiology at the Department of Biomedical and Neuromotor Sciences at the University of Bologna. He is affiliated to the National Institute for Nuclear Physics (INFN), and an associate at the Italian Institute of Technology (IIT). He conducts research in the field of integrative physiology, hibernation, and neuroscience. He is Chair of the Topical Team "Hibernation" of the European Space Agency (ESA); member of the technical panel for Integrative Physiology of the Italian Space Agency (ASI); member of the International Countermeasure Working Group (ICMWG) for ASI; and a member of numerous international scientific societies. He is also a member of the national board of the Italian Society of Neuroethics (SINe) and engages in scientific outreach by writing for popular science magazines.

David Dunér is Professor of History of Science and Ideas, affiliated researcher in Cognitive Semiotics, and coordinator of the research group Space Humanities at Lund University. He is a member of the European Astrobiology Institute

(EAI), the European Exo/Astrobiology Network Association (EANA), the Panel on Social Sciences and Humanities, Committee on Space Research (COSPAR), and a board member of METI International.

Charles Foster is a writer, traveller, veterinarian, taxidermist, barrister, and a member of the Law Faculty at Oxford. At Oxford he is also a Fellow at Exeter College, Senior Research Associate at the Uehiro Centre for Practical Ethics, Research Associate at the Ethox Centre within the Nuffield Department of Public Health, Research Associate at the Health, Law and Emerging Technologies Centre, and an Associate at the Human Rights Hub. He is known for his books and articles on natural history, travel (particularly in Africa and the Middle East), theology, law, and medical ethics.

David Heyd is Chaim Perelman Professor of Philosophy at the Hebrew University of Jerusalem. He was born in Jerusalem and earned his PhD in philosophy at Oxford University. His main areas of research are ethics, political philosophy and bioethics. He has served on many public committees on biomedical issues.

Karim Jebari is a Researcher at the Institute for Futures Studies in Stockholm. His research interests are Metaphysics, Epistemology, Applied Ethics, Normative Ethics, Social and Political Philosophy, Philosophical Traditions, and Social Epistemology.

Alessandra Marino is a Research Fellow in International Development within the Open University's AstrobiologyOU Research Group. Her interest is in critical Development Studies and issues of justice, equality and ethics, with a focus on how postcolonial and decolonial studies can contribute to current debates on knowledge production within space science and to decolonising astrobiology research methods. Together with Derek Matravers, she directs the OU Space Ethics Group.

Derek Matravers is Professor of Philosophy at The Open University and a Fellow of Churchill College, Cambridge. He writes in aesthetics, ethics and the philosophy of mind. He is the Editor, with Paloma Atencia-Linares, of *The British Journal of Aesthetics*. Together with Alessandra Marino, he directs the Open University Space Ethics Group.

Mikko Puumala recently defended his doctoral dissertation on ordinary morality, moral demandingness, and climate change at the Department of Philosophy, Contemporary History and Political Science in University of Turku, Finland. His research interests include environmental ethics, philosophy of sustainability, space ethics, and philosophical methodology.

Juha Räikkä is Professor of Philosophy at the University of Turku, Finland, where he is also Vice Dean of the Faculty of Social Sciences. His research interests focus on ethics and political philosophy. He has published in journals such as *The Monist, Australasian Journal of Philosophy, The Journal of Political Philosophy, Synthese, Utilitas, Res Publica, Metaphilosophy, Theoria, Ratio, Philosophia, The Journal of Value Inquiry*, and *The Journal of Social Philosophy*.

Arden Rowell is Professor of Law at the University of Illinois. Her research interests revolve around environmental law, risk regulation, and human behaviour. Recently, her research has focused on bringing interdisciplinary insights into environmental law. Her past scholarly work has been published in law reviews and interdisciplinary journals, including *Science*, the *Harvard Environmental Law Review*, and the *University of Chicago Law Review*.

Oskari Sivula is a Doctoral Researcher at the University of Turku. His research interests are in space ethics, environmental philosophy, and intergenerational ethics. Recently he was a Visiting Scholar at the University of St Andrews Centre for Ethics, Philosophy and Public Affairs. He has published on topics such as space settlements, human enhancement for space flights and directed panspermia.

Evie Kendal is Senior Lecturer of Health Promotion at the Department of Health Sciences and Biostatistics at Swinburne University of Technology, where she also heads the Ethical, Legal and Social Implications of Emerging Technologies Research Group (ELSIET). Her work focuses on reproductive bio-technologies, health communication and media, and space ethics.

Émile P. Torres is a postdoctoral researcher at the Inamori International Center for Ethics and Excellence, at Case Western Reserve University. Their work focuses on existential threats to civilization and humanity. They have published on a wide range of topics, including machine superintelligence, emerging technologies, religious eschatology, and the history and ethics of human extinction. Their newest book is *Human Extinction: A History of the Science and Ethics of Annihilation* (Routledge 2024).

Natalie Treviño is a Postdoctoral Research Associate of the Open University's Space Ethics Group. She has published on space exploration, decoloniality and ethics. She holds various positions in space-related NGOs, and has had numerous speaking and consultation engagements, including with NASA and MIT.

1

OUTER SPACE AND HUMANITY

History, Concepts, and Themes of a New Philosophical Frontier

Marcello Di Paola and Mirko Daniel Garasic[1]

Contemplation and Execution

Aristotle might have been right, and Spinoza with him, and the mystics, and the Beatles in their early India days, that the good life is a life of contemplation. But outer space exploration is all about execution.

We contemplated the stars from up on our roofs and towers, and then we contemplated their movements and pictured them in the guise of equations in our books. By contemplating the stars, we established modern science on Earth centuries ago. Today we know that among these stars move satellites and orbitals of human engineering, placed there by governments and private companies, and we understand that all that is in our phones, in our hands, flows through those space artifacts. We also know that there should be a golf ball on the Moon, shot by a US astronaut from one spot to another because he understandably wanted to do on the Moon what he loved to do on Earth. The older among us may find that in some way poetic, or at least cute.

But the younger among us will want more than golf and cute. They will ask what happened next – why the Americans stopped going to the Moon, why the Russians never even managed to get there, why no human has ever stepped on Mars yet, though there has been talk of that for decades – and then Venus, and all the other planets' many moons, and all these infinitely many places spinning far above and beyond our satellites and orbitals. Out there, everywhere, is outer space – the space that none of Earth's roofs or towers is tall enough for us to see from, and no phone can ever photograph. So, the younger among us will ask, why are we all still hanging out down here?

Execution, dear friends. It's not easy to get anywhere out there. We are made of Earth and, as organisms, on Earth alone we fit. Anything beyond the earthly spheres is far and apart, and ferociously inhospitable and horrifyingly

DOI: 10.4324/9781003374381-1

indifferent to us. Nothing is easy out there. Any mistake is fatal and final and there is a whole, ineliminable universe of factors unknown. Contemplate all you want, but through your individual local mammal brain you will not even be able to fathom the distances between where you now stand and anything that's in what you now call "outer space". And you can learn and acknowledge and mathematize all the data through some app in your phone – this many lightyears from this or that place – but getting there, and then managing to do something useful and perhaps even meaningful up there, that's a whole other game. It's the execution game, and it is the hardest by far, particularly for a planetary civilization that still uses its energies in ways that are largely inefficient.

Nonetheless *sapiens* we are, and so we do try tottering beyond the sheltering skies of our planet, sometimes even successfully by some standards. But to any expert external observer, were there any of these out there, it would be clear that cosmically speaking we are but rookies. We have powers that can be employed to emanate humanity beyond Earth in various ways, but these powers are still largely unordered. Proof is that humanity is not emanating beyond Earth to explore outer space united as a species: we come in factions and parties if we come at all – though existing international legal agreements regarding outer space will promise you otherwise.[2] Another proof is that very different and only partially coherent rationales and justifications are given in support of our space ventures. So yes, of course, execution is key – but when we try to leave our planet, why and how are we executing what, exactly? Any engineering needs a point and a method; and although it might not really be about contemplation, even outer space exploration needs a philosophy.

After the Moon landings, things kind of cooled off. Or better, nothing very spectacular, or of comparable symbolic significance, has happened since. But in the past few years outer space exploration has made not only a comeback but also significant and accelerating progress, fueled by increasingly more capable technologies, larger investments, and renovated political interests. The promises of a New Space Age are attracting growing attention from science, states, businesses, innovators, as well as the media and society more generally. Space tourism, asteroid mining, exploration within and beyond our solar system, and the possibility of settling colonies on the Moon and Mars are now technically within human reach. To reach them, however – to execute what we contemplate – is a different thing, as different as actualized power is from potential and reality is from fancy. And yet already just the sight of such new horizons raises deep and often disorienting questions on the new forms that being human may take beyond Earth and, more generally – and now as philosophically as is humanly possible – on the very place of humanity within the cosmos.

With our emanations beyond Earth becoming more sustained and the option of pursuing multi-planetary futures becoming more concrete, the premises, promises, values, rationales, meanings, modalities, impacts, and implications of outer space exploration and even colonization – for specific humans, for humanity at large, for being human itself, for the future of Earth and other celestial bodies – call for thematic philosophical consideration with increasing urgency. In addition, many of the philosophical questions that the project of outer space exploration generates are also of great and immediate relevance on Earth, and/or for thinking about Earth. Yet, philosophical theorizing on these themes is still in its infancy, and this potentially immense field of study is far from mainstream yet.

This volume is a philosophical investigation of some challenges and promises of the New Space Age. It is partly reflective and partly speculative. It integrates some of the scientific and societal debates sparked by recent developments in space research with conceptual, existential, ethical, aesthetic, and political concerns regarding this project of expanding the outreach and history of humanity beyond Earth.

Our Place under the Stars

The cosmos is, most likely, all there is. Of it there are no known limits, reasons, or ultimate features. Perhaps the cosmos exists eternally, but it is thought to have begun to expand 13.7 billion years ago, with the explosive generation of space-time. In some languages, such as Russian, cosmos means 'space' in the sense of a container and separator of elements, for example bodies. In Greek, it means "order": non-random arrangement.

There are innumerable bodies in the cosmos. Each body is in turn an evolvable aggregate of some degree of order. The cosmos is thus a swarming of many a cosmos, related to each other by incessant reciprocal remodulation. Each body, once ordered, tends to persist, but its very evolvability makes it essentially unstable and prone to dissipation, and thus to returning to what can be thought of as a disorder that is both an initial generator and a terminal collector – called, again in Greek, "chaos".

While some bodies, such as human bodies – but also all architecture, all machines, all living things – emerge and then unravel into chaos quickly, other bodies have more powerful and persistent degrees of order. Among these bodies are stars – huge, like our Sun or bigger, radiating light and heat. And then planets – smaller bodies, which receive light and heat from the stars and revolve around them. Planets are space bodies that wander orbitally, like tracks marked by a wheel, around a dominating star that determines their wanderings by attraction and repulsion, as Sun does with Earth. In turn, planets orbitally dominate their surroundings, which often include one or more moons, called satellites. Then there are free hitters such as asteroids, meteorites, and comets. All these bodies escape dissipation over long periods of time: some for thousands, some for millions, some – like stars and planets – for billions of years.

Not only do cosmic bodies embody order – they are also hinged to networks of ordered relationships. It is estimated that there are at least two hundred billion galaxies – vast ensembles of stars, planets, satellites, asteroids, meteorites, gases and dust bound together by reciprocal gravitational action. The galaxy of which Earth is part, the Milky Way, has an estimated diameter of one hundred thousand light years, a thickness of between one thousand and twelve thousand light years, and hosts, it is believed, between two hundred and four hundred billion stars, each of which dominates planets, each of which dominates satellites.

Earth's star, Sun, dominates thirteen planets gathered in what is called the Solar System. These include five dwarf planets (Pluto, Ceres, Haumea, Make-make, Eris), four medium-sized ones, closer to Sun and made of rock and metals (Mercury, Venus, Earth, and Mars), and four "gas giants", further from Sun, of vast mass, made of a rocky core wrapped in thick layers of liquids and gases (Jupiter, Saturn, Uranus, and Neptune). Earth has one moon, Mars has two, Jupiter and Saturn have several each. It is estimated that there are a total of 173 moons orbiting the planets of our Solar System, not all of which are of the shape or size of Earth's moon – most often only a few kilometers in size, and of irregular shapes.

One can read order in the cosmos but certainly nothing in there has a name. This is not a "planet", and certainly it is not "Earth" – nor is that "Mars", "Venus", "Kepler-16b", or "HD 189733". Planets only have names because on at least one of them there are conscious beings who give names to the things they are conscious of. These beings for whom one thing, like a name, can mean another, like a body, have christened their planet "Earth" and call themselves *Homo sapiens*. Naming is an exercise without criterion that simply stages the ability to perform it – a form of power concretized precisely by arbitrary catalogues and the arbitrariness of catalo-guing methods. How the catalogue is configured thus reveals, primarily, the characteristics not of what is catalogued but of the circumstances, habits, assumptions, interests, aspirations, and limitations of the cataloguer.

In naming the planets, for example, *sapiens* shows a certain provincialism. It calls them by the names of archaic deities of naive anthropomorphic forms: Mars, Jupiter, Venus, and so on. And being *sapiens* an animal of soil, of *humus* (hence "human"), it calls "Earth" a planet (its own) whose surface is actually seven-tenths water; and then, by analogy, it calls other planets made of rock and metals "ter-restrial". *Sapiens*, by the way, inhabits only a fraction of Earth's material reality, only its crust and outermost mantle – the so-called lithosphere. It has no access to the innards of the planet – to the asthenosphere and down from there into the mantle and to the core. The incandescent magma that is the sap of Earth rejects *sapiens* permanently. The inhuman magma thickens inside Earth, coagulating mainly into iron as pressure and temperatures rise approaching the core. The fer-rous core then generates, it is said by self-excitation, a magnetic field around the planet, which protects it from cosmic radiation and solar winds.

That planetary, magnetic-protective self-excitation also helps to prevent the destruction or dispersion of water and thus allows the configuration and persis-tence, first in the oceans and then in the soils and air of Earth, of organic structures: living beings – a radical remodulation of matter – a remodulation whose origin is unclear. Everything seems to be self-exciting: not only Earth's core but also its sur-face matter, a matter that is initially lifeless, self-excites by organizing itself into molecules capable of self-reproducing, self-assembling, and self-catalyzing, forming cell membranes that then structure living organisms that evolve in sync with and in response to their environments. Like the Baron of Munchausen, who lifted himself and his horse out of the mud by pulling up his own hair, that which lives seems to raise itself out from the inorganic soup of matter that is believed to be inert and then, even more mysteriously, further self-modify, first articulating more-than-automatic forms of intelligence, then informed tendencies, then reactive mental states such as pleasure and pain, and then consciousness, the subjective sense of experience – the how-it-feels-like in experiencing, in being affected in this or that way by our own and other bodies and minds.

Even if relegated to a tiny speck of a planet that is a minuscule speck of the cosmos, *sapiens* have thus passed through at least three ultimately unexplained ontological filtrations: being something rather than nothing, being living matter, being conscious living matter. Statistics would have it that there must be innumerable occasions in the immeasurably vast, possibly infinite cosmos, when this existence–life–consciousness triad is realized. But with certainty, at present, we only know that it is realized on Earth, and only for certain bodies on Earth, and in a particularly remarkable way for human bodies, the bodies of *sapiens*. Humans who then, from Earth, give names to things in the cosmos. And in this as in many other ways, they provincially and misleadingly place themselves at its center.

The New Space Age

The Artemis program – a NASA initiative that aims at landing humans on the Moon again by 2024, in order to mine it but also to establish settlements that may function as both research centers and base camps to other celestial bodies including Mars – should be the first manned step on the way to what promises to be the greatest project that humanity will pursue in the 21st century and beyond: the configuration of extra-terrestrial human futures. But Artemis will not be the last, as the race to space is now an affair open to many – with the Moon alone currently being roamed and studied by Indian, South Korean, and Chinese programs.

Besides sending people to the Moon, NASA is studying the Sun with unmanned spacecraft. Indian and European exploration programs are scheduled to begin doing the same within years. Mercury is an object of research for a European-Japanese program that launched three spacecraft in 2018, scheduled to enter the planet's orbit in 2025. Venus's atmosphere has hosted a Japanese orbiter since 2015, which is scheduled to be joined by US, European, and Indian missions within years. Jupiter is being studied by NASA, and its icy moons Ganymedes, Callisto, and Europa should also be reached by European missions that were launched from Earth in 2022. NASA will launch an exploration of Saturn's moon Titan in 2027. Then there are the exoplanets being figured out by cosmic telescopes like Hubble and now James Webb. And, of course, Mars: besides the Moon, most of the action now and for the foreseeable future will be on and about Mars. There is powerfully trumpeted talk from many sides about sending human visitors to Mars within years.

Currently on missions to or around Mars are China with Tienwan-1 ("Celestial Questions" – 2021), the United States with Perseverance (2021) and Curiosity (2012), and the United Arab Emirates with Hope Mars Mission (2021 – an unprecedented case of space technology, design, and logistics entirely purchased from third parties). Japan is likely to join soon. Before the invasion of Ukraine in 2022, the European Space Agency (ESA) and the Russian space agency (Roscosmos) were engaged in a joint program called ExoMars, a portion of which is ongoing (namely the Gas of the Trace Gas Orbiter, a satellite that is able to read the Martian subsurface based on the intensity of its neutron emissions at the impact of hyper-energized particles known as "galactic cosmic rays" – and which has reported on possible large reserves of frozen water far from the poles, at latitudes relatively more favorable to potential human settlement). The other portion of the ExoMars program (the docking of the Rosalind Franklin rover and the Russian Kazachok surface platform) is currently suspended.

At the same time, Mars-oriented work is in full swing on Earth, with NASA's Mars Dune Alpha project to assemble a crew of four astronauts in the Texas desert in a 3D-printed 160–square meter station, to test the psychological, social, and operational dynamics that can emerge in a situation of confinement, high risk, continuous monitoring, pressing responsibilities, and forced coexistence such as the one in which the first visitors and later settlers of Mars will have to live. This is not the first and will not be the last of these tests, which are necessary to understand ourselves, and our powers and limits, in the face of inhuman environmental and social stresses.

In recent years, the race to Mars has also seen private companies, explicitly interested in pursuing a neocolonial project, establish themselves among its main protagonists. The most important initiative so far is SpaceX, which intends to utilize reusable spacecraft capable of sustaining long journeys (5–10 months) to Mars carrying up to 100 humans at a time. SpaceX is heavily involved in the material and electronic engineering of such vehicles. Its ultimate goal is the erection of a Martian metropolis capable of housing one million colonists, self-sufficient in terms of its bio-regenerative life supports (i.e. microbial, plant, and animal life forms capable of recycling and providing the air, water, and food that the colonists will need) and energized by Martian fuels. The company, owned by currently (as of early 2024) the richest *sapiens* on Earth, has no definite timetable for a human landing on Mars but has repeatedly hinted that a manned mission is a feasible goal within the next 20 years.

All Eyes on Mars

On 9, 10, and 18 February 2021, three probes from Earth reached Mars. In them were not humans but artificial intelligences, of human making and to varying degrees heirs by transfer of human creativity, but without consciousness. The first two probes entered Mars's orbit with the aim of studying the planet's morphology, meteorology, and climatology. One of those then released a rover that would descend onto Martian ground. The third probe instead deposited its rover directly onto the ground, in a crater called Jeziro – with the aim of testing its soils and air, cataloguing its material compositions, and searching for traces of life, past or present.

On the strength of unprecedented technologies, at the beginning of what the majority of *sapiens* call the third millennium, the exploration of Mars is undergoing a tremendous acceleration. The goal is avowedly to prepare not only robotic but also human explorations, with inhabited outposts first and more populous and articulated settlements later, and eventually to colonize the planet, configuring a multi-planetary human future, no longer Earthbound. According to more or less official communiqués from more or less powerful, affluent, coherent, and transparent terrestrial institutions and organizations, at least some flesh-and-blood humans, with their inadequate bodies, complex consciousnesses, and technical apparatuses, should reach Mars within the first half of this century. There would follow, theoretically, the configuration of a new extraterrestrial world and humanity; further exploration of further celestial bodies; and probably further settlements – perhaps beyond the Solar System, perhaps beyond the Milky Way.

Among *sapiens*, such things have been fantasized about for a while. Mars, in particular, has been a topic of human conversation for millennia.[3] Proof of this is the string of names that have been attached to it: *Ma'adim, Simud, Auqakuh, Kasei, Ares, Nergal, Huo Hsing*. Everywhere, Mars has always had a name. *Sapiens* has always followed it closely, partly because Mars is visible to the naked eye – quite bright, with a peculiar reddish hue. Mars is also an orbital neighbor: Earth is the third planet from the Sun, Mars the fourth. The two must have formed more or less simultaneously, some four and a half billion years ago, extracting themselves from the swirls of gases and dust that enveloped the newborn solar body. After a turbulent gestation phase, after being battered by asteroid blasts and comet showers for several hundred million years, Earth and Mars, like the entire Solar System, found some stability. When they cooled enough to allow the formation of solid soil, it is likely that both Earth and Mars had liquid water on their surfaces.

The two planets are in fact in the so-called Interstellar Habitable Zone, or Goldilocks zone, which is the region around a star where it is theoretically possible for a planet to maintain liquid water on its surface. This categorization criterion is, as always, entirely human: the possibility of there being liquid water is only relevant because liquid water is essential for all forms of life as humans know life on Earth. For there to be that kind of life, there must be liquid water. But of course, there could be countless other kinds of life in the cosmos, many of which may not need liquid water. In any case, Mars meets this interesting geo-bio-anthropocentric criterion of habitability. The possibility thus exists that there is, or, more likely, has been, life on Mars.

This interest in life on other planets, especially but not just Mars, is a cornerstone of human thinking about the cosmos. It has ancient roots, partly statistical and partly religious. Already the Greek philosopher Epicurus (341–270 BC) speculated that, given the exorbitant number of cosmic bodies, it was impossible for there to be no extraterrestrial life, similar or dissimilar to that on Earth, and it was also impossible to prove that conditions elsewhere could never be right for such life to develop in the future. Centuries later, close to the modern era but with one foot still in the Renaissance, and with a tuneful mixture of rationalism and esotericism, the heretical monk Giordano Bruno (AD 1548–1600) proclaimed himself in agreement with Epicurus in *De l'Infinito, Universo e Mondi* (AD 1584) – in his characteristically vivid language and following a particularly refined (no less than devilishly refined, according to some of Bruno's most powerful contemporary opponents) set of reflections on the mathematical-philosophical-religious notion of "infinity". A staunch defender of the Copernican heliocentric theory, Bruno claimed there were countless suns, and countless worlds revolving around those suns, and in these worlds were countless inhabitants, similar or dissimilar to earthlings. For these claims and many others, Catholic authorities set Bruno on fire.

Yet even in Christianity one could find a widespread argument, of Platonic derivation, for the existence of life on other planets. Surely, it met with powerful opposition from the upper echelons of Christian intellectualism because it challenged in various ways the idea that Earth and its human inhabitants were God's favorite creatures. Nevertheless, the argument's strength was widely recognized: At the root of the universe is the goodness of God, who transfers his own perfection to his whole creation ("without envy", says Plato in the *Timaeus* – though clearly speaking of a "God" very different from the Christian one). That other planets exist is clear, and that God created them is only obvious. If on these planets, unlike Earth, there were no intelligent inhabitants committed to worshiping God, then these planets would be less than perfect, indeed nonsensical. But divine creation must be perfect because divine goodness guarantees a transfer of perfection to it, and it must be sensible, because the divine intellect knows no senselessness. Therefore, there must be adoring worshipers on all planets. The argument has strengths indeed, but that did not save Bruno from being burned at the stake.

When astronomy also became astro-morphology – when, at the beginning of the 17th century, the use of telescopes made it possible to observe the surfaces of celestial bodies and not only their movements in the sky, Mars became a privileged object of study given its proximity to Earth, which allowed it to be framed telescopically in large dimensions (only Venus among the planets is closer to Earth, but of Venus – as of Mercury – often a slice only can be seen, while Mars is always fully illuminated). And so remarkable and crucial similarities between Mars and Earth were soon found, not least because they were being strongly sought.

As early as 1659, the Dutch mathematician Christiaan Huygens, whose technical mastery in the construction of telescopes and precision lenses was well known, was able to state that Mars, like Earth, rotates around its axis and therefore has a night and a day, and that its rotation cycle is about 24 hours, like that of Earth. Which was far from obvious: Venus takes 243 Earth days to rotate on its axis, while Jupiter takes about 10 hours.

In 1784, the astronomer William Herschel proved that the axis of rotation of Mars is oblique in relation to the plane of its orbit around the Sun, as is that of Earth, and about as oblique as is that of the Earth; therefore on Mars there must be seasons, and when it is winter in its northern hemisphere it must be summer in the south, and those bright spots seen at the poles, advancing and receding with the seasons, must be – as on Earth – ice caps. Herschel also proved that Mars has an atmosphere, which includes clouds that obscure parts of it with a dynamically changing rhythm. In short, Earth has a brother planet. All eyes on Mars.

Within a century Mars would be mapped with sophisticated competence – first by Reverend William Dawes, then by astronomer Richard Proctor, and finally by artist Nathaniel Green, who in 1877 published a series of lithographs of the Martian surface for the Royal Astronomical Society of London. A division into four continents was imagined, and each part of the planet was given a name. The more Mars became known, the more terrestrial it was imagined to be.

The discipline of spectroscopy (the study of spectra of electromagnetic and corpuscular radiation) gave a new impetus to astronomy. Inaugurated by Newton, developed by Herschel, and then perfected and applied on a systematic basis to the study of planetary surfaces by William Huggins from 1860 onwards, spectroscopic analysis allowed inferences about the atmosphere of stars and planets, and from there further inferences about their temperatures, pressures, densities, chemical compositions, motions, and masses. As for Mars, spectroscopy provided evidence of the presence of water in its atmosphere. As *sapiens* wanted to see it, this promised plants. The question then became whether that red color tinging the planet's surface was red rocks or red plants.

Huggins and French astronomer Jules Janssen argued vigorously that there was a lot of water in Mars's atmosphere, and probably also on its surface. Huggins himself and the French astronomer–discoverer Camille Flammarion went further and claimed that the red surface was vegetation. It was supposed to be plants without chlorophyll – but they were plants from another planet, so why not? These proposals, which fed on the wishes of their supporters, retained some credibility in the scientific community for almost a century. But over time, thanks to more powerful technologies, rigorous analytical sifting, and in-depth fact-finding missions such as NASA's Viking explorations in the mid-1970s, the idea that Mars could be not just Earth's brother but its very twin progressively evaporated.

There is, indeed, water in Mars's atmosphere, but much less than Huggins and Janssen claimed. If condensed, it would occupy a few cubic kilometers; if evenly distributed over the surface, it would form a film of some twenty microns (0.020 millimeters). The Martian atmosphere is, therefore, extremely dry. Moreover, that atmosphere, unlike Earth's, is incessantly dissipated through atomic ionization and interaction with solar winds, from which Mars has no magnetic field defense (which further diminishes its ability to retain water in the atmosphere and on the surface).

There must also have been plenty of surface water on Mars, for at least the first half billion years since the planet's formation, because the valleys that innerve it have unmistakably been carved out by watercourses. But then at least four-fifths of that surface water disappeared. There is certainly still some left at the poles, in the form of ice: if liquified, that could be enough to generate a global Martian ocean some thirty meters deep on average.[4] But the mystery remains as to where Mars's water went: dispersed into space, perhaps, or trapped underground. If the latter, and humans found a way to access that water, then colonizing Mars would become a far more plausible hypothesis.

By contrast, the idea that there is vegetation on Mars, however possibly different from that on Earth, is no longer considered at all plausible. Nor is any credibility now accorded to the hypothesis that there is life in the form of lichens or algae. Contrary to what has sometimes been believed, those darker patches that can be observed to appear at the contours of the Martian poles when they seasonally recede are not vegetation that, irrigated cyclically, flourishes rhythmically – as it happens in many terrestrial deserts. Rather, as in terrestrial deserts but with highly superior powers, sandstorms occur on Mars that make surface colors change. No plants, therefore, but shadows and dust. This, however, does not prove that there is or was no life on Mars. Whether there may be any in the future, and of what form, will probably also depend on *sapiens*.

The rovers Perseverance (from NASA, docked on Mars in February 2021) and Zhurong (from the China National Space Administration, docked the following May) are currently searching for Martian life on the soils of the Jeziro crater and the Utopia Planitia region, respectively. What they are looking for are not plants, nor Martians on legs, but traces of ancient microorganisms. Mars is the place in the cosmos where *sapiens* are most likely to find traces of extraterrestrial life because it is close enough to go check and it is relatively Earth-like. Only Venus is closer, but Venus's atmosphere is composed almost entirely of carbon dioxide, with a formidable greenhouse effect that brings its daytime temperatures to, it is estimated, over 450 degrees Celsius. This does not mean that unimaginable life forms cannot exist on Venus, but that *sapiens* will hardly ever be able to see them up close – nor from a distance, really, because Venus's hellish atmosphere is also extremely dense and swathed in clouds, which hide its surface from telescopic observation. If Venusian life-forms can ever be observed, it will perhaps be in the planet's atmosphere, probably its outermost layers – and these will be aerial life-forms, proliferating in suspension, like halos on mirrors.

For other reasons, Mercury is even more hidden from observation than Venus is, and in any case, it is so close to the Sun and rotates on its axis so slowly (a day on Mercury corresponds to about 175 Earth days) that it is toasted at over 400 degrees Celsius on one side, and frozen at −170 degrees Celsius on the other, without any atmospheric protection. If there are life forms on Mercury, they must be biologically schizophrenic, constitutively dual, dizzyingly bipolar. Between Jupiter and Saturn lurk at least four more plausible cradles of life as *sapiens* can imagine it, namely Jupiter's moons Europa and Callisto, and Saturn's moon Titan and Enceladus. As noted above, efforts are being made at studying these moons in ever greater detail. Nonetheless, it is still incomparably easier for *sapiens* to get to Mars.

Mars might harbor or have harbored life, which might have originated on Mars itself or have come there from somewhere else, somehow. Perhaps Martian life shares its ancestral lineage with that of Earth – or perhaps it has developed independently. Finding Martian life forms, no matter how "simple", no matter how "micro", no matter how fossilized and defeated by time, would be one of the most exciting developments in the history of science, one of the most significant in the history of humanity, and one of the most destabilizing in the history of the ideas that *sapiens* has constructed of the cosmos, and of the relationships between humans and cosmos, over millennia. It would also open moral questions of enormous depth, and religious questions of perhaps cataclysmic proportions, equal to those raised by the heretic Giordano Bruno almost five centuries ago. For this reason, NASA has since 2014 funded research projects at Princeton University's Center for Theological Enquiry aimed at exploring the religious implications of possible findings of extraterrestrial life, on Mars or elsewhere.

In addition to looking for traces of life to better understand its adventures and development both on Mars and on Earth, contemporary Martian explorations are, as noted, concerned with the climatological and geological characterization of the planet – including, where possible, the mapping of its resources. All this prepares for manned exploration, which in turn is a step towards settlement and colonization. For a permanent settlement of a human colony on Mars to be successful, several long, complex, and costly steps must be completed. These include: the creation and management of interplanetary supply chains; the creation and management of habitats and infrastructures on Mars; the "terraforming" of the planet, i.e. its remodeling at the level of basic ecological systems to make it more humanly congenial (e.g. the creation of a magnetic field, or the enhancement of its weak greenhouse effect); the transformation (both planned and reactive) of significant elements of the colonists' bio-psychic constitution (and thus the modulation of a new humanity, with new characteristics, powers, and limits); the creation of Martian institutions and the successful management of their relations with those on Earth; and of course the investment of monumental amounts of money, thousands of years of effort, and in all likelihood millions of human lives. At immense costs, a new world on an alien planet may then emerge.

Some Reasons for Human Emanation into Outer Space

Human space ventures, private and public, manned or unmanned, to Mars or elsewhere, can be and have been motivated in various ways. To gain a conspicuous picture, it might be useful to refer to an ancient and incisive taxonomy that the Greek historian Thucydides (ca. 460–404 BC) coined to describe the motivations for every war. The fact that war and outer space exploration, particularly colonization, share some important features – in particular, they both redefine borders and redraw jurisdictions and influences – makes Thucydides's taxonomy applicable at least as a helpful analytical tool. The taxonomy is triadic and inexorable: what moves humans to try and redefine borders and redraw jurisdictions and influences are fear, honor, and interest. As Thucydides himself noted, these three springs of human action are distinct, but they interact constitutively and often blur into one another.

To emanate beyond Earth and successfully lay jurisdiction or even settle on and colonize other celestial bodies would mean for *sapiens* to become a multi-planetary species. The fear to which this would respond is the very first and last of fears: that of physical annihilation and existential disaster – the extinction of the species or a permanent crippling of its potential. If concentrated all on a single planet, everything that matters, has ever mattered, or ever could matter to *sapiens* can be disintegrated by a comet barely five kilometers wide, crashing into Earth after travelling for millions of years in the swollen darkness of cosmic indifference. Or Earth could lose its congeniality at the hands of *sapiens* themselves – due to climate change, nuclear conflicts, resource shortages, pandemics, or dispassionate algorithmic procedures of artificial intelligences that may strip us of all relevance. Since, in principle, humanity can realize enormous potential value if it survives such risks, there are good reasons (according to some, even moral obligations) for becoming a multi-planetary species. Add to this that not only the value of humans and human things, but also that there be anything of value generally, could be erased by an eventual obliteration of *sapiens*. As far as is known, valuing is a cosmically restricted phenomenon, a mostly human phenomenon – and it could be argued that valuing itself is immensely valuable, to be defended at all costs.

There is also honor, then – Thucydides's second motivational spring – in defending the human from that which threatens to dissipate or disfigure it, and in pursuing what in the human is best: curiosity, creativity, solidarity, cooperation, resolute determination towards the pursuit of the Beautiful, the Good, and the True – all qualities that outer space exploration and even colonization enable and require in the highest degree. Understanding things, properly interpreting the inexhaustible physiognomy of the cosmos, its infinite modifications; pushing the horizons of the possible pushing; pursuing new virtues and never stagnating; demanding more, giving more – this is the best part of us. To colonize new planets would be the greatest of challenges, and the visionary spirit and discipline required for the attempt are in themselves exciting sources of inspiration. There is admiration and gratitude, among humans, towards those who inspire, and push, and never give up. And there is also recognition: the honors of history will redeem their arrogance, the patents will reward their ideas, and rights will sanction their order of arrival. Finally, there is pride in acting, in taking the scene, in being protagonists and not just spectators. We would take less pride in discovering the facts of Mars if some alien species were to precede us there and, however amicably and accurately, notified us of everything Martian by bulletin.

And then, still following Thucydides, the third great spring for human action: interest – material, concrete, quantifiable. Working for ourselves, getting stuff for ourselves. Mars, for example: there is water there, and it can be combined with atmospheric carbon dioxide to produce biological support fluids, fuels, oxidants, and plastics; there is oxygen, nitrogen, hydrogen; there is iron, titanium, nickel, aluminum, chlorine, sulfur, calcium, clay-like materials, and there is silicon dioxide, a basic constituent of glass and useful for building fibers and other physical and digital structures and infrastructures. We want this stuff. We can use it. It is legal to take it, or we will make it legal. It is nobody's stuff after all, or everybody's. Practically, it's up for grabs.

Space colonies would be, as every colony has always been on Earth, at once study centers, extractive sites, emporia, ideological powerhouses, and marshalling yards. The Moon and Mars will be refueling stations enabling further routes, perhaps to those satellites of Jupiter and Saturn and those asteroids overflowing with rare sands and diamonds – mines whose treasures, to be robotically extracted, would obliterate all earthly quotations; new markets and practically lawless lands, positioned beyond Earth's economic cycles. It is called the Space Economy, it is potentially limitless, and it is not just money, it's progress. Now that we have the technological and financial means to activate our fears, our cravings for honor and our intellectual and material interests in support of this incredibly innovative multi-planetary adventure, many would see it as a foolish and cowardly waste not to do so – not to pursue, with all our present and future powers, this new horizon that we have procured for ourselves.

Transforming Humanity

The basic alternative that any system that is committed to persistence, be it an organism or an organization, must incessantly negotiate when allocating its energies is whether to innovate or to consolidate – or rather: how much to innovate and how much to consolidate. This negotiation is inescapable because, on the one hand, consolidating also requires innovation and change, and while consolidating the capacities for innovation and change are also consolidated; and, on the other hand, innovating without consolidated foundations is as arduous and hazardous as growing is for a plant with fragile roots. Persistence, then, requires from systems a sort of conservative dynamism, or dynamic conservatism.

Should *sapiens* innovate by increasing its cosmic options, or should it rather focus on consolidating its terrestrial circumstances? This question arises at the delicate and uncertain juncture when humanity – in its historically most globalized, technologized, industrialized, climate-altering, militarized version – is at work to remake Earth, mostly undermining its congeniality for *sapiens* itself and an indefinite number of other species. And the question arises because, strangely, the same anthropogenic forces – capital and technology above all – that are undermining Earth's congeniality are now also proposing alternatives, other possible worlds for humanity: Planet(s) B. They propose transformative experiences at planetary and species scales.

Transformative experiences are distinctive in that they change the experiencer. Making a major scientific discovery, undergoing a religious conversion, having a child, losing a child, fighting a war, going blind, winning an Olympic gold medal, having a dangerous car accident, going to prison, falling in love, undergoing major surgery, and many other and diverse experiences can reshape not only their subject's views and preferences but also their self-conception and fundamental criteria for what matters. Outer space exploration and even colonization can plunge *sapiens* in a most stimulating, but also most disorienting, species-level transformative experience.

The hallmark of all transformative experiences is that one cannot know what the experience will be like and how one will be transformed by it unless one lives it. If one does not live the experience, one will never know what one has missed out on; but before living through the experience, it is impossible to know (if and) what one will gain from doing so – not only because of the uncertainty in which the experience may be enveloped, but also and above all because in experiencing it one will be transformed by it, and thus one's criteria of what counts as a gain and a loss will also be transformed.[5]

In the same way that those who have never had or lost a child "cannot understand" or even imagine what it is like to have or lose a child, so earthly humans are precluded from knowing or even imagining what it will be like to be humans beyond Earth. That experience will transform individual as well as collective points of view, value systems, needs, habits, aspirations, priorities, self-conceptions, and how we will experience being who we are. In short, outer space exploration, and possibly even colonization, will transform what it is like to be human in ways that are largely impossible to predict, evaluate, and even imagine beforehand.

But we know that the transformation will occur along multiple trajectories and take place both on and beyond Earth.[6] Sustained outer space exploration, and even more so colonization, will necessarily enable and require significant technological, social, and cultural changes that are likely to have profound impacts on human societies.[7] There will be investments in research, development, and human capital that could potentially lead to significant advancements in areas such as energy, medicine, and materials science, which could have far-reaching implications for humanity on and beyond Earth.[8] The challenges and opportunities presented by outer space environments may also lead to new ways of thinking about environmental resource management on Earth, while the potential for new discoveries and resources may lead to new economic, organizational, and institutional models. And becoming habitual space-roamers or even a multi-planetary species could also lead to new perspectives on ethics, morality, and the meaning of life. All this is a boon for philosophical reflection; this book hopes to contribute to it, and to a more informed societal debate about the brights and darks of this New Space Age. It does so by isolating for analysis some of its central dimensions and themes, as follows.

Overview of the Book

The volume opens with some foundational issues in outer space philosophy. The first of these concerns what is perhaps the hardest of philosophical questions about humanity's fascination with, and pursuit of, outer space exploration: what's the point of it?

David Heyd looks at this question by considering possible reasons why NASA launched into outer space two Voyager Golden Records in 1977, on the advice of a committee chaired by astronomer and space science communicator Carl Sagan. Voyager 1 and Voyager 2 include collections of earthly images and sounds, and human music and greetings. At the time of writing, they must have reached interstellar space and be powering through galactic plasma. Soon we will no longer be able to receive any signals from them as they speed further out. Why send them out there – why send these earthly and human anthologies into the depth of space?

One reason may be a will to pursue frontier expansion; another an attempt to send a signal to anybody or anything that may appreciate it; and yet another a need to leave a legacy, something that will survive us and is valuable as a testimonial of things of Earth and *sapiens* that were valuable. Heyd considers and rejects these options, arguing that the point of the Golden Records, and by extension of our longing to emanate beyond Earth, is the very attempt to give meaning to our human lives from some perspective other than our own.

But what perspective is that? Outer space is, surely, inhuman. How to conceptualize that inhumanity – how to think of the impersonal, vast, anterior and ulterior forces and entities that constitute all that is out there, including the galactic plasma in which Voyager 1 and 2 are now enveloped? **Vincent Blok** engages this question by reflecting on the ontology of planets – beginning from, but then going beyond, planet Earth. That which characterizes the being of planets, Blok suggests, is material, pre-individual, generative, responsive conativity – and it is from a basic confrontation with this conative material base, with the raw powers of necessary generation and dissipation, that any human attempts to create worlds beyond Earth, and to better understand and experience Earth itself, must necessarily begin.

One thing that Earth does is life. Does anything live, or has anything ever lived, anywhere else in the cosmos but Earth? As far as we know, no other planet or celestial body conates itself into life as Earth does. Yet astrobiologists insist, much on the strengths of the same statistical reasonings of Epicurus and Bruno, that the more probable scenario for the New Space Age is that we will one day find, somewhere – perhaps already on Mars – some signs of biochemical processes that may have their origin in extraterrestrial biological activities. How will we then know that these signs really mean life – or, what grounds will we have to explain them by proclaiming life as their cause? To tackle this general question, **David Dunér**'s chapter concentrates on two central distinctions in astrobiology: that between fossils and pseudo-fossils, and that between biotic and abiotic processes.

Questions of meaning that may be considered technical issues in astrobiology are, for philosophers brought up in any 20th century tradition, issues about language and its powers in shaping and being shaped by forms of life. Who we humans are and how we know things is filtered and possibly produced by our uses of language; and our uses of language are filtered and possibly produced by our social and environmental interactions, and these are terrestrial. If there are extraterrestrial live entities anywhere beyond Earth that astrobiologists could recognize, and these have forms of life – ways of being and knowing – that lie beyond the limits of our earthly language uses, how are we to approach them, existentially and conceptually?

In his contribution, **Charles Foster** speculates about how non-terrestrial entities might be and know, based on research on terrestrial non-human ways of being in and comprehending the world. Investigations of these rich and nuanced non-human ways unveil the large extent to which our own human ways limit the amount and kinds of data that we process when determining what kind of a place the world is, and what our place is in it. Language may perpetuate a variety of sensory and other biases that have the ultimate effect of making us self-referential and self-reverential. These biases should not go unchallenged, Foster argues: not on Earth already and especially not when entering a New Space Age that may open us to innumerable remodulations of life and reality beyond Earth.

Another thing our languages do, and perhaps in this reside their most complex powers, is fashioning stories. It is through and in stories that *sapiens* typically makes sense of things and of its own station within the wider workings of things here on Earth. And even more stories are and will be enabled and required by outer space exploration – the exploration of the inhuman, the overwhelmingly powerful, the unknown and untold. The next two chapters of the volume consider our earthly attempts at imaginatively grappling for glimpses of outer space and at getting somewhat epistemically competent about it.

Marta Benenti discusses portrayals of outer space exploration(s) in literary and cinematic works of fiction. Notably, those works tend to characterize outer space not as an inert setting but rather as a "determiner" of the plot. Outer space often functions like a character, whose impersonal agency is causally active in the story. Among the most common topics in outer space stories are the exploration of new territories, encounters with extraterrestrial life or civilizations, space conquest and colonization, interstellar politics and diplomacy, confrontations with space technologies of various sorts, and engagements with cosmological or physical limits and paradoxes. Benenti argues that, thanks to the limited reality constraints that are characteristic of these stories, and the cognitive validation that they temporarily command within their narrative context, outer space stories offer distinctive opportunities for engaging in thought experiments that can be relevant to test our untutored intuitions, for disseminating basic scientific notions about outer space exploration and even colonization, and for imaginatively but conspicuously framing our first steps towards an increasingly more refined ethical, political, and psychological comprehension of what outer space exploration and even colonization could mean for humanity, and for being human.

But then there are many different sorts of stories. Some are less thought experiments than they are denunciations of received knowledge as deceitful and proclamations that alternative knowledge is true. Some of these stories line up their elements in the shape of a theory and go by the name of conspiracy theories. There are numerous conspiracy theories regarding both Earth as a planet (that it is really flat, for example), things from space that frequent Earth (aliens that already live among us and/or whose starships go in and out of our atmosphere), and outer space exploration (that the Moon landings were a hoax, or that space exploration is merely a cover to conceal the existence of secret military bases or at least appropriate taxpayers dollars).

In his chapter, **Juha Räikkä** discusses these space conspiracy theories, and the widely felt but largely unexamined sense that they be epistemically special: notably strange or particularly complex, in terms – for example – of how they approach data, criticize as well as defend testimonial knowledge, or relate to experts and expertise. Raikka argues instead that, from an epistemological standpoint, space conspiracy theories are no different from conspiracy theories about anything else. They belong to no special epistemic class and have the structurally very same strengths and weaknesses as all other conspiracy theories. Räikkä's carefully defended conclusion may also be precious at the level of political communication and opinion management of outer space exploration, considering that whether to emanate into outer space has all the features of a politically divisive issue, which can feed on controversial technical questions while powerfully probing our ideas of efficiency, legitimacy, and justice, and challenging important tenets of various value and religious systems. It is issues of this sort that tend to trigger both the cognitive mobilization and the deep sentiments off which conspiracy theories often prosper.

Three themes that would be likely to attract heated societal debate are the status of outer space exploration and even colonization with reference and even as a response to various challenges of global earthly sustainability; whether human emanations into outer space will make outer space (or at least the tiny specks towards which humans will manage to emanate) better or worse; and how to articulate and manage the issues of justice that outer space exploration and even colonization trigger both on Earth and, potentially, between planets. These are the subjects of the next three chapters in the volume.

Mikko Puumala examines the conceptual and normative implications of the New Space Age for three notions that are central to our thinking about global sustainability on Earth. These are substitutability – the idea that different kinds of capital, for example natural and economic capital, cannot be substituted (transformed into one another) beyond certain thresholds without jeopardizing thereby the ability of future generations to satisfy their needs; the notion that there are ecological boundaries setting limits to economic development; and the very notion of future generations. Puumala suggests that the New Space Age has the potential to upset both the factual and normative presuppositions that are typically at work when these notions are mobilized in sustainability discourses, and that for sustainability to remain a relevant concept and normative criterion into the future, it must accommodate space activities and abandon its "Earthist" assumption that there be no "Planet B" to inhabit, develop, and sustain life on.

Arden Rowell asks what it would mean for humans to improve outer space rather than make it worse – and in this way questions some widely held assumptions. In particular, based on a widespread perception that humans have degraded Earth and depleted its resources, many of us take it as a given that the relationship between humans and their environments is ultimately predatory and even vandalic, so that the best thing humans can do is often to stop whatever it is they are doing, or plan to do, and leave these environments alone. Bracketing the question of whether this "humans as degraders" picture correctly applies on Earth, Rowell wonders if it applies to outer space contexts. Must outer space exploration and even colonization be a march towards cosmic anthropogenic environmental degradation? Rowell suggests that more positive accounts of human emanations, interventions, and impacts in and on outer space would rather focus on the capacity of humans to consciously cultivate environmental qualities they deem beneficial, where these benefits need not be anthropocentric – at least not substantively: for example, humans may work to enhance outer space biodiversity, bringing life and with it various forms of value and valuing to what are now but mutely enacted portions of the cosmos. Rowell suggests that allowing for and exploring the possibility of anthropogenic environmental improvement as opposed to degradation may reduce ideological antagonisms regarding outer space exploration and sharpen its planning and governance both on Earth and in outer space.

Such planning and governance are not insulated from important issues of global justice. **Derek Matravers, Alessandra Marino**, and **Nathalie Treviño** examine the interdependence of historical and technological processes on and beyond Earth to prove the urgency of redefining the global, and the ways in which principles of justice are typically thought to apply globally, to anticipate or manage the emergence of New Space Age injustices. The authors zero in on three particular issues: the repercussions of earthly global injustices in outer space; controversies regarding the classification of outer space or portions thereof as "global commons"; and the implications for both outer space explorations and earthly global justice of the current proliferation of satellite infrastructures (including so-called "mega-constellations" – systems that use thousands of individual satellites) that currently provide services to earthlings but could, in principle, also be re-fitted to become space stations themselves.

The chapters that follow dwell more specifically with multi-planetary human futures – the justifications for their pursuit, the requirements they will impose on the bodies and minds of individual humans, as well as the threats and opportunities they will represent for both non-terrestrial human societies and outer space environments.

Matteo Cerri provides an overview of current scientific knowledge regarding biological challenges for human life in outer space, some of which can be mitigated by means of advanced infrastructural engineering. Outer space is a hostile environment for life as we know it, including of course our own totally Earth-adapted human life. For humans to endure the inhuman conditions of outer space, they will need – among other things – to construct effective protective environments for themselves, including those of starships (transitional environments where spacefaring humans will nonetheless have to spend the long times needed to cover outer space distances), which must be strategically fitted cabin ecologies technologically responsive to human bodily needs. Cerri discusses obstacles towards the achievement of such bio-technical symbiosis under conditions of extreme constraint and risk, and considers how long-duration space travel may affect the physiology of crews and, potentially, their offspring.

Besides their immediate environments – their cabins and habitats – spacefaring humans and particularly hypothetical first settlers and colonists will need to modify themselves. **Karim Jebari** investigates the bio-technical feasibility and some ethical ramifications of bioengineering-based human adaptation to Mars's inhuman conditions. Jebari explains the distinctive challenges that Mars poses to human biology, and how these remain practically insurmountable even when significant investments in environmental support systems are factored in. He argues that bioengineering – through, for example, genetic engineering or cybernetic implants – can provide significant and indeed indispensable support in making humans fit for the Red Planet, thus enabling paths of evolutionary adaptation otherwise ever foreclosed. He then considers some topics in the ethics of human bioengineering for outer space exploration.

And then of course, besides human bodies and habitats, there might be whole planets, or large portions of them, to be fitted for human fruition. Mars is the usual suspect, and **Oskari Sivula** considers the hypothesis of terraforming it as a way into a larger discussion on the (un)naturalness of human interventions in outer space. Discussions regarding (un)naturalness are staples in environmental ethics as well as in bioethics literature on human enhancement. In both fields two concerns are central. First, is naturalness morally pertinent at all – and if not, should it nonetheless influence decision-making on some other, non-moral grounds? Second, how is this elusive (un)naturalness property to be baselined and articulated in different contexts and cases? Sivula proposes to first analyze the ways and senses in which terraforming Mars and its biosphere would be unnatural and then consider whether its (un)naturalness would diminish the value of the newly man-made Martian biosphere. The results of this exploration can provide us with at least one criterion for determining whether we can justifiably terraform extraterrestrial environments.

And once our habitats and bodies will be fit for Mars, and Mars will be fitted to our habitats and bodies, there will be extraterrestrial humans, and these will generate extraterrestrial lineages. As **Evie Kendal** notes, the process of creating such human communities off Earth will allow for the exploration of alternative reproductive futures and family structures. On Earth, human societies have various moral and legal protocols that rely on precedent, and the very fact that some act, practice, or policy has always been enacted in a certain way is often enough to justify its continued performance. For these and other reasons, challenging cultural norms on Earth can be extremely difficult, and laws are frequently sluggish to evolve. In this picture, emerging technologies are frequently represented as a threat to social values, with reproductive technologies constituting a particular cause for concern if they pose a threat to conventional notions of kinship and family structure. But on a different planet, and generally in outer space, there are no precedents. As social norms for non-terrestrial human communities have not yet been established, it is possible to consciously contemplate and deliberately plan innovations of various kinds concerning their formations and proliferations. As family formation is a crucial aspect of societal development, Kendal examines emergent reproductive technologies in the context of future space exploration and possible off-Earth human settlement.

In the chapter that closes the book, **Émile Torres** ties some strings together by re-examining one rationale that is often offered when publicly justifying outer space exploration and the pursuit of multi-planetary futures for (what is now) *sapiens*. This is a longtermist rationale, which suggests that immense amounts of value would be lost or never realized if humans went extinct or the human trajectory was permanently crippled. Because the probabilities of such existential disasters are much higher if humans are all on one planet, they should become a multi-planetary species (or a source of various rivets of multi-planetary speciation). As seen, this will necessitate extensive bioengineering and geoengineering, but there will be innumerable cases in which even that won't do. To generate the "astronomical" quantities of "value" that the longtermist vision promises for the distant future, we will need to also emanate to portions of the universe whose inhumanity is for us totally intractable. Our only option then will be to usher our bodies out of the scene and become digital entities who live in digital worlds, as Torres dubs them. But these worlds and our digital being in them will be radically different from anything we have any experience of. For example, digital entities would likely take the form of hive minds, collective intelligences, distributed selves, and protean entities that share parts of themselves with other entities in their environments. We are largely clueless regarding the consequences of such transformative changes to our being; accordingly, evaluating the justifiability of these changes in terms of their consequences is practically impossible. Yet longtermists do frequently use expected value calculations, which involve allocating probabilities to known outcomes with determinable values and then averaging these probability-weighted values. Torres argues that these calculations are impossible given cluelessness before transformative experiences. In addition, to recognize these "astronomical" amounts of longtermist "value" as such, the digital entities that will populate outer space on our behalf will – problematically – need to be conscious; or else, somewhat grotesquely, it will all have been for naught.

Outer Space and Humanity: Paving the Way for Further Investigations

It is clearly not possible to constrain all the philosophical dimensions of outer space exploration and even colonization in one book. All that *The Philosophy of Outer Space* aims at is mapping some of the terrains that present and future scholars are or will be navigating as they reflect upon this unprecedented option of leaving Earth to emanate into outer space. The hope is that this will also help to structure a sustained, rich, and nuanced societal debate about this impending, incredibly stimulating, and somewhat disconcerting New Space Age.

Notes

1 Di Paola is responsible for the opening six sections of this chapter. Garasic is responsible for the final two. The entire chapter was co-edited.
2 *The Outer Space Treaty* of 1967, ratified by over 100 countries, establishes that outer space, including the Moon and other celestial bodies, is not subject to national appropriation and is available for exploration and use by all states for peaceful purposes. It also prohibits the stationing of weapons of mass destruction in outer space. *The Rescue Agreement* of 1968 obligates states to help astronauts in distress, regardless of their nationality. *The Moon Agreement* of 1979 reaffirms and elaborates on many of the provisions of the Outer Space Treaty, underlying that the environments of the Moon and other celestial bodies should not be disrupted, that the United Nations should be informed of the location and purpose of any station established on those bodies, that the Moon and its natural resources are the common heritage of mankind, and that an international regime should be established to govern the

exploitation of such resources when such exploitation is about to become feasible. None of these documents regulates the operations of non-state space venturers.

3 For a more extensive treatment of the history of human fascination with the Red Planet, see Weintraub (2020).
4 For evidence that there might be more water below the surface of Mars, see Lauro et al. (2021).
5 For a dedicated technical treatment of transformative experiences, see Paul (2014).
6 For discussions of some of those trajectories see Garasic (2021, 2022).
7 See Schwartz and Milligan (2016); Szocik (2019); Green (2021); Garasic (2022).
8 See Milligan (2015); Arnould (2017); Szocik (2020).

References

Arnould, J. (2017). *Impossible Horizon: The Essence of Space Exploration.* Adelaide: ATF Press.

Garasic, M. D. (2021). The War of Ethical Worlds. Why an Acceptance of Posthumanism on Mars Does Not Imply a Follow-Up on Earth. *Medicina e Morale* 70 (3): 317–327.

Garasic M. D. (2022). What Happens on Mars Stays on Mars: A Reply to Balistreri and Umbrello. *Medicina e Morale* 71 (3): 323–332.

Green, B. (2021). *Space Ethics.* New York: Rowman & Littlefield.

Lauro, S., Pettinelli, E., Caprarelli, G., *et al.* (2021). Multiple Subglacial Water Bodies Below the South Pole of Mars Unveiled by New MARSIS Data. *Nature Astronomy* 5 (1): 63–70.

Milligan, T. (2015). *Nobody Owns the Moon: The Ethics of Space Exploitation.* Jefferson: McFarland & Company.

Paul, L. A. (2014). *Transformative Experience.* New York: Oxford University Press.

Schwartz, J. and T. Milligan (2016). *The Ethics of Space Exploration.* Dordrecht: Springer.

Szocik, K. (2019). *The Human Factor in a Mission to Mars: An Interdisciplinary Approach.* Dordrecht: Springer.

Szocik, K. (2020). *Human Enhancements for Space Missions.* Dordrecht: Springer.

Weintraub, D. A. (2020) *Life on Mars: What to Know before We Go.* Princeton: Princeton University Press.

2

A MEMORIAL WITH NO OBSERVERS

Carl Sagan's Golden Record

David Heyd

A Realistic Phantasy

Kant's concluding remarks in his *Critique of Practical Reason* are well known:

> Two things fill the mind with ever new and increasing admiration and
> awe ... the starry heavens above me and the moral law within me ... The
> former begins with the place I occupy in the external world of sense, and it
> broadens the connection in which I stand into an unbounded magnitude of
> worlds beyond worlds and systems of systems and into the limitless times
> of their periodic motion, their beginning and their continuance.
>
> *(Kant 1956, 166)*

And, continues Kant, the second source of awe is our moral conscience, which
is infinite in its own way. This famous passage has been quoted again and again
but almost always in the context of the second, moral source of awe. But here I
am drawn by Kant's philosophical reflection about the "starry heavens", the
boundlessness of the physical universe, since the focus of this chapter is the
impact of the immensity of space and time on our consciousness and the sense
of our place in the world. The following discussion aims to show that Kant's
first source of admiration also raises interesting questions about the nature of
value and the meaning of human existence. Our absolute importance as intelligent beings is for Kant grounded in our moral capacity and dignity, but if we
view ourselves from the perspective of a future human-less world, far away in
space and time, this privileged standing may lose its grand status. Evolutionary
theory and space technology, which were not available to Kant, provide us with
tools for the adoption of such a perspective.

DOI: 10.4324/9781003374381-2

The space project that is the focus of this paper is, unlike future projects such as the human settlement of Mars, not imaginary; it is already four-and-a-half decades old. Yet it may last for a much longer time than any Mars settlement or indeed any human or post-human existence. It combines a highly advanced technological know-how with a thoughtful attempt at reporting the best expressions of the achievements of human civilization. Unlike other space missions, which were all aimed at widening our scientific knowledge, this project had an extra purpose of a more philosophical nature: a thought experiment that stretches our imagination yet at the same time is based on a real possibility.[1] It does not search for further understanding of the world (because the mission will not be able to deliver any information) but rather tries to explore the meaning of the search itself. Most of the literature on space philosophy is engaged with the continuation of humanity on planets other than Earth and its transformation into a post-human species. But here we are concerned with post-human *existence*, that is to say a world where there are only beings who have no relation of continuity with us or a world with no living beings at all. We mean here "post-human" in the most literal sense.[2]

In 1977 NASA launched the spacecraft Voyager 1 for a long mission the purpose of which was to study the faraway planets of the solar system. It was designed to continue its trip after completing its main mission with the hope of exploring the edge of the solar system and then roaming the vast interstellar space. In 2022, forty-five years later (when these lines were written), traveling at the speed of 60,000 km/h, it is about 23 billion kilometers away from Earth, which means that the time it takes to send an electronic message to the spacecraft and receive a response amounts to 45 hours. Only in 80,000 years' time will it reach the vicinity of Proxima Centauri, the nearest star to the sun. By 2025 all communication with the spaceship will terminate and its scientific mission of supplying data about the nature of its surroundings will come to an end. But we know that it will continue travelling in great speed in the darkness of outer space. One's philosophical fascination arises when we read that NASA conjectures that "Voyager is destined – perhaps eternally – to wander the Milky Way". This means that Voyager could not only outlast the existence of the human species (in "evolutionary time") but also the existence of our planet and the solar system as a whole, which will come to an end at some point (in "astronomical time").

For reasons related to this not unrealistic prospect of Voyager, the famous scientist Carl Sagan and his team proposed to design for the spacecraft a "Golden Record" with a collection of 116 images and an assortment of sounds describing the way human beings, other living animals, and non-living entities look and sound. It would also include images and recordings of the main achievements of human civilization, particularly in science and music. The idea was to give possible extraterrestrial intelligent beings, who one day might bump into the spacecraft, an idea of who we were and where we came from even if no other trace remained of us and of our great accomplishments.[3] The record's cover was made of aluminum and electroplated upon it was an ultra-pure sample of the isotope uranium-238, which is said to have a half-life of 4.468 billion years. The Dutch astronomer Nick Oberg hypothesized that the record can last three to five billion years even under the "sandblast" of microscopic dust in the interstellar space, and after the Milky Way clashes with Andromeda, its neighboring galaxy, it may have an even longer life expectancy.[4] These assessments demonstrate Sagan's wild ambition, since in three billion years there will certainly be nothing left of the human race and probably also no trace of Earth and our sun. Sagan wanted to leave one single memorial of humanity and of the planet on which it had lived.[5] This seems to be as close as one can get to eternity.

It is interesting to compare the Voyager thought experiment with an older version of a similar nature which related to a technologically more modest feat but felt to be no less dramatic. In the Prologue to *The Human Condition* Hannah Arendt recounts the experience of the first satellite (*sputnik*) launched into Earth's orbit in 1957, a human artifact that "has been admitted tentatively to [the] sublime company of the heavenly bodies". It was, in her words, an event "second in importance to no other" (Arendt 1958, 1). But, continues Arendt, the immediate reaction described the event as the first step "toward escape from men's imprisonment to the earth". Together with the attempt to create life in an artificial way, this escape should be interpreted as an attempt to transcend "the human condition" and separate human beings both from their physical environment of planet Earth and from their association with all other living things on it. And, continues Arendt, this separation has been achieved with the acquired ability of human beings both to break away from the forces of gravity binding them to their natural habitat and to destroy all organic life on earth.

It seems that Sagan's way of looking at Voyager's voyage was more like Arendt's perception of the *sputnik* than like NASA's rationally based expectations of scientific benefits from the expensive enterprise. After all, the chances of the existence of other intelligent beings in the universe are quite slim and the chance that even if they existed, they would be able to intercept the spacecraft are infinitesimally small,[6] let alone to decipher the record's content and make sense of it. Biologists like Peter Ward and Donald Brownlee remind us that the evolutionary gap between microbial life and intelligent life is wider than the gap between non-life and life (Dick 2009, 167). So even if due to similar climate and physical conditions there is some chance that life could be found on a distant planet, the evolution of simple forms of life into intelligent beings like us would be a miracle. It seems, therefore, that the act of sending aimlessly a disc with a concise summary of who we are has neither scientific or epistemological value nor a communicative purpose. But then, does it have any value at all? How could Sagan justify the idea of the Golden Record, which imposed some extra costs on NASA's limited resources?

Sagan himself opens his book with the story about the Babylonian king Esarhaddon who, like so many mighty rulers in the past, took seriously the idea of a "time capsule", burying deep under the foundations of a majestic monument inscriptions in cuneiform (Sagan 1978, 3). We do not know whether Esarhaddon believed that they would ever be discovered; and if they were, would people understand their meaning? But many of the grander enterprises of ancient kings, like the pyramids, were surely meant to last far beyond the temporal horizon of their builders. Esarhaddon was probably not sure that his inscriptions would ever be excavated, but he knew that there was such a possibility and he could imagine that the discoverers would be human beings like himself. But with the Golden Record, the two assumptions of Esarhaddon are not realistic: it is far from certain that there will be any recipients of the message, and even if there are such discoverers whether they would be sufficiently similar to us as to enable them to read and understand it.

This article will consider four possible motivations behind the project of the Golden Record: expanding frontiers, sending a message, leaving a mark and searching for meaning. All four motivations raise fundamental philosophical problems, which were not given systematic reflection by the team that designed the record. First, what does the expansion of the frontiers of knowledge mean if there are no actual humans who can make use of it? Or, in other words, what is the difference between what Arendt calls the real "escape" of humans from their natural environment and the virtual escape of humanity in the case of Voyager (an escape by proxy)? Secondly, what are the conceptual limits of a communicative act like sending a message, including the constraints of language and the dependence of language on common environmental experience? What can be the role of a unidirectional act of delivering a message with no chance of getting a response? Thirdly, leaving a mark is not merely a communicative act but also an attempt to maintain some sort of presence after one's demise. Is such presence conditioned by the existence of observers who are also motivated by leaving a mark? And fourthly, is the meaning of life (and of human existence as a whole) an "internal" matter, i.e. decided *within* one's life (like the meaning of a novel, which derives exclusively from its form and content) or an "external" matter tested in terms of its effects on people and circumstances beyond one's life? And in more general terms, what is the nature of value and is it a feature of the world or just a feature of the way human beings are affected in various ways? Obviously, this chapter cannot answer these deep philosophical questions. Its more modest aim is to show how the unique perspective of the Golden Record can serve as a sharp test to the way we deal with them.

Expanding Frontiers

The metaphor of frontier has both geographical and epistemological senses. The idea of going beyond the geographical border has a powerful pull on the American mind, but the same applies to the way American culture has always viewed the effort to transcend the limits of scientific knowledge and technological capabilities. Rachel Schmitt (2017) has argued that the frontier is the fundamental metaphor in the rhetoric of scientists involved in NASA's enterprises like Voyager. She persuasively points out that the move beyond the frontier is associated with adventurous loners exploring new and uncertain territories in a hopeful spirit. And, indeed, the small and fragile spacecraft wandering in the unmapped intergalactic space with little knowledge of what lies beyond is a beautiful expression of that frontier mentality.

However, Schmitt associates the frontier mentality primarily with *colonization*, with the aim of conquering, appropriating, and ultimately settling new territories with human beings. And, indeed, Sagan has also the vision of human settlements on other planets of the solar system as a solution to the threat of nuclear or demographic explosion of life on Earth. But the frontier metaphor does not fully work in the case of Voyager and its gilded message (at least after completing its very productive exploration of the Jovian planets). It does not aim and is not able to declare sovereignty over any piece of territory, not even by symbolically sticking a flag (like Neil Armstrong did on the moon). It will never be the pioneer for others to follow, let alone prepare the ground for a settlement. Even if it encounters other intelligent beings, it will have no power over them or ability to exploit their resources. And it will never benefit us, its launchers, materially or scientifically, since we will lose contact with it forever. And although cultural critics of the Golden Record were quick to note the white male bias in the material selected for the record, there is no chance that Voyager will exercise cultural colonialism as so many conquests of territories on Earth have done. So although it continuously breaks the record of the farthest human artifact in space, it expands only virtual frontiers. Even the name given to the spacecraft – Voyager – expresses its difference from other NASA missions, which were given names such as Pioneer, Mariner, Explorer, Ranger, Surveyor – all referring to some practical or scientific purpose. Voyager's task now is just to go on traveling forever.[7] Voyager is roaming in uncharted territories without charting them.

Sending a Message

Despite anecdotal reports about the arrival of extraterrestrials on Earth and despite the serious scientific efforts to detect by sensitive radio telescopes signals from other stars, we still have no real sign from any intelligent beings out there. But if other beings do not connect with us, we might try to communicate with them. We can send to the outer space radio signals and now also a physical object. But the chance that we succeed in directing our radio signals exactly to an intelligent addressee in such faraway locations is miniscule, and if some intelligent community in our galaxy happens to get hold of the Golden Record, it will be too late for us to get their response, for by that time we will not be here anymore.[8] The futility of sending such a message is similar to sending a message in a bottle from a desert island: even if it eventually reaches someone, it will be too late to save the stranded sender of the message. But that in itself is no reason not to dispatch such a message. Esarhaddon's motivation is perfectly understandable despite his full awareness that he will never know the impression that the message left on its recipients in the distant future. On a grander scale this is after all the whole idea of leaving our descendants with our heritage. Communication may make sense even if it is unidirectional. There is value in passing on important information to people far away in time and space since it could be of value to them.

Still, even if we do not expect to get an answer to our messages, sending them makes sense only on the assumption that someone can read and understand them. This is a precondition of any valuable communicative act. In the temporal and spatial distance Voyager is expected to wander, the intelligibility of its message is not a trivial assumption. Sagan and his team were well aware of this challenge.

Xenoarchaeology (or astroarchaeology) is the field that tries to interpret remainders of alien civilizations in faraway stars. Although it is restricted today to science fiction writers because scientists have no evidence-based material for their study, we should try to imagine the work of the xenoarchaeologists of those stars who in the deep future might one day be studying *our* remainders, such as the Golden Record. This is an interesting reversal in methodology: rather than reflect on the way we might have to interpret signals from outer space of senders whose existence and nature are completely unknown to us, we should try to imagine our addressees about whom we know nothing but can devise the means that with some chance might both reach them and communicate our message to them. We have the archeological experience of how difficult it is to decipher human signs, symbols, or the function of material objects of the ancient past. Till the work of Champollion on the Rosetta stone the ancient Egyptian language was incomprehensible to us. And the old language of the Cretan Minoans (Linear A) has not been deciphered yet. How can Sagan hope that the sounds and pictures he chose for the record will make sense to non-human intelligences in a million or a billion years' time on a planet that is light years away from us?

Consider rational beings in Kant's sense – beings who have reason but no senses, no body, not perhaps even the forms of intuition of space and time. They would be completely blind to the symbols on the material Golden Record. But even if they have bodies, how can we even hope that they function in the same way as ours? After all, their bodies would be the product of some evolutionary process, which like all evolution develops in response to particular physical environments and challenges and is partly guided by random genetic mutations. So these beings can be easily imagined to have reason (and brain) but no eyes and ears. Furthermore, eyes and ears are not enough to make sense of the vocal greetings in dozens of human languages that have been recorded on the Golden Record or of the drawings of the male and female body trying to explain human reproduction. Even if they have, as Kant surmises, the a priori categories of thought, they could easily lack the schemas to make them applicable to their experience since that experience would be so different from ours.

The barriers of comprehension are very high, possibly insurmountable. There are limits to the translatability of language. As Quine argues, sharing the non-linguistic experience of reality is a precondition for being able to learn the language of a remote tribe.

> Language is a social art. In acquiring it we have to depend entirely on intersubjectively available cues as to what to say and when. Hence there is no justification for collating linguistic meanings, unless in terms of men's dispositions to respond overtly to socially observable stimulations.
>
> *(Quine 1960, ix)*.

In the case of extraterrestrials these socially observable stimulations would not be shared by the two communities and hence the translation of the Golden Record would not be only "indeterminate" but simply impossible. Normally the task of the translator is aided by prior linguistic knowledge – either of the actual language to be translated or of some related language. Quine envisages a case in which the translation of a language must proceed without any prior linguistic knowledge and solely on the basis of the observed behavior of the speakers of the language in conjunction with the observation of the basic perceptual stimulations that give rise to that behavior. He calls this challenge "radical translation" (28). But in our case, it is not only prior knowledge of an interpreter that is lacking but the conditions of learning a completely foreign language with no behavioral evidence of the way people of the source language move or respond to environmental stimuli (32). For the alien receivers of the Golden Record human beings would be considered as "a hitherto untouched people" (28) and the aliens would be at a loss to interpret the language of the record due to the absence of any interpreter and of the conditions to question us and watch our non-verbal and verbal responses. The way to bridge the linguistic gap between two completely alien communities is – as anthropologists attest – long and arduous, and involves intensive interaction and observation, which is blocked by the time and space gap stretching between us and the aliens. And note again that in the anthropological setting we know that the tribe we meet for the first time consists of human beings having the same five senses, human bodies, and a human language; and that they live in a similar natural environment – conditions that we cannot presume that extraterrestrials share with us.

So the reversal of xenoarchaeology – rather than studying past signals sent to us from outer space, imagining how future people in that space would interpret signals we send to them now – teaches us an important lesson of humility. The obstacles we face in trying to understand prehistoric artifacts and artworks such as cave paintings or Cycladic figurines are slight in comparison to the job of those alien extraterrestrials who in a million or billion years' time are expected to make sense of the strange Golden Record. With our prehistoric ancestors we share the same genome, we live in a more or less similar environment, and we know quite a lot about the continuous history spanning their time and ours. Future beings in a different galaxy will have none of these conditions that bridge the spatio-temporal gap between the sender of the message and its addressee. In that sense sending a message on Voyager turns out to be a futile idea. Even if by some infinitesimally small chance it is received by somebody, it will not make sense to the receiver, let alone be reciprocated by a response (for which there would also be no receiver, and even if there were, they would encounter similar insurmountable obstacles in interpreting it). Trevor Wolfram searched for some kind of universal language based on computation which could serve as the means of communication with complete aliens, but he always stresses that even that language can serve for communication only if at least *some* of the historical and cultural context in which it is interpreted is shared by the two sides to the communication (Wolfram 2018). Even if we showed extraterrestrials a thousand different chairs (which would be more than enough to teach a foreigner on our planet the English word "chair"), it would mean nothing to intelligent alien creatures who cannot bend their bodies to a sitting position.

There still might be one aspect of the spacecraft and its record that could serve as a "message": to its finders it would look different from all they know; it would be identified as an *artifact*. It would look like the watch found in the middle of the desert by a savage who has never seen a machine of any kind. Even if they won't be able to perceive it as a message intended to them, they would be able to understand that it is an object that was crafted by someone as they craft their objects, and accordingly treat it as a relic from another world. But still, it would look to them more incomprehensible than the way extraterrestrial objects depicted in sci-fi movies look to us; for the objects designed by movie directors always share with our real-life objects some important features that make them interpretable by the spectator. There is no similar guarantee in the way the human artifact would look to an alien. Furthermore, we should take seriously Bernard Williams's insightful proposition that the dividing line between nature and culture is itself culturally dependent. To the untrained eye a hexagon shape in the desert sand may look human made; but scientists know that such a shape is often created by the wind (Wolfram 2018). The same applies to radio signals we often took in the past to be signals from extraterrestrials but now know to be the effect of natural processes on other planets. So we cannot even be sure that the future receivers of the Golden Record would perceive it as an artifact. They could understand it as part of nature, a divine miracle, a hallucination, etc. If that is correct, Timothy Ferris's hopes (in his contribution to Sagan's *Murmurs of the Earth*) seem to be somewhat overblown:

> But any creature who comes across Voyager and recognizes the record as an artifact can realize that it was dispatched with no hope of return. That gesture may speak more clearly than music. The record says: However primitive we seem, however crude this spacecraft, we knew enough to envision ourselves citizens of the cosmos. It says: However small we were,

something in us was large enough to want to reach out to discoverers unknown, in times when we shall have perished or have changed beyond recognition. It says: Whoever and whatever you are, we too once lived in this house of stars, and we thought of you.

(Sagan 1978, 167).

It is not fully clear whether Sagan and his team really believed that their message would be received by anyone, and if it were, whether it would make sense to the recipients. They surely put a lot of effort in trying to make the messages on the record as simple as possible (as we shall see below) but that does not mean that their assumption was that they would play the role of a communicative act. So maybe their motivation was different than sending a message.

Leaving a Mark

Our stranded person on the desert island may throw the bottle with his message into the ocean without having any hope or rational expectation that it would ever be found, let alone serve his efforts to be saved. He could equally carve in the tree "I was here" and sign his name, with the knowledge that even if by some happenstance someone ever reaches the island the name would mean nothing to her. We know that leaving a mark is a kind of desire we all share although it takes different forms among people.

Unlike sending a message, leaving a mark is not a communicative act. It does not aim to deliver information, let alone get an answer. It is an attempt to guarantee our presence after we are gone – either to another place or completely gone. Therefore, there is something inapt in the widespread use of the terms "mission" and "probe" by NASA scientists in describing Voyager's intergalactic trip, for there is no addressee to the mission out there or recipient of discoveries down here. There can be no explorers without anyone for whom a new territory is discovered. Voyager's only function is simply leaving a mark or serving as a memorial. But what is the meaning or point of leaving it?

There are two competing theories of value. According to the *impersonal* theory goodness can be ascribed to states of affairs or to the world. According to the *person-affecting* theory, good is always good for somebody, a person. While for impersonalism the promotion of the overall goodness in the world is valuable, as it is in Bentham's utilitarianism, for the person-affecting theorist only the promotion of the good of actual human beings is of value. The difference between the two theories can be best illustrated in the dilemmas of procreation: is the addition of (happy) people to the world in itself something good, or is it only good to advance the goodness of existing people? Or in the common formulation of this dilemma, do we have to make happy people or to make people happy? For the person-affecting view, making happy people is not the way of doing good unless by creating them we make actual people better off. For the impersonalist, the more the merrier – more well-being in the world makes a better world (Parfit 1984, part IV).

The relevance of this debate about the nature of value to our concern here is obvious. If there is no intelligent or living being in the universe after the extinction of the human race, then it does not seem that even an object that was of great value to us may maintain its value in that human-less world. For the person-affecting view, there is no value without evaluators and hence in the case there are no intelligent beings capable of evaluation, reality becomes value-neutral. The world before the evolution of the human species had no value, as will be the case when the species dies out. For the impersonal approach, it is good that even after nothing is left of the valuable products of human civilization there will be at least one single object left that encapsulates some of its valuable achievements.

Nietzsche (1969, 42) seems to have held a person-affecting view of value. The idea of humanity leaving an eternal mark in a human-less universe looked to him "mendacious":

> In some remote corner of the universe, poured out and glittering in innumerable solar systems, there once was a star on which clever animals invented knowledge. That was the highest and most mendacious minute of "world history" – yet only a minute. After nature had drawn a few breaths the star grew cold, and the clever animals had to die.
>
> One might invent such a fable and still not have illustrated sufficiently how wretched, how shadowy and flighty, how aimless and arbitrary, the human intellect appears in nature. There have been eternities when it did not exist; and when it is done for again, nothing will have happened. For this intellect has no further mission that would lead beyond human life. It is human, rather, and only its owner and producer gives it such importance, as if the world pivoted around it.

For Nietzsche, a mark of the kind Sagan was so eager to leave would look pathetic since the "intellect has no further mission that would lead beyond human life". Building a monument to "the clever animals", which no human (or human-like) intellect can appreciate, is an arrogant act since from the point of view of the non-human universe there is no value to the human intellect and its achievements.

A test for our intuitions regarding the impersonal vs. the person-affecting views is the Last Man thought experiment. Imagine the last man in the process of the dying out of humanity. He holds, let's say, the original painting of the Mona Lisa from the Louvre. He can either wrap it well so as to protect it from natural damage or set it on fire. Can he be said to act wrongly if he does the latter? After all, there will be no one in the future who would be able to examine the painting, satisfy her curiosity, derive aesthetic satisfaction, or feel a sense of the sublime. The painting will become a mere physical object with no value of any kind. Putting it on fire does not deprive any individual – actual or future – from the joy of watching it. In such circumstances can the last man be described as heartless? Cynical? Vengeful? Would we prefer him to make the Mona Lisa the last and only testament of humanity in the human-less universe?

The Last Man thought experiment is often discussed in environmental ethics with regard to the source of responsibility of human beings to maintain the integrity of nature and its beauty. The "deep ecologists" adopt the impersonal point of view, which holds that the Grand Canyon has a value independently of its appreciation by human beings. But "shallow ecologists" argue that we should keep nature's beauty only for our descendants for whom it would be a grave loss if it was damaged. However, in the case of the Golden Record we have a reversal of the relations between nature and culture: rather than the effort to preserve nature from the violent assaults of modern technology and industry, we are concerned here with the desperate effort to preserve at least a tiny specimen of culture from the natural processes of erosion, which ultimately will lead to the total annihilation of all human artifacts. On the grand astronomical scale, the attempt to save culture from nature seems more urgent and unique than sparing the beauty of nature from the damages of human culture, especially since this nature is going to be destroyed when the sun becomes a red giant in due course.

Leaving a mark seems to be as futile as sending a message at least from the point of view of the person-affecting conception of value. It may be a pleasing phantasy to think of a post-human world that still contains one single product of the long and arduous development of humanity. But all monuments in past history were erected for the sake of future human beings who at some point might encounter them and who would have the conceptual tools to interpret their meaning. The Pharaonic king who instructed his treasures to be buried with him in a way that they would be impossible to find may have thought that their value is not dependent on being appreciated by any human being in the future. But he may have thought that these treasures would serve *him* for eternity and in that sense that they had a person-affecting value. We know that gravestones are not usually visited by anyone after a while, but we still build them of sturdy materials. I am not sure we would build them if we knew we were the very last generation of the human race. Voyager may be seen as such a gravestone for the human species, a pointless phantasy of being remembered even if there is no one left to remember.

Searching for Meaning

If the Golden Record venture proves to be futile both as an act of communication with possible extraterrestrials and as an attempt to secure the value of human civilization, what could be its point? The real motivation of the team of scientists and experts is somewhat clouded by their passion and enthusiasm while engaging in the construction of the physical and the intellectual components of the record. But from their reports and writings about the project it occurs that the communication phantasy was for them an opportunity to seriously reflect on the deep structure of artistic media, the multi-cultural nature of humanity, the universal elements of our experience. It was an exercise in abstraction, an attempt to reveal the most elementary components of the language of science and the arts, those that we can hope can serve as a bridge between us and intelligences of another world (whether they actually exist or not). The scientific mission of Voyager (which was meant primarily to study the more distant planets in the solar system) provided the opportunity to reflect on the possibility of a human artifact outlasting humanity as a whole. Stretching the imagination to such an unprecedented spatio-temporal extent proved helpful in assessing the limits of knowledge, meaning and communicability, which we usually test in facing other human cultures and other epochs in human history but not beyond them.

Sagan seems to have captured this meaning of the record when he tried to vindicate the project by quoting his colleague, Bernard Oliver: "There is only an infinitesimal chance that the plaque will even be seen by a single extraterrestrial, but it will certainly be seen by billions of terrestrials" (Sagan 1978, 11).[9]

It is *we* who are the real addressees of the Golden Record. It is a celebration of the most advanced technological competence and of the general achievements of human civilization in its long history. But it also raises our phantasy of putting ourselves in the shoes of extraterrestrials so as to look at ourselves from the outside, or from nowhere.[10] So compiling the contents of the record is a deep exercise in self-awareness, and this exercise is also of a major historical significance since it will be part of the heritage of 20th century humanity.[11] In two hundred or two thousand years' time, our (human) terrestrial descendants will carefully study the content of the record and the hard choices of selection that had to be made by Sagan's committee. And they might wonder what made us make such choices and express such preferences, which would probably look to them naïve or outdated. (Wouldn't it be very illuminating if we found a time capsule from 1500 with a summary of what they thought to be the most significant information for their distant descendants?) However, unlike standard thought experiments in philosophy or sci-fi scenarios, the power of the Voyager journey lies in its empirical possibility. We have scientifically based grounds for believing that the spacecraft and the record can outlive humanity and planet Earth, and that if there happen to be other intelligent beings in the universe they might intercept Voyager and examine the Golden Record.

An illuminating illustration of the idea that the Golden Record ultimately serves our research into the nature of our cultural products is the work of the musicologist Alexander Rehding. In his "Intergalactic Music Theory of Everything", he suggests a theory that provides a new definition of music, one that may make as much sense to aliens as it does to humans.

> We need to reduce the idea of music to its most basic components, to bare vibrations and to build it up from there.
>
> By reducing music to its most basic components, Rehding hopes to create a portal into music analysis that anyone can enter. That includes aliens.
>
> *(Sweet 2020)*

This is an interesting proposal that is aimed at bridging the huge gap between us and aliens who are deprived of the context that makes our music intelligible to our ear. The assumption is that physics is more basic than the auditory experience and may thus reach the comprehension of people who have no ear for music or no ear at all. The basic structure of a Bach fugue (of the kind that was uploaded on the record) can be detected on a more abstract level and hence made more universally accessible. If, as the Pythagoreans theorized, music is concerned with proportions of movement, then the movement of a string, an airwave, or the stars themselves may all have a common mathematical basis, which may be intelligible to non-human minds lacking the historical context of music appreciation.

Carl Sagan formulated this idea in more general terms as his strategy of choice of the contents for the record. The laws of physics and chemistry are uniform and apply in the whole universe and hence they should serve as the language in which the record carries its message (Sagan 1978, 6).[12] Furthermore, although we do not know how the environment of extraterrestrials looks and how it shapes their experience, we can be certain that they are exposed to physical matter, chemical composition, mountains and stars – an environment they share with us. Biology, on the other hand, may be special to our world if it is the only place in which life in its biological-evolutionary form exists. Music can, as we have seen, be given a more abstract mathematical or physical form, but painting cannot. That is why the human accomplishments in biology and the visual arts were not included in the record. But again, the strategy of both Sagan and Rehding is valid for *our* way of framing scientific knowledge and the hierarchy of its different branches. That epistemic structure is by no means necessary: our aliens may have a perfect musical ear and the ability to enjoy musical harmony without having a clue about Pythagorean physics or the mathematical basis of octaves and major thirds. So the strategy may work for communicating the beauty of harmony to human deaf people but fail to do so for extraterrestrials. The struggle of making ourselves understood to complete "others" requires of us epistemic humility: not only is our knowledge of the world very limited; we do not know what other possible intelligent beings know or are capable of knowing.

For this reason, despite being enthusiastic about his "space music", Rehding is sober about its meaning: "Even as we turn our attention to distant planets, the benefits we may reap from this post-human musicology are ultimately geocentric and distinctly human" (Sweet 2020).

But whether the Golden Record was meant to communicate a message to unidentified extraterrestrial beings or to leave a mark in the uninhabited universe, or to reflect on the meaning of our human life and history – Sagan's fully conscious decision to exclude from it the negative aspects of human history is surprising (Sagan 1978, 40). The possible receivers will not know anything about the evils of war, hunger, cruelty, crime, illness and suffering. They will receive peaceful greetings in dozens of languages, but no expression of violent intention; they will get a schematic view of the contours of the male and female body, but no sign of handicap or pathology; they will get a chance to enjoy a prelude and fugue by Bach, but no cry of a tortured prisoner. If we wish to leave a mark of who we were, shouldn't that be faithful to the truth? Is the Golden Record a grand PR project to look good to people who will get to know us long after we are gone (what the team referred to as showing "the best of ourselves")? As Sagan conceived it, the record is a "celebration" of human scientific (and artistic) achievements. And as Jon Lomberg, chief of the team responsible for the visual images said, "we decided the worst in us needn't be sent across the galaxy" (Sagan 1978, 76). The pride in the contents of the record is not in harmony with the humility of humans in the face of the immensity of time and space and especially of the open possibility that the receivers (actual or imaginary) of the message may turn out to be much more civilized and lead a life of a much higher moral quality. Shame and care for our reputation should not play any role here since by the time our character and deeds are discovered by the aliens, we will have been dead for a very long time. And if the real addressees of the record are our fellow (present and future) humans, isn't it somewhat ridiculous to ignore the darker side of our civilization of which they will be acutely aware?

Trevor Paglen is skeptical about the very possibility of there being any extraterrestrials not to speak of any such aliens who could decipher the Golden Record. But he respects Sagan's project in terms of "what we would like to say and how we would like to represent ourselves [to those imaginary aliens]".

> I believe in continually asking the questions that designing for extra-terrestrials implies, because thinking about aliens is a way to think about ourselves and our relationship to the future. The impossible questions of representation and form are fruitful to consider.
>
> *(Paglen 2013, 19)*

The title of Paglen's article includes the phrase "why talk to aliens even if we can't?" and the answer I propose is that the Golden Record project is at the same time futile but meaningful. It is a deep exercise in experiencing the limits of our knowledge and of the fact that the value of our existence and civilization is only "for us (and our descendants)" and that there would be no value after we are gone when no one else remains in the universe. Nevertheless, we are creatures who have an insatiable thirst for self-transcendence and refuse to be constrained by the person-affecting nature of value. The thought that the grand story of human civilization will come to an end without leaving any value in the world is intolerable and despite knowing that this is inevitable we still put an effort in leaving at least some memorial to it, which we delude ourselves would be itself of value. So the meaning of the Golden Record project consists of the deep respect we have for that urge for self-transcendence. Despite knowing that we are merely a "passing shadow" in the history of the universe, we can still leave our footprint in it for an indefinite time in incomprehensibly remote locations.

Conclusion

What can we learn from the grand thought experiment designed by Sagan and his team? Take the four possible motivations for undertaking the project around which this chapter was structured:

1. Expanding frontiers. Although Voyager 1 has already reached a geographically (or rather spatially) unprecedented distance and will eventually break any imaginable limit on such a distance, this expansion of frontiers is vacuous since in intergalactic space there are no real frontiers, limits, or obstacles. There are no lines to be crossed. More importantly, the spacecraft will not break any epistemological borders because by entering into new territories it will not advance our knowledge of outer space (at least once it stops sending signals to Earth in two years' time – 2025). Expanding frontiers is of value only if beyond the frontier humans can settle, colonize, exploit, or learn something new. The only frontiers of knowledge that the Golden Record can in principle break are those of extraterrestrials who might encounter it one day. The spacecraft itself is obviously a technological and scientific victory over all the obstacles to the "escape from Earth", but the Golden Record as such is not. Thus the analogy to the 19th-century movement to the West in the U.S. (or for that matter to Magellan's adventurous travels trying to map the globe) is only partial and mostly metaphorical.
2. Sending a message. The hypothetical encounter between extraterrestrials and the Golden Record is a sharp test for the limits of communication, particularly if it is unidirectional. Although unidirectionality characterizes also the signals we get from the distant past, archeologists have so much background information about the kind of people who sent us "the signals" in the form of signs, pictures, and artifacts; we know a lot about the natural environment in which they lived, and we rely on a high degree of anthropological and cultural continuity and in the similarity in mental and psychological functions between us and them. The xenoarchaeology that would be exercised by extraterrestrials who might discover the Golden Record will have none of this background knowledge and hence would not be able to apply any of the methods of scientific archeology. Only an evolutionary miracle would make them sufficiently similar to us biologically, neurologically, and socially to make our messages comprehensible to them – independently of their intelligence. Even identifying Voyager as artifact cannot be guaranteed or assumed since the distinction itself between the natural and the artificial is culture dependent. If Quine's conditions for translatability do not hold (either by some mediating language or by an ongoing sharing of a social and natural environment), then it seems that the gap between our effort to make ourselves comprehensible and the extraterrestrials deciphering capacity would remain unbridgeable.

3.   Leaving a mark. Here we move from conceptual and empirical constraints to the debate between conceptions of value. If the very existence of humanity (and civilization) is considered valuable, then leaving a memorial for it after its demise is also valuable. This makes sense from the perspective of impersonalism, i.e. the view that features or conditions of the world can have value independently of their being appreciated by or in the interest of human beings. But from a "person-affecting" point of view, a memorial without any observer does not have any meaning, let alone value, because according to this view there is no value without valuers. This fundamental debate resists a clear rational resolution. But the question whether the Golden Record will have any value in a billion years is surely a pure and clean test to our intuitions.

4.   The search for meaning. Sagan's project served as a rare opportunity for distilling the most essential and most important achievements of humanity under extreme constraints of space and intelligibility. It demanded an effort to overcome the obstacles of language, communication, and biological conditions, and forced the team to make some morally and politically controversial choices. Such an enterprise makes humans proud but also modest. However, beyond the value of the celebration of human achievement the deeper meaning of the feat of the Golden Record lies in the recognition of the unique struggle of human beings with their insatiable drive for bootstrapping, the futile but unquenchable desire to give meaning to our existence by looking at ourselves from the outside. This, I believe, is ultimately the real meaning and justification for the project of the Golden Record.

Notes

1   I call the project a "thought experiment" because despite involving a real-life high-tech artifact, the way it actually behaves, its life expectancy, and the way it is interpreted and understood by whomever encounters it will never be subject to experimental observation or testing.

2   Thus, when the scientific advisor to NASA, Carl Sagan, says that "if our long-term survival is at stake, we have a basic responsibility to our species to venture to other worlds", he is concerned with the continuity of the human species. But beyond that Sagan ponders about Voyager in terms of astronomical time in which all humans will become extinct even if they succeed in settling "other worlds".

3   There were two camps in the controversy over the question how to justify NASA's budget in the eyes of the taxpayer: those who underlined the military and technological importance of the development of space exploration and those who appealed to the scientific value and to the imagination of the possible existence of extra-terrestrials. Sagan was a very effective leader of the second camp since he was an astronomer and a popularizer of science while his rivals were engineers and military people McQuaid (2006, 148–149).

4   Personal communication with Nick Oberg.

5   To do justice to the facts, there were two previous projects in the early 1970s in which "plaques" were sent on Pioneer 10 and 11 spacecraft with a similar mission to the outer space and in 1977 Voyager 2 was also launched, equipped with the same Golden Record. But Voyager 1 is by far the fastest and farthest from Earth. There is

also the SETI (Search for Extraterrestrial Life) program (which searches for laser flashes that other societies might use to signal their presence). But these are attempts at electronic communication rather than leaving physical evidence for the existence of humanity. They also raise similar questions about the interpretability of such signals if and once they are received. For these and other attempts to transmit our heritage to the deep future in outer space, see May and Holtorf (2020, ch. 20).

6   Years before the missions to the outer space R. N. Bracewall hypothesized that our only real chance of communicating with extraterrestrials would be through radio signals, which can bridge the immense distances between stars. And according to his calculations only a more advanced civilization has the chance to do so by sending probes to our solar system and trying to get from us a response to their radio signals (which would take only minutes rather than years). Bracewall could not imagine that only 17 years after his short paper humanity would become able to send similar probes to distant stars (although it will not be able to send radio signals to alien civilizations since its radio will die out already in 2025). See Bracewall (1960, 670–671).

7   The fascination with the very idea of the spacecraft constantly speeding away from us, with no specific purpose beyond getting as far as possible, is demonstrated by the interest people show in NASA's internet site for Voyager. It shows day and night the number of kilometers it travels each second and counts its continuously growing distance from Earth in mind boggling numbers.

8   Bracewall (1960) was acutely aware of the short time span in which there is a chance of creating interstellar communication. The life span of an intelligent civilization like the human species is limited and short in astronomical terms. And the chance that the signal sent in a particular direction would reach the addressees when they have reached a sufficiently advanced stage so as to be able to spot the signal and before their species dies out is very small. I should add that being "more advanced" does not necessarily entail being able to understand (us): there are so many signs and symbols of less advanced human civilizations that we do not comprehend; why should a more intelligent and sophisticated extraterrestrial civilization be able to decipher our "primitive" drawings and sounds on the Golden Record?

9   In a similar vein, Jon Lomberg, a member of Sagan's team who was responsible for the selection of the visual images and contributor to Sagan's *Murmurs of the Earth*, says that there have always been two audiences – the human and the extraterrestrial. We can never know if there will be an extraterrestrial audience, but the response from the human audience has been more positive and enduring than we ever expected. In a world where so much is ephemeral, it is not easy to make a classic, and that is what the Golden Record has become [personal communication].

10 See also another quotation from Sagan: "Perhaps the Voyagers would never be recovered by some extraterrestrial society. But making the record had provided us with a unique opportunity to view our planet, our species and our civilization as a whole and to imagine the moment of contact with some other planet, species and civilization" (Sagan 1978, 41). Still, in a biographical note on Carl Sagan, Oliver Marsh comments that he "proved adept at incorporating metaphysical and spiritual references in his work while preserving a separation from religion" (Marsh 2019, 476).

11 Take the dozens of multilingual greetings recorded on the Golden Record. I guess that most people thinking about the content of their greeting did not believe that they will ever reach a recipient, but that the greeting was an opportunity for them to reflect on what they value most and wish other people to have (peace, good will, and friendship). It is an exercise similar to the custom of making three wishes when one sees a falling star: one does not believe in the chance of satisfying those wishes but still enjoys the challenge of selecting what one really hopes to get. In both cases the act is primarily reflective and expressive.

12 This idea, which today looks to us quite obvious, goes back to the revolutionary idea of the ancient Greek and Roman atomists (like Democritus and Lucretius), who

argued that since the universe is composed of an infinite number of atoms and their possible compositions, we should surmise that there are infinite worlds beyond our perception and comprehension, and that these worlds could also consist of intelligent beings. See Dick (2009, 168–169).

Bibliography

Arendt, H. (1958). *The Human Condition*. University of Chicago Press.

Bracewall, R. N. (1960). "Communication from Superior Galactic Communities". *Nature* 186, 670–671.

Dick, S. J. (2009). "A Historical Perspective on the Extent and Search of Life". In C. M. Bertka (ed.), *Exploring the Origin, Extent, and Future of Life: Philosophical, Ethical and Theological Perspectives*. Cambridge University Press.

Kant, I. (1956). *Critique of Practical Reason* (trans. Lewis White Beck). Bobbs Merrill.

Marsh, O. (2019). "Life Cycle of a Star: Carl Sagan and the Circulation of Reputation". *British Journal of the Philosophy of Science* 52, 467–486.

May, S. and C. Holtorf (2020). *Heritage Futures*. UCL Press.

McQuaid, K. (2006). "Selling the Space Age". *Environment and History* 12, 127–163.

Nietzsche, F. (1969). "On Truth and Lie in an Extra-Moral Sense". In W. Kaufmann (ed.), *The Portable Nietzsche*. Viking.

Paglen, T. (2013). "Friends of Space, How Are You All? Have You Eaten Yet? Or, Why Talk to Aliens Even if We Can't". *Afterall: A Journal of Art, Context and Enquiry* 32, 8–19.

Parfit, D. (1984). *Reasons and Persons*. Oxford University Press.

Quine, W. v. O. (1960). *Word and Object*. MIT Press.

Sagan, C. (1978). *Murmurs of Earth*. Ballantine Books.

Sagan, C. (1994). *Pale Blue Dot: A Vision of the Human Future in Space*. Random House.

Schmitt, R. (2017). "Archiving 'The Best of Ourselves' on the Voyager Golden Record". M.A. Thesis submitted at the University of Colorado.

Sweet, J. (July–August 2020). "One Small Step for Music". *Harvard Magazine*.

Wolfram, S. (2018). "How to Design Beacons for Humanity's Afterlife". *Science*. January 18. http://www.wired.com/story/how-to-design-beacons-for-humanitys-afterlife/.

3

EARTH AND THE ONTOLOGY OF PLANETS

Vincent Blok

Introduction

The perseverance of climate change and inability of humanity to safeguard a sustainable future on our planet gives rise to speculations about the possibility of space exploration and the settling of human colonies on other planets. While Mars colonies were still science fiction in the 1950s, nowadays the experience of our dying planet revitalizes the ambition to explore the universe to find a new home for humanity (Burges, 2014). In Frank Herbert's book *Dune* (1965), the terraforming of Arrakis to make it more habitable for humans was still science fiction. Nowadays, terraforming is a serious field of scientific research – interested in, for instance, how human interventions can help the self-regulation of the Martian biosphere to support life and make Mars a habitable planet (McKay et al., 1991), for instance by creating a greenhouse effect (Sagan, 1994). For instance, the Persephone project envisions to "prototype exovivaria – closed ecosystems inside satellites, to be maintained from Earth telebotically, and democratically governed by a global community".[1]

Philosophers like Hannah Arendt conceive the promise of a space age impossible because "the earth is the very quintessence of the human condition" (Arendt, 1958: 2–3). According to Arendt, the colonization of other planets testifies to human escapism – our tendency to move away from the *givenness* of our existence on Earth and to replace it with a world of our own construction. While Arendt could still ask whether we should use our human abilities in this direction, the perseverance of climate change outdates her position. Even if we reject the possibility of the terraforming of Mars because humanity is an Earth-bound creature, it can be argued that climate change enforces the terraforming of Earth to keep it a viable habitat for human existence in the future. After all, the Earth is correctly understood as a planet like any other, and it is also

DOI: 10.4324/9781003374381-3

increasingly depicted as a spaceship (Buckminster Fuller, 2008): not primarily "given", but the subject of management and control by humanity (Blok, 2022).

Whatever our ambition with terraforming might be, and before we can ask whether it is feasible or not, we need to ask the preliminary question how this "terra" has to be understood – irrespective of whether our subject is planet Earth or any other planet. This brings us to the main question of this chapter: what is the ontology of planets? Philosophical questioning of the ontology of planets is still in its infancy; yet some understanding of it seems necessary, if we are to theorize about the premises, challenges, and promises of space exploration. In this contribution, we map the philosophical terrain for our understanding of the ontology of planets as a core concept in the space age.

Our access point to this question is the ontology of planet *Earth*. Although the presence of life marks planet Earth as special among other planets, Earth shares a basic commonality with them – namely, its material existence. We take this commonality as a point of departure for our reflections on the ontology of both planet Earth and other planets. In this chapter, we ask for the ontology of this materiality of planets. We consult the ontology of planet Earth as I developed it in an earlier contribution (Blok, 2019), explore the ontology of planets as absolute boundary of the natural habitats on Earth, and reflect on the opportunities and limitations such ontology provides for future human colonies on other planets.

In the next section ("A Unique Feature of Planet Earth: the Disaster of Climate Change as Access to Earth and World"), we distinguish between Earth and World and argue that Earth, not World, provides access to the ontology of planets. In the section that follows ("The Ontology of Planet Earth"), we develop three principles of the ontology of planet Earth. In "The Ontology of Planets", we consider these principles as constituents of the ontology of planets. In this context, we also consider to what extent other Worlds can also be conceived on other planets that are founded on the materiality of planets. In the final section of the chapter, we draw some conclusions.

A Unique Feature of Planet Earth: The Disaster of Climate Change as Access to Earth and World

We start our reflection with a negative indication on the ontology of planets, as provided by the climatic disaster that threatens human survival on planet Earth. Etymologically speaking, a disaster concerns the loss of a guiding star that determines our destiny, fortune, or fate – the loss of ground beneath our feet. What is this star that can take away its guidance due to climate change?

In the phenomenological tradition, World is the meaningful environment in which we are intentionally involved and know how to live and act with other human and non-human beings. It concerns a relative stable background condition for our engagement with human and non-human beings, which is rather in the foreground. The climatic disaster confronts us with the experience that this stable worldly background is not freestanding but embedded in the instabilities and volatilities of the Earth system. In times of climate change we learn that World depends on Earth. In this sense, climate change shifts our attention from World to Earth (Blok, 2022).[2]

With this reference to the disaster of climate change, we also receive a first indication of the difference between planet Earth and other planets. Human and non-human beings already live in a meaningful World in which they are intentionally involved. This World not only happens but depends on Earth. We could then say that human and non-human acting and living in a meaningful World is a characteristic that distinguishes planet Earth from other planets.

Climate change shows us that the Earth is the ground of our living and acting in the World. The givenness of Earth is not only a prerequisite for the emergence of human and non-human beings at an ontic level, i.e. at the level of beings. In the philosophical tradition, a distinction is made between the ontic and the ontological, between beings and the being of beings, their essence or meaning. Traditionally, the origin of the being of beings is for instance found in a transcendent *idea* (Plato), in the categories of thinking (Kant), in our being-in-the-world (Heidegger), etc. But if human and non-human beings always live and act in a meaningful World in which they are intentionally involved, we see that the givenness of Earth is a prerequisite also at the ontological level – the condition of possibility of our living and acting in a meaningful World.

As a geological entity, the Earth was there long before human and non-human living beings emerged. Our living and acting in the World emerges, unfolds, and expands out of Earth, and threatens to go back into the Earth again due to climatic disaster. After our extinction, the Earth would no longer have the human and non-human World as its unique characteristic, but it would continue to exist. The disaster of climate change doesn't concern the Earth. So the notion of a disaster tells us that our normal vocabulary doesn't really concern the ontology of planets, but rather the World in which we are intentionally involved.

Relational philosophers like Bruno Latour acknowledge Earth's history before humans, but nonetheless think of the Earth only in relation to human existence – as World. This is less a mistake than a habit: philosophers generally tend to think of the materiality of planet Earth from the perspective of organic life or the biosphere, rather than from the geophysical, elemental perspective of the inanimate realms of the lithosphere, hydrosphere, and atmosphere (Harman, 2009). If we want to discuss the ontology of planet Earth, rather than World, we should reject any characteristic that is derived from our human and non-human involvement in the World. With this, we do not want to claim a priori that Worlds on other planets are impossible (we come back to this question in "The Ontology of Planets" later in the chapter), but that we should start with the materiality of planet Earth, when reflecting on the ontology of planets, not with the ontology of World.

To think the Earth beyond World is a difficult task, as it seems to reach beyond our living and acting in the world and, therefore, to challenge the very grounds of our thinking. Maybe the Earth is something like Kant's thing-in-itself; or the exterior milieu that remains exterior to any interiority of World. This exterior milieu cannot be objectified by science, as it would become World thereby, something measurable and calculable – yet according to formulas that are strange to Earth as planet. We can only access this exteriority by allowing ourselves to be responsive to it as exteriority.

The Ontology of Planet Earth[3]

a) The Principle of Conativity as Characteristic of the Ontology of Planet Earth

The disaster of climate change enables us to experience the volatility of the Earth system and its destabilizing powers over our everyday World. Yet this volatility also provides a first positive indication on the ontology of planets.

The starting point for our considerations is an old philosophical insight that is nowadays increasingly accepted in science: the idea that not only humans, but all things, have agency (Latour, 1993). One of the sources of this idea that inanimate beings have agency is the philosophy of Spinoza. According to Spinoza, "each thing, as far as it can by its own power, strives [*conatur*] to persevere in its own being" (Spinoza, 1992, part 3, proposition 6). According to this view, not only trees, animals, and humans, but each and every being is conative, including stones, sand dunes, and volcanoes. For Spinoza, this conativity is not an *ontic* will or impulse of *living* systems toward self-preservation, but an *ontological* principle of *all* beings: "The conatus to preserve itself is the very *essence* of a thing" (Spinoza, 1992: part 3, proposition 7 (emphasis added)). We can take inspiration from Spinoza and frame Earth's conativity as a cosmogenic or worldbuilding capacity to generate and establish the being or identity of material entities that constitute our reality.

We are legitimized to refer to a worldbuilding capacity of the Earth, because conativity is not limited to living systems.[4] All bodies are conative, from stones to humans (see Bennett, 2010: 2–3). Conativity is not only a principle of living nature, but a more general principle of the materiality of the Earth. But conativity also extends agency, traditionally thought to pertain to the living, or some of them, and to the inanimate – thus establishing something like "living matter" as a key element in Earth's generation and self-regulation as a dynamic system (Vernadsky, 1998; Clark, 2011).

To what extent can we consider conativity to be *essential* for the materiality of the Earth? Differently put: to what extent does conativity articulate the very *identity* of material entities? In Spinoza's view, only one common substance – *Deus sive Natura* – constitutes the universe. All separated material entities that compose our reality are *modes* or *modifications* of this one substance. As such a mode, each material entity is resistant to everything that can take its existence away, and this resistance is precisely the conativity or striving to preserve oneself as such a mode of the common substance (Spinoza, 1992: part 3, proposition 6). Conativity is essential, then, because it *differentiates* the identity of material entities from the common but undifferentiated substance – it articulates and establishes the self or identity of the tree and the stone, for instance, *as* modes of this common substance (*self*-perseverance) – and prevents at the same time their relapse in this common substance (self-*perseverance*).

Spinoza's idea of an undifferentiated common substance is not an example of a "demented ontology", "bending a continuous plastic material without separation" (Neyrat, 2019: 19), but the condition of possibility of separation, i.e. of differentiated identities of material entities. If we frame Spinoza's idea of a common substance in more profane terms and highlight the "naturalistic" framework that our ontology of planets is interested in, we could argue that all the material entities that we encounter on Earth – the stone, the tree, human beings, any artifact – are modes or modifications of the materiality of the Earth. We could then be tempted to bring the ontological fact that each material entity strives to preserve itself (*self*-perseverance) down to an ontic level – namely to the metabolic relation to the Earth as resource that constitutes the tree, the stone, human beings, and artifacts in their striving for self-preservation. But that would be a mistake. If that striving is indeed *essential* for each material entity, then conativity cannot be understood, at an ontic level, merely as powering a struggle for persistence in and by each individual entity. It must remain at an ontological level – as that impulse[5] in the undifferentiated materiality of the Earth to differentiate and establish material entities as modes (of the undifferentiated materiality of the Earth).

The essentiality of conativity for material entities shows that conativity is not a will or power of material entities to preserve themselves – a form of *autopoiesis* (Maturana and Varela, 1980) – but rather a principle of the *appearance* of Earth's materiality *as* stone, tree, human, artifact, and so on. Earth's conativity is literally an endeavoring, an effort – and its essentiality consists in the fact that it articulates and establishes the differentiated identities of material entities *as* modes of the undifferentiated materiality of the Earth.

The importance of these two aspects of conativity is also confirmed by recent insights into earth systems sciences; Earth's history is characterized by an inherent instability in which life forms but also inanimate conditions of life like climate changes emerge, adapt to the changing environment, and disappear again: "The vision that has been emerging, through a succession of discoveries, controversies and convergences, is one in which instability and upheaval, rhythmical movement and dramatic changes of state are ordinary aspects of Earth's own history" (Clark, 2011: xii). This rhythmical movement of the Earth indicates the mobile and active conativity of the undifferentiated materiality of the Earth, out of which differentiated material entities or relatively stable bodies like stones and trees up to the world of the biosphere and noosphere emerge (*self*-perseverance) and maintain (self-*perseverance*) themselves before they recede again in the undifferentiated materiality of the Earth.[6] This recession in undifferentiated materiality does not only apply to organic life that composts after its death; a stone also dissolves due to erosion in the course of (deep) time.[7]

A first round of reflection reveals the principle of conativity as the principle of planet Earth, which is not an ontic will or impulse of material entities but an ontological endeavor to differentiate the identity of material entities up to the world of the biosphere and the noosphere, and as such, deviations from this undifferentiated materiality. Conativity as *self*-perseverance and self-*perseverance* of Earth is the first characteristic of the ontology of planet Earth that we can discern.

b) The Pre-Individual Generative Capacity as Characteristic of the Ontology of Planet Earth

As a consequently of the principle of conativity as the first characteristic of the ontology of planet Earth, "I", as a material entity, am not primarily conative. On the contrary, "I" am the performative constituent of the conativity of the undifferentiated materiality of planet Earth. This means that conativity as a principle of planet Earth consists in the endeavor to differentiate and preserve the identity of material entities like stones and trees, me and you, from undifferentiated matter – as modes of this materiality of planet Earth. As such an origin of the identity of material entities, the undifferentiated materiality of planet Earth itself has to be understood as non-identity or pre-individual generative capacity. The material entities are transgressing the non-identity of the undifferentiated materiality of the Earth and remain at the same time embedded in this conative or "vibrant" materiality of the Earth (cf. Bennett, 2010), like a ripple in the water that emanates from the ocean and remains embedded in it at the same time.

The dynamic character of Earth's conativity can be conceived as *metabole* in the broadest sense of the word, i.e. change.[8] Unlike the metaphysical tradition, which finds its point of departure in a steady material being that can subsequently change, the movement of the Earth shouldn't be understood out of that which is generated by *metabole*, i.e. the material entities that are performatively constituted by the conativity of the materiality of the Earth. Conceptualized this way, the movement as character of the Earth's conativity is reduced to what is moved in favor of its presence as a being, while the Earth is not such a being; the being of the Earth *is* in the way of such movement. We can compare this endeavor to differentiate the identity of material entities with Kauffman's ideas about the *origins of order*, i.e. the spontaneous emergence of order out of chaos by the self-organization of complex systems (Kauffman, 1993). Earth's history with its evolution of a wide range of landscapes and species shows the limitlessness of the undifferentiated materiality of planet Earth as a domain of generative capacity out of which such differentiations emerge and in which they in the end recede again.

This second round of reflection on the Earth as planet reveals, then, a second characteristic of its ontology. The Earth has to be conceived as a pre-individual generative capacity that spontaneously articulates and emits the identity of individual material entities. The Earth is a reservoir of spontaneous material flows as a condition of possibility for the emergence of each and every material entity. The materiality of planet Earth is not only characterized by a non-identity or a pre-individual generative capacity, but is also always heterogeneous to, and always res-cends (as opposed to the idea of trans-cendence) any actual material entity as differentiation from this undifferentiated materiality of the Earth. With this, we introduce a dualist notion of the ontology of planet Earth, namely as undifferentiated materiality that constitutes a domain of spontaneous generative capacity out of which the identity of material entities emerges as differentiations. The undifferentiated materiality of the Earth concerns the non-identity or pre-individual whereas differentiated material entities concern the identity of material entities up to the world of the biosphere and the noosphere in which we live and act.

c) The Responsive Conativity of a Subset of Conative Material Entities as Characteristic of the Ontology of Planet Earth

According to Spinoza, the materiality of the Earth is not only conative but also *associative*; this means not only that the conativity of the Earth articulates and establishes material entities as differentiated modes of undifferentiated materiality that can *affect* other such differentiated entities in the environment, but also that these differentiated entities are at the same time always already *affected* by other entities, which are in their turn also performatively constituted by the conativity of the materiality of the Earth. From a Spinozian perspective, each mode of the materiality of the Earth has to be seen as a composition of simple modes that affect and are affected by one another, i.e. that they are primarily *responsive* to one another and form the relatively stable bodies that we encounter in the environment, ranging from simple bodies like stones and minerals that constitute the geosphere, to complex bodies like human beings and to complex networks and alliances of bodies like the world of the biosphere and the noosphere. Or as Jane Bennett puts it:

> Because each mode suffers the actions on it by other modes, actions that disrupt the relation of movement and rest characterizing each mode, every mode, if it is to persist, must seek new encounters to creatively compensate for the alterations or affections it suffers. What it means to be a "mode", then, is to form alliances and enter assemblages: it is to mod(e)ify and be modified by others.
>
> *(Bennett, 2010: 22)*

While Spinoza inspires new materialists like Bennett to see a convergence between the geosphere, biosphere, and noosphere, as all these spheres can be characterized by conativity and associativity or responsiveness, we reject such a convergence.[9] While the world of the biosphere and the noosphere are constituted by alliances of material entities that affect and are affected by each other and constitute a meaningful World in which these material entities are responsive to each other, this is not the case with the geosphere of the Earth. Stones and minerals, elements like water and air, Earth dynamics like plate tectonics, volcanoes and hurricanes *affect* this World by its destabilizing perturbations, may *afford* the responsiveness of the biosphere to sustain the Earth as condition for biological life (Lovelock, 1987), or may afford the responsiveness of the noosphere to sustain the meaningful World in which we humans live and act in times of climate change, but the Earthly geosphere is not itself *responsive* to affordances set by these human and non-human entities in the World.

A first indication of the non-responsive conativity of the geosphere of planet Earth is that the Earth as a planet emerged in the cosmic history long before human and non-human responsiveness emerged on the planet. The emergence of the Earth in Earth history is a necessary condition for the emergence of human and non-human responsiveness, but not itself responsive to these human and non-human entities. Although the worlds of the biosphere and the noosphere are actually generated by the spontaneous generative capacity of the Earth (and the Sun),[10] it is in no way necessary; it would have been perfectly possible that World never emerged in the Earth history, just as Mars or Jupiter didn't give rise to a biosphere beyond their geosphere so far. The conativity of the Earth generates the identity of material entities, ranging from rocks to animals and from trees to the built environment. But to the extent that human and non-human entities always live and act in alliances, ecosystems, or worlds in which these entities are responsive to the Earth as geosphere and to other entities that constitute the world of the biosphere and the noosphere, the conativity of the Earth is a *prerequisite* for the responsiveness that constitutes World (Blok, 2022), but not necessarily responsive itself. The conativity of the Earth is a necessary condition for World constitution, but not a sufficient condition yet.[11] In fact, not only human activity can destroy the existing world in times of climate change, but also the elementary forces of the conativity of the Earth can affect, alter, or even disrupt existing worlds. This is indicated by historical examples like the eruption of Mount Vesuvius that disrupted the world of Pompei, the earthquake that disrupted the world of Haiti, or hurricane Katrina that disrupted the world of New Orleans, but constitutes a spontaneous generative domain that is devoid of any given responsiveness to these worlds.

The constitution of World requires the emergence of material entities that are not only constituted by their conativity, but also co-constituted by their responsiveness to other material entities; this responsiveness constitutes the World in which human and non-human entities are at home. While the conative material entities that constitute the Earth are a necessary condition for the emergence of life on Earth and our living and acting in the World, the responsiveness of a subset of conative material entities constitutes the sufficient condition for the emergence of the World in which entities become responsive to each other. An example of this responsiveness is the responsiveness of material entities to the conativity of the Earth, that constitutes the world of the bio-sphere as atmospheric homeostasis of the Earth system (Lovelock, 2006).

If we conceptualize the conative responsiveness of material entities at an ontological level, i.e. at the level of the articulation and establishment of the identity of material entities in the World, we can conclude that the identity of these material entities is not only performatively constituted by the con-ativity of the Earth as its ground (first principle of the conativity of the Earth), because the identity of material entities in the World is at the same time constituted by their responsiveness to other material entities. In the differentiation of material entities by the conativity *of* the Earth, a subset of these conative entities is thus co-constituted by its responsiveness *to* other conative and responsive conative entities that constitute the world of the biosphere and the noosphere, in which these entities are interconnected and interdependent. Together, these conative and responsive material entities constitute the World in which we live and act. A third round of reflection on the materiality of the Earth thus reveals the *responsive* conativity of a subset of conative material entities as a third principle of the ontology of planet Earth.

With this, we introduce a dualist notion of the conativity of material entities, allowing us to limit the first principle of the ontology of planet Earth to the conativity as *self*-perseverance and self-*perseverance* of all material entities. This principle enables us to acknowledge the Earth as rock and mineral, Earthly rhythms like plate tectonics and volcanoes, etc., which constitute the geosphere. The third principle of the ontology of planet Earth enables us to identify a subset of conative material entities, which are not only constituted by their conativity but are also co-constituted by their responsiveness to other material entities, ranging from their responsiveness to conative material entities like volcanoes and earthquakes to other responsive conative material entities like trees, animals, and humans.

This dualist notion of the conativity of material entities implies a funda-mental *asymmetry* between the conativity of Earth and the responsive conativity of World. This asymmetry is not only an epistemic asymmetry as limitation of what is known – the Earth as *terra incognita* – but also an ontological asym-metry; the Earth as pre-individual generative capacity that differentiates and emits the identity of material entities without the possibility of being identified itself (second principle of the ontology of planet Earth). This generative capa-city of the Earth constitutes the material entities that are characterized by self-perseverance (first principle of the ontology of planet Earth). This Earth is a condition of the possibility for the constitution of World. This World is not only constituted by the generative capacity of the Earth that constitutes material entities, but co-constituted by their responsiveness to the conativity of the Earth (third principle). Earth and World are interconnected but not interdependent – the conativity of Earth is a necessary condition for the responsive conativity of the World but not the other way around – and Earth remains heterogeneous in relation to each and every World. World is dependent on Earth, which can disrupt it by its perturbation, and can spontaneously generate new conditions for the World.

The Ontology of Planets

Until now, our ontology of planet Earth didn't take into account that this particular planet is characterized by human and non-human life as the peculiar characteristic that marks this planet out as unique in the universe. For this reason, we were able to refer not only to stones but also to trees and humans as performative constituents of the responsive conativity of Earth that constitutes World in the previous section. If we now want to try and transfer this ontology of planet Earth to other planets, the question is how to distinguish between the responsive conativity involved in the constitution of Earth and World in comparison with the conativity involved in the constitution of other planets.

In "A Unique Feature of Planet Earth: the Disaster of Climate Change as Access to Earth and World", a distinction between Earth and World was introduced. We later suggested that, in building an ontology of planet Earth, we should reject any characteristic derived from World, In "The Ontology of Planet Earth", we reflected on the materiality of planet Earth, pivoting it on the notion of conativity. Although we concentrated on the principle of conativity to establish the identity of material beings on Earth, we can argue that the same principle of conativity functions on other planets like Mars, leading to another set of material entities, such as stones, sand dunes, and minerals. To the extent that each material entity is resistant to everything that can take its existence away, *self*-perseverance and self-*perseverance* occur as much on/with planet Earth as they do on/with Mars or any other planet that exists. The conativity of planets differentiates these material entities from the undifferentiated materiality of planets in which they are embedded (*self*-perseverance) and prevents their relapse into the undifferentiated materiality of planets again (self-*perseverance*). The conativity of the materiality of planets is the first principle of the ontology of planets. It establishes the identity of material entities like sand or rocks that constitute planet Earth or any other exoplanet as differentiation of the undifferentiated materiality of planets.

If the principle of conativity of planets differentiates the identity of material entities like rocks and stones that constitute planets from the undifferentiated materiality of planets as modes of this materiality, then the ontology of planets is twofold. The principle of conativity differentiates the identity of material entities (stone, sand, rock, minerals) that constitute the planet, which remains embedded in the non-identity or pre-individual generative capacity of the undifferentiated materiality of planets, like a grain of sand emanates from the desert and remains embedded in it at the same time. The ontology of planets is not only characterized by the non-identity or pre-individual generative capacity that constitutes the identity of individual material entities, but this non-identity of the materiality of planets is always heterogeneous to, and always res-cends, actual material entities as differentiations form this undifferentiated materiality. The materiality of planets is limitless and undifferentiated as a domain of generative capacity out of which differentiations emerge, such as certain rocks and minerals. The non-identity or pre-individual generative capacity of the materiality of planets constitutes the identity of material entities and always res-cends actual and possible material entities as differentiations from this undifferentiated materiality of planets, and is the second characteristic of the ontology of planets.

In the case of planet Earth, the principle of conativity is accompanied by the principle of responsiveness that also differentiates plants, animals, and humans from the undifferentiated materiality of planets as modes of this materiality, while in the case of planet Mars, plants, animals, and humans are not differentiated until now. Based on the dualist notion of planets as undifferentiated materiality (non-identity) out of which the identity of the material entities emerge that constitute these planets, we can argue that the commonality has to be found at the level of the conativity of material entities (first principle) and the non-identity or pre-individual generative capacity of undifferentiated materiality (second principle), while the difference has to be found at the level of the responsiveness of a subset of differentiated conative material entities that constitute the World (third principle), which differs in the case of Earth and Mars. At the level of differentiated entities, several commonalities can be found – i.e. oxygen, iron, magnesium, aluminum, and similar composite rocks can be found on both planet Earth and Mars – but planet Earth also contains different differentiated entities like trees and animals that are not only conative but also responsive, and constitute the World in which we live and act.

While the first two principles of the ontology of planet Earth can be extended to the ontology of planets, we can argue that the difference might be found in the responsiveness as the third principle of the ontology of planet Earth. In the previous section, we saw that material entities are not only conative but also affected by other conative entities, which are in their turn also performatively constituted by the conativity of planet Earth. The responsive conativity of planet Earth constitutes material entities that are responsive to one another and form the relatively stable bodies that we encounter in the environment, ranging from stones, seas, and landscapes in which we live and act. These types of complex entities, ecosystems, or worlds have not been found on Mars or any other exoplanet so far. We can argue, therefore, that the first two principles of the ontology of planet Earth are common with other planets, while the principle of responsiveness is the unique characteristic of the ontology of planet Earth. For this reason, we can say that the World in which we live and act is a unique characteristic of planet Earth, which cannot be found on other planets.

If the principle of conativity is understood as a necessary yet not sufficient condition of possibility for the emergence of World (first principle), this principle has to be seen as a necessary condition for the emergence of material entities on each and every planet. In the case of Mars, the principle of conativity solidifies the magma on Mars and constitutes an igneous rock (self-perseverance), which due to wind and water is pulverized again in sand in the course of time. The difference has to be found in the particular arrangement of material entities in the case of planet Earth and in the case of planet Mars, for instance. In the case of Mars, the conativity differentiates a particular arrangement of sand dunes, rocks, and minerals that are incomparable with the arrangement of planet Earth.

In the case of planet Earth, different Worlds are nested within each other. The world of the noosphere exhibits unique properties like cultural phenomena, and is nested in the world of the biosphere in which plants and animals constitute a dynamic ecosystem on which humans living and acting in the World depend, which is again embedded in a "bacterial" World of metabolic processes of "microbial intra-actions [which] have nothing to do with humans", on which animals and humans living and acting in the World depend, etc. (Hird, 2009: 26). The condition of possibility of human and non-human metabolism in the human World has to be found in the bacteria that constitute the bacterial World, and in this regard we can say that the world of the noosphere is *grounded* in the world of the biosphere as its condition of possibility. In a similar vein, we can argue that this world of the biosphere is nested in the Earth as minerals, elements and rocks that constitute the planet on which human, animal, plant, and bacterial life depends.

While material entities like sand and stones can be found on both planet Earth and planet Mars, at least to a certain extent, the world of the biosphere or the noosphere cannot be found on planet Mars. With this, however, we don't necessarily have to argue for an evolution starting with the conativity of material entities, moving forward to the responsive conativity of material entities like bacterial, plant, animal, and in the end human life if certain conditions are met. First, although material entities like sand and minerals serve as a necessary condition of possibility for the emergence of World, in the case of planet Earth it is not necessary to assume that the principle of conativity is always accompanied by the principle of responsivity and will always lead to the world of the biosphere via a bacterial World in the future. Second, it might be the case that we discover planets in the future that are governed by conativity and responsiveness, or that responsiveness will emerge in Mars history, for instance. But this doesn't mean that Mars would necessarily evolve in a similar way as planet Earth. It might be the case that other planets evolve heterogeneously in completely different directions due to crisis – like the dinosaur World disappearing by accident due to an asteroid impact on Earth, or like the world of the noosphere that might disappear one day due to climate change. Other planets might evolve heterogeneously in different directions due to the unlimited richness of the conativity and responsivity of material entities, which continuously generate new material entities (*self*-perseverance) and probe new ways to preserve its own existence (self-*perseverance*), as speculative biologist Gert van Dijk shows with his fictive planet Furaha.[12] Third, our World is not necessarily an end state of the World but remains open-ended, as the responsive conativity of the materiality of Earth is generative and evolves iteratively, with the responsive conativity of material entities generating novel material entities responsive to each other in unforeseeable ways and constituting new emerging Worlds. There is not one unique World, but open-ended Worlds that are nested in each other in a variety of heterogeneous ways.

The embedding of the open-ended futurability of Worlds in the conativity of planets has the advantage that it prevents our overly investing in future Worlds while neglecting the rich potentiality that the concrete materiality of planets provides (Blok, 2019). The limitlessness and complexity of the materiality of planets consists in the fact that this materiality is never exhausted by the material entities it constitutes, is always richer and more complex than any actual material entity, and res-cends all actual and possible material entities. The conativity of planets is indeed characterized by the non-identity or pre-individual generative capacity that constitutes the identity of the materiality of planets, and as such *grounds* the futurity of any possible World that we will find on exoplanets in the future.

The conativity of the materiality of planets is not only the ground for the emergence of material entities like stones, rocks and sand dunes that constitute planet Earth and planet Mars at an ontic level. If a subset of these conative material entities are already responsive to each other in the world of the biosphere or noosphere, the conativity of the materiality of planets is also the ground of each and every World at an ontological level, whether it is a world of the biosphere or the noosphere we find on planet Earth or any other World we might find on other planets in the future. Each and every World emerges, unfolds, and expands out of the conativity of the materiality of planets, and goes back to that undifferentiated materiality when it ends.

Conclusions

In this chapter, we raised the philosophical question of the ontology of planets, as this is a prerequisite for theorizing about the premises, challenges, and promises of space exploration. In the first section, we mapped the philosophical terrain for our understanding of planets as a core concept in the space age, by reflecting on the ontology of planet Earth. We argued that the ontology of the Earth provides access to the ontology of planets. In the second section, we developed three principles of the ontology of planet Earth: 1) the conativity of the materiality of planet Earth establishes the identity of material entities that constitute the planet; 2) the non-identity or pre-individual generative capacity of the materiality of planet Earth constitutes a domain of generative capacity that articulates and emits the identity of material entities and always res-cends actual and possible material entities as differentiations from this undifferentiated materiality; 3) the responsiveness of a subset of conative material entities to other material entities constitutes the world of the biosphere and noosphere of planet Earth.

In the third section, we considered these ontological principles in the context of other planets. While the first two principles seem to also apply beyond Earth, the third principle enables us to distinguish between planet Earth and other planets. This does not mean that we should reject the possibility of discovering Worlds on exoplanets in the future. Although future research is needed to reflect on the interdependency of Earth and World in case of planet Earth, in order to explore the possibility of World constitution on other planets, the embeddedness of the open-ended futurability of Worlds in the conativity of planets enables us to engage the cosmogenic or worldbuilding capacity of planets to explore new future Worlds, whether on planet Earth or any other planet.

Funding Information

This work is part of the research program Ethics of Socially Disruptive Technologies, which is funded through the Gravitation program of the Dutch Ministry of Education, Culture, and Science and the Netherlands Organisation for Scientific Research under Grant number 024.004.031.

Notes

1 https://www.persephone-project.com/ourstory-1 (last visited July 5, 2022)
2 The notions World and Earth remind us of Heidegger's use of the terms, for instance in his essay on the origin of the work of Art. Although I am inspired by Heidegger's notion of World, I have also been very critical about his conceptualization of the Earth (Blok, 2016a). This criticism has been a major inspiration to develop a concept of World and Earth that can help philosophical reflection in times of climate change.
3 Parts of section 3 are based on an earlier contribution (Blok, 2019).
4 The distinction between *living* nature and *dead* matter is already questioned as a typical *modern* distinction (Jonas, 1966). Also for Spinoza, conativity is not limited to living systems. In this chapter, we conceive conativity as a principle of Earth's materiality, thus including nature.
5 *Conatio* is a translation of the Greek *horme*, impulse or onset.
6 In this conceptualization of the conativity of the Earth, we deviate from Spinoza's original intuitions, which were precisely monist by nature.
7 It should be clear that we only took inspiration from Spinoza's idea of conativity, without claiming that our philosophical reflection is in any way consistent with his framework or system. For instance, the idea of a recession in undifferentiated materiality is not to be found in Spinoza's work. Also, while I claim that "I" am not conative whereas the materiality that constitutes "me" is, Spinoza would disagree.
8 Originally, the Latin word *planeta* indicates a roaming or moving star.
9 In this, we do not only criticize Bennett, but also our own earlier work (Blok, 2016b).
10 In fact, the biosphere is as much generated by the Earth as it is generated by the Sun, as Vernadsky (1998) already indicated. The further discussion of the role of the Sun in World constitution is beyond the scope of this chapter.
11 The question how non-responsive conativity (Earth) can give rise to responsive conativity (World) is beyond the scope of this chapter.
12 www.planetfuraha.org/ (last visited: 14–7-22).

References

Arendt, H. (1958). *The Human Condition*. Chicago: Chicago University Press.

Bennett, J. (2010). *Vibrant Matter: A Political Ecology of Things*. Durham: Duke University Press.

Blok, V. (2016a). "Thinking the Earth after Heidegger: Critical Reflections on Meillassoux's and Heidegger's Concept of the Earth". *Environmental Ethics* 38 (4): 441–462.

Blok, V. (2016b). "The Human Glanze, the Experience of Environmental Distress and the 'Affordance' of Nature: Toward a Phenomenology of the Ecological Crisis". *Journal of Agricultural and Environmental Ethics*, 28 (5): 925–938. doi:10.1007/s10806-015-9565-8.

Blok, V. (2019). "Nothing Else Matters: Towards an Ontological Concept of the Materiality of the Earth in the Age of Global Warming". *Research in Phenomenology*, 49: 65–87.

Blok, V. (2022). "The Earth Means the World to Me: Earth- and World-Interest in Times of Climate Change", Di Paola, M., Pellegrino, G. (Eds.), *Handbook of Philosophy of Climate Change*. doi:10.1007/978-973-030-16960-2_105–101. Cham: Springer.

Buckminster Fuller, R. (2008). *Operating Manual for Spaceship Earth*. Zurich: Lars Müller Publishers.

Burges, K. (2014). "Space Ark Will Save Man from a Dying Planet". *The Times*, April 28.

Clark, N. (2011). *Inhuman Nature. Sociable Life on a Dynamic Planet*. Los Angeles: Sage.

Harman, G. (2009). *Prince of Networks: Bruno Latour and Metaphysics*. Melbourne: Re. press.

Herbert, F. (1990). *Dune*. Woodbury: Ace.

Hird, M. J. (2009). *The Origins of Sociable Life. Evolution after Science Studies*. New York: Palgrave MacMillan.

Jonas, H. (1966). *The Phenomenon of Life*. New York: Harper and Row.

Kauffman, S. A. (1993). *The Origins of Order. Self-organization and Selection in Evolution*. Oxford: Oxford University Press.

Latour, B. (1993). *We Have Never Been Modern*. Cambridge: Harvard University Press.

Lovelock, J. (1987). *Gaia: A New Look at Life on Earth*. Oxford: Oxford University Press.

Lovelock, J. (2006). *The Revenge of Gaia. Why the Earth Is Fighting Back – And How We Can Still Save Humanity*. New York: Penguin.

Maturana, H. R., and Varela, F. J. (1980). *Autopoiesis and Cognition*. Dordrecht/Boston: Reidel.

McKay, C. P., Toon, O. B., and Kasting, J. F. (1991). "Making Mars Habitable". *Nature*, 352: 489–496.

Neyrat, F. (2019). *The Unconstructable Earth. An Ecology of Separation*. New York: Fordham University Press.

Sagan, C. (1994) *Pale Blue Dot: A Vision of the Human Future in Space*. New York: Ballantine Books.

Spinoza, B. (1992). *Ethics: Treatise on the Emendation of the Intellect, and Selected Letters*, Trans. S. Shirly. Indianapolis: Hackett.

Vernadsky, V. 1998. *The Biosphere*. New York: Copernicus.

4

SIGNS OF LIFE

The Epistemology of Indirect Sensing

David Dunér

Introduction

The search for extraterrestrial life has increasingly consolidated a multi-disciplinary research program, astrobiology, dealing with empirical content that can be studied with scientific methods and theories (Horneck et al. 2016). At this very moment a rover, Perseverance, is rolling around on the surface of Mars searching for signs of life, particularly past microbial life, in environments that may have been suitable for harboring life in ancient times (NASA 2020). It landed successfully in the Jezero Crater on 18 February 2021 and will, with time and luck, give some answers to the long-disputed question as to whether Mars might have or have had life.

Now and then, reports have been published claiming that traces or indices have been found of existing or past life on Mars. Photographs of structures on the surface of Mars, some researchers conclude, reveal growing forms that are reminiscent of mushrooms, stromatolites and other morphological similarities found on Earth. As Joseph et al. (2019) claim: "There is no definitive proof, only a lot of evidence which shouts: Biology". The question is: did they see what they wanted to see, or, in other words, what can we conclude from a bare similarity? Without in situ and in vitro investigations, the proposed connection between the expression (biosignature) and the content (life) would be difficult to establish with an acceptable degree of certainty. Many research articles also discuss the possibility of spectroscopic analysis of exoplanet atmospheres which could reveal biogenic gases (e.g., Seager et al. 2016; Catling et al. 2018; Meadows et al. 2018; Olson et al. 2018). On 18 December 2020 it was announced that Breakthrough Listen, a privately funded search for extraterrestrial intelligence, had detected its first official candidate signal from outer space, named BLC-1. The news, without further confirmation of its accuracy, was leaked to

DOI: 10.4324/9781003374381-4

The Guardian, *The Washington Post*, *National Geographic*, *Scientific American*, and other media. BLC-1, it is claimed, stems from Proxima b, a planet of the red dwarf star Proxima Centauri – our nearest star, located 4.2 lightyears from Earth. The signal was received by Parkes Observatory, Australia, over 30 hours during April and May 2019.

This chapter concerns the epistemology of biosignatures individuated via remote sensing, as in each of the studies mentioned above: the question is how to tell whether these remotely sensed signs that we interpreted as possible signs of life really have a biogenic origin.

In the quest for life in the Universe, the most likely scenario is that we will one day find signs of life, or "biosignatures", indicating the occurrence, past or present, of certain biochemical processes originating in extraterrestrial biological activity. Biosignatures may be chemical substances (elements, molecules, etc.), but also physical features (structures, shapes, morphology, etc.), and physical phenomena (electromagnetic radiation, light, temperature, etc.). They may vary in scale from atomic to planetary magnitude, or perhaps even larger. They may be searched for on our nearest planets and moons as well as in other solar systems. Until we find ways to physically move around the cosmos, biosignature searches will mostly be done via remote sensing.

Coming across observable and verifiable biosignatures, we will consider the tenability of connecting them causally to the workings of organic life – that is, of considering these signs as expressions of a specific content, namely biochemical processes of extraterrestrial life. We will make or refute this connection from our human perspective, with our inventive minds that are a result of a particular biocultural evolution here on Earth (Dunér and Sonesson 2016; Dunér 2016). This chapter is concerned with how astrobiologists, as interpreters, establish these connections between expression and content. It is thus concerned with the criteria used to access, interpret, and understand possible life in outer space.

A Semiotic and Epistemological Problem

The problem of biosignatures is a semiotic and epistemological problem: how meaning can be discovered, deciphered, interpreted, and invented (Dunér 2019). At the extreme, one might say that the science of astrobiology cannot but invent connections between the signifier and the signified, the expression and the object, "signs of life" and "life", because of the distance between what terrestrial astrobiologists know about life, and conceive of as life, and the potentially infinite variations and versions of life that might in principle exist.

The first semiotic problem that arises with extraterrestrial biosignatures is spotting them as such – that is, realizing that there is a sign at all. Some regularity and order, such as finding a repetition in some pattern, is insufficient. The interpreter needs to identify the physical phenomenon as containing semiotic meaning, and a particular meaning that refers to the content "life." On Earth, both in the day-to-day and in science, the expression of a phenomenon can in most cases easily be connected to its content. Seeing the footprints of an animal, we can infer – based on previous knowledge – what kind of animal it is, its weight, and its direction. However, this semiotic confidence is drastically reduced when we turn to biosignatures of unknown forms of life. We are then compelled to make assumptions about both the expression (what counts as a sign) and the content (what counts as life). Our assumptions might be mistaken, which would lead to wrong interpretations, for example taking for a sign of life what is in fact just a remnant or outcome of some unknown or known abiotic process. Or, possibly worse in some cases, we might fail to make any assumptions at all and just miss it: the phenomenon encountered, "the signature", may not be recognized as a meaningful sign.

The difficulty here is that a physical phenomenon is meaningless as long as there is no one to recognize it as meaningful. Phenomena that we call biosignatures become meaningful when we interpret them as such – that is, as signs. Signs are the tools we use to make sense of the world, approach it, get access to it, and differentiate things from one another. Accordingly, biosignature detection is one tool among many to make sense of the data we receive from outer space. It is in our meaning-making practices that the "biosignatures" become biosignatures. And the biosignatures we detect exist as biosignatures just insofar as we approach them as meaningful. In this perspective, biosignatures are not solely "out there" – rather, to a decisive extent, they are in our own minds, marking ways in which these minds interact with the outer world. When the astrobiologist is interpreting biosignatures, then, he or she is involved in a meaning producing semiosis (Dunér 2018). This semiosis is triadic, containing expression, content, and interpreter – which in our case respond to "biosignature", "life", and "astrobiologist". Depending on how the interpreter makes or interprets the connection between the expression and the content, we have basically three types of sign relations, *icon*, *index*, and *symbol* – that is, sign relations based on similarity, causality, or convention. In the case of astrobiology, a Martian fossil would be an icon in the sense that it shows a morphological similarity with a living organism. A certain gas detected in the atmosphere of an exoplanet would be an index of life, not because it shares a similarity with the actual living organism, but because of the causal connection between the expression and content. And finally, an interstellar message would be a symbolic sign relation, when the signal received has no intrinsic similarity or causality with the content or meaning of the message, but has just an arbitrary connection that is a product of a cultural convention. The following will focus on the iconic and the indexical sign relations involved in the search for biosignatures.

The search for biosignatures is based on the human endeavor of connecting things with each other, and of selecting the right elements for the connection among a wider range of possible elements. We ask ourselves, what are the meaningful properties of the information we gather through spectrometers, radio or optical telescopes, etc.? Which signatures (phenomena) have meaning, and which others are just meaningless noise – and how to tell these apart? The signifier is directly given, but the signified is only indirectly present, through the hypothetical link with the signifier: the "life" (the signified) that we are searching for is just indirectly reachable for us, and we must content ourselves with the only thing that is directly given, the biosignature (the signifier). As interpreters, we determine the relation between the signifier and the signified by picking out those elements we assume to be relevant. The challenge of the astrobiologist is to pick the right elements (properties) of the signifier. For example, when examining a Martian rock, we need to pick out all and only those elements (shapes, molecules, etc.) that direct us to the signified, the living organism. And we need a reasonable explanation of the link between the signifier and the signified. Why, and how, would this particular gas be a metabolic result of a living organism? In what way is this shape a remnant of the morphology of a living organism? We need to know the physical processes that let us link the signifier with the signified. In outer space, we are likely not to know what we need to know.

Next, I will focus on two major cases in the search for signs of life, through in situ investigation and remote indirect sensing: (1) the differentiation of fossils and pseudofossils; and (2) the differentiation of biotic or abiotic processes.

Case 1: Fossils or Pseudofossils?

A perennial theme in paleontology is how to distinguish real remnants of living organisms from structures that just mimic living forms – or, how to distinguish fossils from pseudofossils. Pseudofossils, for example branching structures like manganese dendrites in limestone, kidney ore, moss agates resembling moss leaves, and other patterns in rock that arise through geological – not biological– processes, can easily be mistaken for fossil marks of life. This is a challenge already when tracing early life on Earth, and the challenge is only compounded when expanding our gaze to outer space. One obvious problem has to do with limitations on control samplings and experiments. For example, in 1996 announcements were made that fossilized life had been found in the Martian meteorite ALH84001 (see McKay et al. 1996). Viewed under an electron microscope, certain tube-like structures in the meteorite resembled fossilized bacteria. But there was no way to exclude that these structures had formed through abiotic processes, and more experiments on the same sample could not fix that. The only way to do so would have been to collect more meteorite material to control for hypotheses made regarding the first sample (Westall et al. 1998).

Fossil biosignatures are different from those individuated via remote-sensing not just because they are found in situ, but also because of their distinct sign relation. Fossil biosignatures share a morphological similarity with living organisms, and can thus be called bio-icons – expressing a sign relation based on similarity, where the expression shares some of the object's morphological properties, perceived against the background of other, dissimilar, properties. The most obvious examples of bio-icons are of course body fossils – those imprints of the hard parts of animals and plants, such as skeletons or foliage. In these cases, it is the very morphological complexity of the expression (the fossil) that directs us to infer the object (life), based on the supposition that it is highly improbable that such a complexity is the result of any (known) abiotic process.

Microscopic fossils, or microfossils, are more challenging. All life as we know it shares the characteristic of having internal volumes isolated from the surrounding environment by a cell membrane (Persson 2019). Based on this shared morphology, one can search for microscopic cellular structures – particularly because well-preserved fossil cells can be identical in size, shape, and structure to living single-cell organisms. But because these structures show little complexity overall, it is hard to distinguish them from structures of abiotic origins. For example, on Earth the Apex chert from Western Australia, dated at ~3.5 Ga, has been claimed both to be fossilized cells of filamentous bacteria or just a result of abiotic processes (Schopf 1993; Brasier et al. 2005).

But morphological similarity alone, be it macro or micro, is in any case not enough. Establishing the connection between the fossil and the living organism calls for a theory that explains the connection. To proclaim a fossil biosignature as such, we also need an explanation of how a living organism can become that fossil – a reverse theory, as it were, linking the supposed living organism with the biosignature. In other words, whatever morphological correlation is adduced, its dynamics must be theorized. This, of course, is problematic, because by themselves fossils are insufficient evidence for a complete understanding of the lives to which they refer: they do not give us complete information on the biochemical nature and dynamics of the living organism.

It is also a question of finding methods that let us detect this connection. Based on chemical analyses, the researcher sees similarities between the expression and the content, not because of structural similarity, but because they share some chemical properties. In the case of chemical biosignatures, some are bio-icons in the sense that the discovered biosignature has a chemical similarity or shared characteristics with the living organism; for example, complex biological macromolecules, such as carbohydrates, lipids, proteins, and nucleic acids (RNA and DNA). Most common biomolecules, however, usually modify and degrade, and the products (also called "molecular fossils") of this chemical breakdown (the diagenesis) have instead an indexical relation to the biological macromolecules, that is, they do not share a similarity, but rather has causal connection to the biomolecules.

Case 2: Indices of Biotic or Abiotic Processes?

As a sign caused by its object, the index has an unintentional, causal link or contact with its content. Indexicality is, in this respect, meaning by proximity or contiguity. This contiguity does not necessarily have to be of real physical causality: it could consist of mere closeness in space. The interpretation of indices requires empirical knowledge about recurrent connections between the sign and what it refers to.

The clearest examples of bio-indices in astrobiology are atmospheric, chemical biosignatures that may be traced back to the metabolic processes of living organisms.

Remote sensing of planetary environments for habitability and biosignatures goes back to the nineteenth century. In his *Cours de philosophie positive* (1830– 1842) the French positivist Auguste Comte said, concerning the celestial bodies, that "we will never by any means be able to study their chemical composition or their mineralogical structure" (Comte 1835, 2; Crowe 2008, 312). Some few decades later spectroscopy was developed – a new, powerful tool for searching extraterrestrial life. By analyzing the spectra caused by the molecular absorption or emission at molecule-specific photon wavelengths, the spectroscopists can infer the chemical composition of the atmospheres of distant planets. The first spectroscopic observations aiming for detecting oxygen and water in the Martian atmosphere were made by the astronomers William Huggins and Jules Janssen in the 1860s. By assuming water as a necessary condition for life, and by linking planetary environmental conditions (presence of water vapor in the atmosphere and liquid water on the surface) with the possibility for life to emerge and subsist, they found a way forward. Detection of water vapor in the atmosphere of a planet would then be a crucial indication that there might be life on its surface. In 1867, Janssen claimed to have discovered the presence of water vapor in the Martian atmosphere, but in fact it was probably a signature originating from Earth, not Mars (Raulin Cerceau 2013).

There are hopes that in the future we will be able to observe the absorption or emission properties of the atmospheres of small, rocky exoplanets (Seager 2014; Seager and Bains 2015). In the future, the European Extremely Large Telescope (E-ELT) will make it possible to perform spectroscopic analysis of the faint light of an exoplanet, and this might result in the first individuations of exoplanetary atmospheric biosignatures – although the interpretation of these spectra will obviously involve many difficulties. A first step in the search for biosignatures of exoplanets would be to study the temperature, size, mass, density, gravitation, and light conditions of the exoplanet; next, to search for indications of atmosphere, liquid water, clouds, surface, plate tectonics, daily rotation, seasons, and weather. The third step would be to look for bio-indices. All the while, our hopes rest on the assumption that certain gases in the atmosphere are produced by life (as we know from studies of our own terrestrial atmosphere), such as oxygen, ozone, methane, and carbon dioxide. Oxygen enrichment in the atmosphere could indicate the presence of oxygenic photosynthesis. Ozone, which is produced photochemically from biologically produced oxygen, could be another indication of biological activity; and methane could likewise be connected to the metabolism of living organisms. However, these gases could also be produced by abiotic processes and exist without any biological activity. Also, some gases that are the products of life on Earth, such as chloromethane, methanethiol, nitrogen dioxide, and ammonia, would not be detected with current exoplanetary sensing technologies, due to low amounts.

It might rather be the combination of gases and the quantity of them, that better reveals if there is life on a planet. Earth-like atmospheric bio-signatures disappear relatively quickly on a planet where life has ceased to exist. If there were to be a certain amount of a biosignature gas, it would need to have a continuous source. That such gases could be diagnostic for life was first suggested by Joshua Lederberg and James Lovelock in 1965 (Lederberg 1965; Lovelock 1965; Catling and Kasting 2007). This atmospheric phenomenon is also detectable by spectroscopy, as in the case of spectral analysis of Earthshine (Arnold et al. 2002, 2008). The simultaneous presence of oxygen and methane in a specific ratio could be assumed as spectral evidence of life. The sustainable source of these gases is life. The discovery of significant amounts of methane in the atmosphere of Mars then implies that there must be a recent or current source, otherwise the methane would rather quickly disappear. The source could be geological activity and water in the subsurface – or subsurface biology (Domagal-Goldman, Wright, et al. 2016).

Conclusion

The general epistemological problem of biosignatures is to recognize the signatures as meaningful, as signatures of life – as expressions of a content. One also needs to establish the connection between the expression and the content with some degree of certainty that will be acceptable for the scientific community and be able to rule out abiotic explanations for the signatures. The main message of this chapter is that the search for signs of life in the Universe is not just a question of scientific methods and theories, as a continuing endeavor of gathering empirical data – it is a question for philosophy and semiotics concerning the meaning-making processes of the human mind. The chapter aimed to bring some semiotic order among the profuse number of potential signs in the Universe by paying attention to the sign relations involved in the interpretation of biosignatures.

The central problem is about how we interpret signs, differentiate biosignatures from signatures that have no biological origin, and thus on what grounds we resolve to endow the world with meaning and identify signs of life from among a profuse number of signs in the universe. The scientific enterprise is an intrinsically human, Earth-bound cognitive-cultural endeavor. In order to solve these epistemological problems, astrobiology as a multidisciplinary scientific enterprise needs to, besides formulating general, tentative definitions of life (or of those life-like phenomena or processes that we are seeking, which remind us of Earth-like life), keep on searching for more material evidence and perform a greater number of in situ investigations that enable astrobiologists to rule out all abiotic explanations and come up with conclusive explanations of the causal connection between the "sign of life" and "life".

References

Arnold L (2008) Earthshine observation of vegetation and implication for life detection on other planets: a review of 2001–2006 works. *Space Sci Rev* 135:323–333. https://doi. org/10.48550/arXiv.0706.3798.

Arnold L, Gillet S, Lardière O, Riaud P, Schneider J (2002) A test for the search for life on extrasolar planets: looking for the terrestrial vegetation signature on the earthshine spectrum. *Astronomy and Astrophysics* 392 (1):231–237. https://doi.org/10.1051/ 0004-6361:20020933.

Brasier MD, Green OR, Lindsay JF, McLoughlin N, Steele A, Stoakes C (2005) Critical testing of Earth's oldest putative fossil assemblage from the *3.5 Ga Apex chert, Chinaman Creek, Western Australia. *Precambrian Res* 140 (1–2):55–102. https://doi. org/10.1016/j.precamres.2005.06.008.

Catling D, Kasting JF (2007) Planetary atmospheres and life. In *Planets and life: the emerging science of astrobiology*, eds. Sullivan WT, Baross JA, 91–116. Cambridge: Cambridge University Press.

Catling DC *et al.* (2018) Exoplanet biosignatures: a framework for their assessment. *Astrobiology* 18 (6):709–738. https://doi.org/10.1089/ast.2017.1737.

Comte A (1835) *Cours de philosophie positive: tome 2, contenant la philosophie astronomique et la philosophie de la physique.* Paris: Bachelier.

Crowe, MJ (2008) *The extraterrestrial life debate, Antiquity to 1915: a source book.* Notre Dame IN: University of Notre Dame Press.

Domagal-Goldman SD, Wright KE, co-lead eds. *et al.* (2016) The astrobiology primer v2.0. *Astrobiology* 16 (8):561–653. https://doi.org/10.1089/ast.2015.1460.

Dunér D (2016) Science: the structure of scientific evolutions. In *Human lifeworlds: the cognitive semiotics of cultural evolution*, eds. Dunér D, Sonesson G, 229–266. Pieterlen and Bern: Peter Lang.

Dunér D (2018) Semiotics of biosignatures. *Southern Semiotic Review* 9:47–63. http:// doi.org/10.33234/ssr.9.4.

Dunér D (2019) The history and philosophy of biosignatures. In *Biosignatures for astrobiology*, eds. Cavalazzi B, Westall F, 303–338. Cham: Springer. doi:10.1007/978- 3-319-96175-0_15.

Dunér D, Sonesson G, eds. (2016) *Human lifeworlds: the cognitive semiotics of cultural evolution.* Pieterlen and Bern: Peter Lang. doi:10.3726/978-3-653-05486-6.

Horneck G*et al.* (2016) AstRoMap European astrobiology roadmap. *Astrobiology* 16 (3):201–243. https://doi.org/10.1089/ast.2015.1441.

Joseph RG, Dass RS, Rizzo V, Cantasano N, Bianciardi G (2019) Evidence of life on Mars? *Journal of Astrobiology and Space Science Reviews* 1:40–81.

Lederberg J (1965) Signs of life: criterion system of exobiology. *Nature* 207:9–13. https:// doi.org/10.1038/207009a0.

Lovelock JE (1965) A physical basis for life detection experiments. *Nature* 207:568–570. https://doi.org/10.1038/207568a0.

McKay DS, Gibson EK Jr, Thomas-Keprta KL, Vali H, Romanek CS, Clemett S, Chillier XDF, Maechling CR, Zare RN (1996) Search for past life on Mars: possible relic biogenic activity in martian meteorite ALH84001. *Science* 273 (5277):924–930. doi:10.1126/science.273.5277.924.

Meadows VS *et al.* (2018) Exoplanet biosignatures: understanding oxygen as a biosignature in the context of its environment. *Astrobiology* 18 (6):630–662. https://doi. org/10.1089/ast.2017.1727.

NASA (2020) *Mars 2020 Mission Overview*. https://mars.nasa.gov/mars2020/mission/overview/ Retrieved 9 February 2023.

Olson SL *et al.* (2018) Atmospheric seasonality as an exoplanet biosignature. *The Astrophysical Journal Letters* 858 (2):7. doi:10.3847/2041-8213/aac171.

Persson, E *et al.* (2019) How will the emerging plurality of lives change how we conceive of and relate to life? *Challenges* 10 (1):32. doi:10.3390/challe10010032.

Raulin Cerceau F (2013) Pioneering concepts of planetary habitability. In *Astrobiology, history, and society: life beyond earth and the impact of discovery*, ed. Vakoch DA, 115–129. Berlin and Heidelberg: Springer. doi:10.1007/978-3-642-35983-5_6.

Schopf JW (1993) Microfossils of the Early Archean Apex chert: new evidence of the antiquity of life. *Science* 260 (5108):640–646. doi:10.1126/science.260.5108.640.

Seager S (2014) The future of spectroscopic life detection on exoplanets. *Proc Natl Acad Sci USA* 111 (35):12634–12640. https://doi.org/10.1073/pnas.130421311.

Seager S, Bains W (2015) The search for signs of life on exoplanets at the interface of chemistry and planetary science. *Science Advances* 1 (2):1–11. doi:10.1126/sciadv.150004.

Seager S, Bains W, Petkowski JJ (2016) Toward a list of molecules as potential biosignature gases for the search for life on exoplanets and applications to terrestrial biochemistry. *Astrobiology* 16 (6): 465–485. doi:10.1089/ast.2015.1404.

Westall F, Gobbi P, Gerneke D, Mazzotti G (1998) Ultrastructure in the carbonate globules of Martian meteorite ALH84001. In *Exobiology: Matter, Energy, and Information in the Origin and Evolution of Life in the Universe*, eds. Chela-Flores J, Raulin F, 245–250. Amsterdam: Kluwer. doi:10.1007/978-94-011-5056-9_34.

5

ALIEN WAYS OF KNOWING AND BEING

Speculations from the Lives of Earthly Non-Human Animals

Charles Foster

Introduction

Epistemology has a good claim to be the most fundamental of the philosophical disciplines. At least where X represents some kind of propositional knowledge, unless one knows how meaningfully one can say 'X exists, and has the following attributes', all other philosophising about X is rather in vain.

Many of our conclusions about the world depend on deductions we make from sense data. All our *philosophical* conclusions are a result of thinking – of a cognitive process. That is the case even if, on investigation, a train of philosophical inquiry is shown to have originated in our intuitions: we have still *thought* about whatever it is was prompted by our intuitions. That thinking is what makes our processing philosophical.

Epistemologists have three problems that are seldom recognised. The first is that we are very visual animals. We tend to neglect senses other than vision. The non-visual senses convey information. If, in reaching conclusions about the world outside our heads, the information conveyed by non-visual senses is ignored or not given the priority that visually mediated information is given, our conclusions are, to say the least, unlikely to be as epistemically satisfactory as they would be if all available information were taken into account. I return to this issue below. The second problem is a consequence of the first: for reasons that lie far back in our evolutionary history, our vision and our cognition are intimately related – so much so that it is often impossible to disentangle them (Pylyshyn, 1999; Collins and Olson, 2014; but cp Firestone and Scholl, 2015). In humans there is far more entanglement of cognition with vision than with other senses. We see this (and that phrase itself exposes our visual bias) in our speech. 'I see', we say, when we mean 'I understand'. 'Seeing is believing', we assert: it is also comprehending. This means that there is no such thing as

DOI: 10.4324/9781003374381-5

pristine thinking about thinking. Even our thinking about our modes of thinking is contaminated by visual reference.

The third problem is that our cognition (which is the only part of our functioning typically valued by philosophers, who are professional cognitisers) is (even for non-philosophers) framed in terms of language. Language determines to a large degree the use we make even of that small sample of information delivered via our eyes.

Robin Dunbar convincingly speculates that language evolved as a form of social grooming, to facilitate the brokering and maintenance of relationships that confer a survival benefit (Dunbar, 2009). In primates, actual, tactile grooming does this job well, but there is insufficient time to groom physically the number of desirable relatees. Language, which can groom many relatees at the same time, and very efficiently in terms of time and energy, steps in to fill the gap.

In humans, then, there is a coalition between vision, language and cognition. I will call that coalition *VLC*. It has given us much as a species. It has also inhibited us in significant ways. The VLC has infected our cognition. The infection makes cognition a poor instrument for determining fundamental questions about what we are and the place we inhabit.

We cannot decontaminate our cognition entirely. There is, indeed, little we can do by way of mitigation, because the faculties that might otherwise have been able to diagnose and treat the infection have themselves been badly affected. All we can do is recognise that our cognition is contaminated, and try to understand (while realising how our understanding has been hijacked by vision) how the contamination might have affected our view (there I go again) of reality.

So far, then, I have suggested that vision and language have colonised our understanding and are running most of the essential services. But how might that colonisation have affected us (if vision and language will, in an unguarded moment, let us ask and stammer out an answer to the question)?

The first observation (yes, sight again) results from the mere fact of the entanglement of vision, cognition and language. For we tend to regard our cognition and our language as essentially – quintessentially – *ours*. Whatever cognition is, we insist that it is related closely to our *self*. Certainly we choose our own words. Vision itself might have this tendency to a greater degree than, for instance, olfaction. Vision gives the illusion of the projection of our self out into the world (rather than gathering the world into us) in a way that olfaction and hearing and perhaps touch do not. In any event we can say that the effect of the vision–cognition axis is to promote an account of reality that is self-centred. When data stream into my eyes and images are formed on my retina and sent to my visual cortex, the images are translated almost instantaneously – and in terms of propositions framed in language – into things that have little or nothing to do with the source of the images or the naked, uncognitised images themselves. They are translated into my reflections on the images; my recollections of other experiences that my mind tells me are related to the images, and so on. All these reflections and recollections are parcelled up in language; and, crucially, in *my* language. On my retina, as I look out of the window now, are images of specific trees. By the time they have had even the most minimal processing in my brain, they have been transmuted into Charles Foster's thoughts about trees in general. So far as I'm concerned there are no *real* trees outside. I've magicked them away into self-referential and self-reverential abstractions. I've not *really* seen a tree for more than a millisecond since early childhood. As soon as I became an incurably VLC creature, trees vanished from the world.

This is unfortunate. I expect that trees are much more interesting than my thoughts about trees. This would seem to follow from the fact that my current appreciation of trees takes much less information into account in the consideration of trees than would be the case if all my senses were fully switched on and their inputs properly evaluated. More information – or simply the same basic information delivered in different sensory modalities – is unlikely to render a tree more boring. My childhood memories of trees tend to bear out this expectation. As the Romantics observed, childhood landscapes shimmer epiphanically. They are fuller than mine are now. They contain not just more significance, but more information. It seems reasonable – at least taken with our consideration of the demerits of the VFC – to lay some of the blame for my current epistemic poverty on my cognition. As a child I was a less cognitive creature. The flow of data into my brain was less restricted, and when the data got there it was less mangled by my cognition. Plato observed that all real knowing is *anamnesis:* unforgetting. It's the process of stripping away the delusions about the nature of the cosmos (including the nature of trees) that have been generated by the VFC. Wordsworth didn't just have 'Intimations of Immortality from Recollections of Early Childhood'; he had more reliable intimations of the appearance and nature of trees.

The vanishing of trees, or their misconstruction, or the painting of trees in far fewer dimensions or far dowdier colours than they deserve, isn't just unfortunate; it's epistemologically troubling in a much wider and more fundamental sense. Can I know anything about anything other than my own thoughts?

I suspect, though I cannot know, that this connection between vision and cognition is a necessary connection, inherent, for the reasons I have suggested above, in the nature of vision itself.

There are, of course, senses other than vision. The dominance of vision is so great that unless our attention is specifically drawn to other senses, we tend not to be aware of those senses at all. As you are reading this chapter, scent molecules are being drawn constantly over your nasal epithelium, but unless there is a particular noxious or pleasant smell, you almost certainly will have been unaware of those scent molecules until I invited you to consider them. That is not because we have a poor sense of smell: it is very good. A master of wine, sniffing a claret, may be able to identify not only the vineyard and the year, but, if she knows the vineyard well, the field from which the grapes came.

It is troubling on many levels that we neglect our non-visual senses. It is troubling because we may be missing out on a great deal of pleasure that might otherwise have been ours. We are wired to receive so much more than we can be bothered to process – and there is reason, from wine tastings and other arenas where we do pay unusual attention to normally neglected senses, to suppose that a good deal of un-regarded sensation may be pleasurable, and that being switched more fully on produces a net hedonic benefit.

But it is philosophically troubling, too. For it means that even if we discount entirely the distorting effect of cognition on vision for which I have argued, we are still construing the world (and founding our speculations about the nature of the world) on the basis of a small proportion of the available data.

Let us suppose that there are only the five conventionally recognised senses. In fact, there are many more than that (Macpherson, 2011) and the others tend to be ignored by our conscious, world-construing minds even more systematically than hearing, olfaction, touch and taste, but I'll ignore these others for the purposes of this discussion. By and large we use only one of the five: vision. This means that we draw our sensory conclusions from (and base our philosophical speculations on) 20 per cent of the available information. One is unlikely to come to a remotely accurate or useful conclusion about the sort of place we inhabit if that is the evidence base. If I'm right, and that 20 per cent is twisted unrecognisably by our cognition, the situation is far worse. No wonder we are confused and unhappy and our philosophical sophistication vain. If you put rubbish into a system, you get rubbish out. If you put little information in, you will not get an accurate and nuanced answer. Our intuitions often are not hamstrung in the way our senses are. They may paint a more accurate picture (vision again) of the cosmos, and so allow us to inhabit it in a more informed way. But cognition insists that it, cognition, is the sole or best arbiter of the nature of a place: the tension between deluded cognition and enlightened intuition may be the source of some of our ontological queasiness.

There are two more neurobiological facts to take into account before we move into outer space.

The first is the basis of Aldous Huxley's famous observation that one of the functions of the brain is to act as a reducing valve, slowing the flow of data to a manageable dribble, and perhaps selecting, too, the types of information that are useful for survival (Huxley, 1954). The brain, on this view, is a gatekeeper and editor.

Huxley's metaphor appears to represent accurately the neurobiological facts. Various types of psychopathology are characterised by an overload of data (Lipowski, 1975). The result can be shutdown or breakdown. And various types of spiritual or ecstatic experience are best conceptualised as a slackening of the valve – letting in a greater amount of data – sometimes leading to an encounter with what is seen as a new type of reality (which may in fact be *more* of the reality that is always there but is generally presented in manageable aliquots, or with some of the more dramatic highlights deleted) (Foster, 2011).

The second neurobiological observation relates to brain lateralisation. All animals that exist or have ever existed have neuronal asymmetry. One can see it in, for instance, nematodes, but it is most obvious where there is an obvious brain. Brains are anatomically asymmetrical and functionally distinct. One hemisphere (the right in humans) has a holistic appreciation of the world. It considers the big picture. It takes context into account. And the other hemisphere (the left in humans) is essentially executive. It governs, in most humans, the usually dominant right hand: the do-er. The right hand manipulates the world. The left hemisphere's job is to manipulate, following the instructions given to it by the right hemisphere. Iain McGilchrist has argued that human history is characterised by a growing usurpation by the executive. The executive is good at narrow focus, but poor at wider vision; a polariser, fond of algorithms, literal, incapable of appreciating the implicit, and unable to appreciate the coincidence of opposites that is a characteristic of wisdom (McGilchrist, 2009; McGilchrist 2021).

The purpose of mentioning these characteristics of human sensory processing and cognition is not simply to bemoan our sensory poverty, or the tyranny of the VLC and the biases that come with it. Nor is it to suggest ways (and I think there are ways) of being less sensorily poor, more epistemically satisfactory, and less hemispherically unbalanced. It is, rather, to draw attention to the very unusual ways that humans perceive the world; to highlight the anthropocentric biases that make us think that the world has to be read the way we read it, and to suggest that there are other modes of being, some of which can be seen in animals on this planet, which might plausibly be adopted by non-terrestrial beings.

The World According to Non-Human Animals

Ed Yong has surveyed the range of animal senses (Yong, 2022). There are many more than our conventionally recognised five. The more comprehensible others include magnetic senses (used in navigation and in determining – by foxes, for instance – the distance to nearby prey) and ultrasound (used, for instance, by cetaceans in creating ultrasonic maps). If a dolphin shot a pulse of ultrasound at you, it would 'see' the chambers of your heart contracting and your last meal being squeezed through your gut. Other senses, though notionally comparable to ours, are so different in sensitivity that the difference becomes practically a difference in kind. Some spiders have light receptors on their legs that are triggered by a fraction of the energy in a single photon.

But even if we examine in non-human species only those senses that we have ourselves, it is immediately clear that many occupy a dramatically different Umwelt from ours. That should not be a surprise. The Umwelt of other humans is fairly inaccessible to us – and our ability to comprehend it is frustrated by the VLC both of the would-be perceiver and the target. We simply can't explain ourselves adequately. The very act of explaining confounds the explanation – such is the nature of the VLC. It may in some ways be easier to enter the Umwelt of non-humans (there's no VLC to obfuscate), but overall, surely we can get further inside the head of even the most slippery human than into the head of even the simplest and most forthcoming giraffe.

Nonetheless, we know enough about the behaviour of the non-visual senses and some of the ways that non-human animals use those senses to be able to make some informed speculations about their Umwelt (Foster, 2017).

Take, for instance, an almost entirely olfactory animal, living in a forest.

Scent is released from the forest floor by water. After it has rained the animal will live in a much more intense sensory world. Scent rises with increasing temperature: the animal will always inhabit a *gradient*. If it raises its nose higher, it will get a bigger dose of scent particles. That will not mean that the ground from which the scent has come is higher. Some scent will come from a long way off, but will arrive at the nose at the same time as scent from immediately beneath the nose. Distance does not mean the same as it does for us. Nor does time. Scenting involves time travel: when sniffing a piece of rock, the animal will get at the same time, in its nose and its brain, an instantaneous olfactory transect of millions of years – from the Carboniferous animals fossilized in the rock to the mouse that walked across the rock a moment before. Olfactory animals have to be geometers too, for scent bounces, ricocheting off trees and rocks like balls in a pinball machine. An animal needs to know if it is detecting a smell that has arrived directly, or whether it is smelling a ricochet. Some sort of trigonometry must be going on.

Decoding and sorting all this information are tasks very different to any that we undertake – although perhaps not so different from the tasks we once undertook when, as hunter-gatherers, we were more switched on.

An auditory world, too, has different rules. Imagine an animal that hunts primarily by sound, underwater at night, but on land during the day. Sound travels in salt water about 4.5 times faster than it does in air. That means that prey 45 metres away in the sea will seem to be 10 land-metres away. The arithmetic of the day is different from the arithmetic of night. The night is auditorily claustrophobic as the day is not.

Radically different Unwelten may be created, also, by different combinations of or different ways of integrating senses. We (if we allow ourselves to be) are splendid sensory all-rounders. But we choose (albeit under duress from the VLC) to be visual. If we recruited the other senses – so increasing the ingress of information above the fifth of the available data that we usually use – the world would no doubt seem very different. It would be a much closer approximation to the way the world objectively is, and it would be less self-referential.

I cannot deal properly here with the issue of whether non-human animals may use language. When humans have looked for language in animals, they have looked, generally, not for faculties that do the job of language, but for faculties that do the job of language in the way that human language does it (Safina, 2015). One may think that a much wider net must be cast in order to catch the quasi-linguistic modes of communication that may be out there. Suffice it to say that although a case may be made for something akin to language in cetaceans, and at least the capacity to learn some elements of human-type language has been shown in non-human higher primates, nothing has yet been demonstrated that could in principle have the tyrannous effect on epistemology that language has in our case (Meijer, 2019). Vision or olfaction or touch (or whatever) may rule a non-human's perception of the world (perhaps in a distorting way), but the L part of the VLC coalition, if L is present at all, does not seem to dictate terms as it so often does for us.

I have said nothing here about non-conventional senses such as telepathy. It should not be assumed that I discount them, or that I think that if they exist they do not or could not exist in non-human animals (Sheldrake, 2004; Hamilton, 2021). I return to such senses as we leave this planet.

Into Outer Space

As we go into outer space, all options are open. But we can surely conclude something from our terrestrial experience about the constraints within which the possible sensory and cognitive options are likely to operate. I consider here only the options inherent in the notion of some sort of embodiment. Without bodies, rather different considerations would doubtless apply, but our experience is so crucially determined by the fact of embodiment that it is hard to say anything meaningful about those considerations. In what follows I assume that non-terrestrial organisms (which I will call NTOs) exist, and avoid cumbersome conditionals.

It seems likely that some selective pressures will have affected the evolution of NTOs, and that those or other pressures will affect the way that NTOs experience and behave in their worlds.

We cannot speculate usefully about what those pressures might be. They will be wholly dependent on the specific environments concerned. There is no reason to presume that the pressures will include predation or be otherwise competitive in the way that we usually conceive of biological competition. It is generally thought that predation produced or (at least) accelerated the innovation of animal forms at the time of the Cambrian Explosion, but predation is not a necessary fuel for the engines that generate biological innovation and diversity. There are many potential engines, and many potential fuels. Co-operation and community are undoubtedly profound forces shaping the biological world here on earth (Foster, 2010). Other worlds, full of nature *not* red in tooth and claw (and indeed toothless and clawless) are entirely plausible.

Probably, though, extrapolating from Earthly biology, sensory apparatus is likely to be more sophisticated the more competition there is of the sort familiar to us.

I of course cannot here do justice to the debate about the existence of consciousness (by which I mean, broadly, the ability to have subjective experiences) in non-humans. My position, for what it is worth, is that the existence of some sort of consciousness in that sense has been conclusively demonstrated in many non-humans, including cetaceans, higher primates and some birds. I suspect, too, that our inability to find it in other species is a result of our poor experimental methods. The better we get at looking for consciousness, the more we find it. I should also admit (without having space to argue for it) my own conviction that some kind of panpsychism is likely to be true. I can see no plausible way in which consciousness could even in principle have emerged from unconscious matter, and so join Whitehead, Nagel, Strawson and others in what seems to me to be the parsimonious conclusion: it *did not* emerge from unconscious matter (Skrbina, 2017; cp Humphrey, 2022). Kripal puts it well: it is obvious that mind is in some way mattered: it seems that matter is also minded (Kripal, 2020).

That conclusion necessarily means that I am sympathetic to the idea that minds might speak more directly to minds (by something like telepathy) than we are used to supposing. Perhaps it happens here on Earth. But even if one rejects the idea of panpsychism, there is no reason in principle to suppose that a mind could not transmit to and receive from other minds – of the same or different type – without the need for intermediaries such as sound, vision and language to which we have become accustomed (James, 1902). It would obviously be useful. The problem is not one of principle; it is merely an engineering problem. If minds can transmit to and receive from minds other than the mind of another similar NTO, the transmitter and receiver would both be integrated into the cosmos in a way articulated by many Earthly religions – and particularly those of the east. Our experience of that integration – the *advaita* experience that occurs when the boundaries of ourselves are dissolved – brings ecstasy. We cannot intelligently suppose that NTOs experience ecstasy – or that they do not.

There may be a need to control the influx and efflux of transmissions – or at least to be able to broadcast and tune specifically into wavelengths of particular importance.

This raises the general issue of reducing valves. In humans the brain seems to act as a sluice gate. We simply don't know if it does in non-humans. Perhaps in non-humans the necessary filtering occurs at the level of sense reception: the sense receptors may not let into the brain information that is deemed unnecessary for painting a picture of the world. Or it may be that everything is allowed in, and more efficiently processed than it is in us – which would mean that a fox (say) is epistemically hugely superior to us. In any event, bigger neuronal capacity (more raw processing power) would seem, in principle, to be able to do away with the need for reducing valves. Perhaps that's the direction evolution took in outer space. Perhaps the NTOs really do know a lot more about their places than we do about ours. If so, perhaps they occupy their places more intimately and satisfactorily than we do ours. Perhaps they feel more at home than we do.

There is no reason to suppose that if NTOs have language and vision, and indeed cognition, they are subject as we are to the disadvantages of the VLC. Again, the problems inherent in the VLC are just engineering problems. There is no reason in principle why vision should be the all-trumping sense, or that the lead sense (whatever it is) should be in a toxic coalition with cognition. Cognition could be more deferential to the announcements of sense data without losing any of its ability to deal with the world. Similarly, a non-propositional mode of representing the world is not only imaginable, but present in some fortunate humans and (no doubt) at least many non-human animals. My son Tom has the great gift of dyslexia. He doesn't reduce the world to a set of statements. He sees the things that are there and relates to them much more directly (and much more epistemically satisfactorily than I do). Most human ways of representing the world seem, courtesy of the VLC, to have taken a wrong turn. Humans might have benefited in the short term – in a very narrow, neoliberal way (there are lots of us) – from cutting out much of the information that could help us to understand the web and weave of the world, but the dangers inherent in our consequent misunderstanding are now ontologically threatening (McGilchrist, 2009; McGilchrist 2021). I doubt that evolution has permitted the same mistake in distant galaxies.

If the VLC is a probably unrepeated human anomaly, it may mean that the sense of self has a less atomistic inflection in NTOs than it does in us. Certainly if the NTOs are panpsychically or otherwise tuned in to a wide range of other minds, it is likely to generate a more communitarian ontology and politics than we enjoy.

Many of the other imaginable ways of being of NTOs are imaginable by direct extension from what we know of terrestrial senses. We have seen how, even in an Earthly wood, time and distance behave in strange ways, and that neurological software has evolved to decrypt the strangeness. If millions of years can be compressed into a single bundle of scent and delivered to a badger's nose, or scent from across the world wrapped up with the scent of a worm in the badger's mouth, why should an NTO not be able (for instance) to participate simultaneously both in the NTO's immediate world and in the world of a distant galaxy (whose light reaches the sense receptors of the NTO 300 million years after it was generated)? The NTO may, for all we know, be able to manipulate the fact of quantum non-locality, and influence that distant galaxy instantaneously, rather than being a mere spectator. I think it's unlikely, but really, all bets are off.

There are two remaining matters. Both relate to brain lateralisation.

The first is that, given the ubiquity of neuronal lateralisation on planet Earth, it seems that lateralisation addresses a fundamental way of *paying attention*. Narrow focus and wide focus need to be kept distinct in order to have the functional conversation, which is what we call ontology.

It is hard to imagine any creature that is sensate in even the most basic sense that does not need to pay attention in these two ways. Indeed, the fact of neuronal asymmetry in even the most basic creatures, together with the fact that no hypothesis for that asymmetry other than wide/narrow focus has coherently been suggested, hints strongly that this is the case. This is not in itself an argument for the ubiquity of consciousness; it is simply a reflection of two facts:

one, that there will always be aspects of the world that are of more immediate concern to an organism than others; and two, that everything in the world has a wider context, which, in the context of organisms, is relevant to survival and thriving. I therefore suspect that a conversation between broad and narrow attention will have been somehow facilitated by evolution in every galaxy.

The second point is that there is no reason at all to assume that an NTO's left-hemispherical executive will have arrogated the position of its holistic, reflective right hemisphere. The conditions for that arrogation were probably local. I hope so.

Conclusion

Human and non-human ways of being can hint at other ways of being – or at least some of the constraints on possible ways. (McGilchrist, 2009; McGilchrist 2021). But the possible ways of being are infinite, and the constraints few.

References

Collins, J.A. and Olson, I.R. (2014). Knowledge is power: How conceptual knowledge transforms visual cognition. *Psychonomic Bulletin & Review*, 21(4), pp. 843–860.

Dunbar, R.I.M. (2009). The social brain hypothesis and its implications for social evolution. *Annals of Human Biology*, 36 (5), pp. 562–572.

Firestone, C. and Scholl, B.J. (2015). Cognition does not affect perception: Evaluating the evidence for 'top-down' effects. *Behavioral and Brain Sciences*, 39. doi:10.1017/s0140525x15000965.

Foster, C. (2010). *The Selfless Gene*. Nashville: Thomas Nelson.

Foster, C. (2011). *Wired for God: The biology of spiritual experience*. London: Hodder.

Foster, C. (2017). *Being a Beast: Adventures across the species divide*. New York: Picador.

Hamilton, D. (2021). *Why Woo Works*. London: Hay House UK.

Humphrey, N. (2022). *Sentience: The invention of consciousness*. Oxford: Oxford University Press.

Huxley, A. (1954). *The Doors of Perception*. London: Chatto & Windus.

James, W. (1902). *The Varieties of Religious Experience*. London: Longmans, Green.

Kripal, J.J. (2020). *The Flip: Who you really are and why it matters*. London: Penguin Books.

Lipowski, Z.J., 1975. Sensory and information inputs overload: Behavioral effects. *Comprehensive Psychiatry*, 16(3), pp. 199–221.

Macpherson, F. (2011). Individuating the senses, in: *The Senses: Classic and contemporary philosophical perspectives*, F. Macpherson (Ed.), pp. 3–43. Oxford: Oxford University Press.

McGilchrist, I. (2009). *The Master and His Emissary: The divided brain and the making of the western world*. New Haven: Yale University Press.

McGilchrist, I. (2021). *The Matter with Things: Our brains, our delusions, and the unmaking of the world*. London: Perspectiva.

Meijer, E. (2019). *Animal Languages: The secret conversations of the living world*. London: Hachette UK.

Pylyshyn, Z. (1999) Is vision continuous with cognition? The case for cognitive impenetrability of visual perception. *Behavioral and Brain Sciences*, 22(3), pp. 341–365.

Safina, C. (2015) *Beyond Words: What animals think and feel*. New York: Henry Holt.

Sheldrake, R. (2004) *The Sense of Being Stared At, and Other Aspects of the Extended Mind*. London: Arrow.

Skrbina, D. (2017). *Panpsychism in the West*. Boston: MIT Press.

Yong, E. (2022). *An Immense World: How animal senses reveal the hidden realms around us*. London: Bodley Head.

6

THOUGHT EXPERIMENTS AND THE (FICTIONAL) EXPLORATION OF OUTER SPACE

Marta Benenti

Introduction

As is well known, science fiction is a vast and varied narrative genre. Scholars do not agree on how to define it, and a lively debate is still ongoing as to whether it must be conceived as a genre identified by necessary and sufficient features (Suvin 1979), or rather as the result of a tradition that "comprise[s], or involve[s], people, books, objects, places, institutions, styles of music, and many other things" (Evnine 2015, 5). A plausible solution to this conundrum has recently been pointed out, which suggests taking works as belonging to the science fiction genre if they possess a cluster of features that can be considered *standard* for the genre. Such a cluster is not rigid nor fixed once and for all. On the contrary, it is open to historical changes, thereby accounting for the inherent mutability of cultural products' traditions (Terrone 2021).

The features that have been proposed as being standard for science fiction are those formerly introduced by Darko Sauvin, namely the presence of a "novum", that is, something new with respect to the author's epoch, which is "cognitively validated within the narrative reality of the tale" (Suvin 1979, 80). In other words, the novelty introduced in the world depicted by the narrative must be justified (usually in scientific terms) from within that very world. This allows the definition to exclude those stories where something new at the time of writing is introduced and simply accepted as such, without further justificatory efforts (Terrone 2021).

Once such a dynamic definition of science fiction is agreed upon, one can try to zoom in and explore features, themes, and topics that are particularly recurring in works of science fiction – though not participating in the genre's definition. One first, quite natural remark is that science fiction stories have always offered their authors and recipients the perfect opportunity to speculate

DOI: 10.4324/9781003374381-6

on meanings, values, priorities, and the possible fate of humankind. According to Suvin, science fiction has, throughout time, become: "a diagnosis, a warning, a call to understanding and action, and – most important – a mapping of possible alternatives" (Suvin 1979, 378). One can thus reasonably wonder why – that is, in virtue of which features science fiction happens to be a genre so devoted to speculating on the present and future condition of its recipients? In order to deal with this question, and given how broad and varied the nature of the genre is, I need to narrow the scope of my analysis. In this chapter I will therefore focus on those works that feature outer space exploration.

In the next paragraph I will give an idea of how space exploration appears and is treated in (most) science fiction works. After presenting this scenario, in the third paragraph I will suggest that the reason why such works foster imaginings and reasoning on the human current and future conditions is that they work as thought experiments. I will outline what thought experiments are and how they relate to fictional narratives in general and to science fiction in particular. In the fourth paragraph I will go back to outer space and suggest what specific kinds of thought experiments are elicited by works featuring its exploration.

Science Fiction and the Exploration of the Outer Space

Space exploration has inspired innumerable works of fiction both in literature and in cinema. Typically included in the science fiction literary and movie genre, stories about outer space exploration can hardly be considered a genre – or even a subgenre – *per se*. The exploration of the universe, its galaxies, planets, or spatio-temporal niches is better to be considered as a theme that characterizes many science fiction works and its subgenres. Take, for example, so-called *space opera* in which outer space provides the scenario where space vessels bring human characters from one planet to another (Westfahl 2000), or *planetary romance* portraying alien planets' customs and traditions (Clute & Nicholls 1993), or *space western*, which exploits typical tropes of westerns against an intergalactic background (Abbott 2006), or else *science fictional space warfare*, where the narrative device of an interstellar or intergalactic war fuels adventure and often military-inspired plots.

These works are characterized by the presence of the outer space not much as an inert scenario, but rather as what we may call a "determiner" of the story (see Benenti & Giombini 2023 for another occurrence of the – still tentative – notion of determiner). Space operates, in such narrations, almost like a character, an ingredient without which those very stories could not develop as they do. This said, the space-character takes innumerable different forms, depending on the story's (sub)genre, focus, or aim. The exploration of new territories featuring futuristic spaceships and spaceports, encounters with extraterrestrial life or civilizations, and interplanetary cultural exchanges; intergalactic wars with the presence of space-cowboys or soldiers and their technologically advanced equipment; space conquest and colonization, interstellar politics and diplomacy, along with their possible ethical consequences, are among the most frequently recurring tropes in science fiction, outer space exploration works. Here are some examples that help lay the common ground for further elaboration.

In *2001: A Space Odyssey* by Stanley Kubrick (1968) – inspired by writer Arthur C. Clarke's short story "Sentinel from Eternity" (1951) – a mysterious black monolith is discovered on the Moon, and the spacecraft Discovery One is sent out to investigate. The crew encounters an artificial intelligence called HAL 9000 that threatens the safety and survival of the crew. Also concerned with the exploration of other planets, *The Martian* by Andy Weir (2011) follows the adventures of an astronaut stranded on Mars after a dust storm, who struggles to survive and find a way back to Earth. The exploration of outer space is famously at the core of the much acclaimed *Star Trek* TV series (1966–2020), set in the 23rd century and reporting the voyages of the *USS Enterprise* space vessel sent by the *United Federation of Planets* to explore new worlds and unknown civilizations, while in *Hyperion* by Dan Simmons, a group of pilgrims travels to a mysterious planet to visit the Time Tombs and confront the Shrike, a deadly creature that controls time and space.

The seminal novel *The War of the Worlds* by H.G. Wells (1898) provides instead a paradigm of military science fiction, in which a war against alien species is staged. Another example of this subgenre is the series *Ender's Game* by Orson Scott Card (1985), where the young protagonist is trained by the military to lead a war against the Formics alien population. A famous planetary war is portrayed by the *Star Wars* saga (1977–2018), in a setting sometimes reminiscent of Frank Herbert's *Dune* (1965), which depicts the desert planet Arrakis where a rebellion takes place for the control of energy resources. We also encounter a highly technological war in *The Sten Chronicles* series by Chris Bunch and Allan Cole (1982–1993) whose protagonist is catapulted into a world of spying, secret military operations, and galactic politics.

In addition to these elements, science fiction set in outer space often explores the social and psychological impacts of space exploration on individuals and societies, as well as the ethical dilemmas and consequences of space travel and colonization. Take for instance Christopher Nolan's *Interstellar* (2014) in which a group of astronauts travels through a wormhole in search of a new home for humanity, as Earth is dying. The film delves into the psychological toll of being away from loved ones and the moral and ethical consequences of their mission in space-time. In 2009's *Moon*, a solitary astronaut is sent to the moon for mining purposes, suffering the psychological effects of long-term isolation and dealing with the moral dilemma raised by the astronaut's discovery of a shocking truth about his mission. Analogously, the protagonist of *Ad Astra* (2019) by James Gray travels to the edge of the solar system to find out challenging truths about his missing father and the aerospatial mission during which he had disappeared 20 years before. Once again, themes of loneliness, family, and the human desire to explore the unknown are put on screen exploiting the narrative devices of space exploration. Ethical dilemmas connected to colonization are finally explored by award-winning *Avatar* (2009) where humans threaten the indigenous population of a distant moon in order to exploit its resources.

Thought Experiments and Science Fiction

Science fiction stories typically rely on what Kendall Walton named the "Reality Principle", applied without particular constraints (Terrone 2021). In reading or watching these works, the audience is, accordingly, allowed to infer what is true or false or possible in a story by relying on what is true or false or possible in their own world (Walton 1990). In other words, more than stories belonging to other fictional genres, such as fantasy, science fiction works are as compatible as possible with laws and truths governing the audience's (and authors') world. In particular (yet with some exceptions), they invite us to (make-)believe that facts such as the historical timeline that precedes the narrated vicissitudes coincide with those holding in our real world. Similarly, unless it is explicitly stated (and cognitively validated – or explained in the story) physical laws in force in the fictional world are the same as those of our own reality.

Given their relation to reality, it seems that works of science fiction are particularly well suited to invite imaginings and speculations about the recipients' own world. They provide scenarios and contexts based on which the audience is often invited to make comparisons between the world they live in and the one depicted by the story. Scholars in philosophy – especially philosophy of literature and epistemology – have noticed that such imaginings might have the shape of thought experiments (Grau 2006; Wiltsche 2021; Terrone 2021; Benenti & Giombini 2023).

The philosophical notion of "thought experiment" has a long tradition that crosses over into fictional narratives. Broadly conceived, thought experiments are imaginative processes that allow one to get a grip on some aspect of reality by imagining a certain experimental set-up from which certain consequences are expected to follow (Brown & Fehige 2019). When performing thought experiments, we imagine – often we visualize – a given situation, we attend to what happens, and possibly draw some conclusion. Typically, such conclusions are meant to apply not only to the situation we are asked to imagine, but to extend or to generalize beyond it, to facts taking place in the actual world, to cases that are analogous in some respects to the one evoked by the experiment, to theories about the world or about a specific portion of it.

Just to make some trite examples. One classical philosophical thought experiment invites the audience to imagine a color scientist who lives in a black and white room so that, although she has a complete physical knowledge of colors, she has never seen them. What if she escaped the room and saw colors for the first time? Another experiment asks to imagine oneself as a brain connected to a sophisticated computer software that perfectly simulates the experiences of the outside world. How would one discriminate actual experience from this Matrix-like scenario? Or else, what if we could decide to divert a trolley running along the railway tracks so as to save someone's life but condemn someone else thereof?

Like fictional narratives, thought experiments have a basic narrative structure, that is, they introduce a set-up scenario, a development, its consequences, and, eventually, a conclusion. These basic features, along with the fact that they mobilize the audience's imagination, made some scholars argue that thought experiments are overall akin to fictional narratives (Davies 2007; Swirski 2007; Elgin 2007, 2014; Egan 2016, among others). More specifically, thought experiments have been playing a crucial role in the debate about the cognitive value of literature. Just like thought experiments – it has been argued – literature can make readers better understand certain aspects of the real world starting from fictional elements and the imaginings they elicit.

Not only, it is claimed, do both fiction and thought experiments invite us to counterfactually imagine what would happen should certain conditions be satisfied, but they both also require the suspension of disbelief, for their narratives often imply that the set-up conditions are not real. And yet neither fictional narratives nor thought experiments let our imaginations run free. On the contrary, they impose implicit or explicit constraints on what should or should not be imagined within the proposed scenarios (Elgin 2014).

Admittedly, this broad overlap between fictional narratives and thought experiments has been downsized. In particular it has been noticed that not all genres of fictional narratives can be adequately treated as thought experiments, for not all genres of fictional narratives are experienced by readers – or viewers – as if they were inviting us to create a model in our mind, let it run, observe what happens, and draw some conclusions that transcend the boundaries of the story (Huemer 2019; Vidmar 2013; Arcangeli 2021). As Wolfgang Huemers cleverly states: "we should not expect to be able to find a short, clear-cut, and homogeneous answer to the question concerning the nature and value of 'literature' ... we should rather be prepared to end up with a long, detailed, and multifarious account" (Huemer 2019, 72). In spite of this fair criticism, however, it can be argued that it is not necessary to endorse this view as applying to all sorts of fictional narratives. One can instead acknowledge that this account is particularly effective when it comes to science fiction. Not by chance, science fiction is often mentioned as one clear example of fiction that works just like a thought experiment (e.g. Swirski 2007; Vidmar 2013; Wiltsche 2019; Brown & Fehige 2019; Terrone 2021).

Among the many available accounts of the nature of thought experiments, the one that turned out to be particularly helpful and consistent with the nature of fictional narrative is the one that appeals to *mental models* (Nersessian 2018). Like actual models created in labs, a mental model is structurally analogous to what it represents. Better said, it *simulates* what it represents. In a nutshell, the mental model account of thought experiments claims that, when we conduct a thought experiment, we construct in our minds and manipulate through simulation a mental model – where actual experiments manipulate physical models (Nersessian 2018, 319). From this perspective, the narrative by means of which a thought experiment is introduced functions as a sort of "user manual" that instructs recipients on how to build the model required by the experiment: the isolated colors scientist condition, the brain-in-a-vat scenario, and so on.

Accordingly, the common denominator of fictional narratives and thought experiments would be their power to establish mental models, providing the imaginers with the instructions to manipulate them and see where they lead. A particularly enthusiastic defender of this view applied to fiction, Derek Matravers, has suggested that, when confronted with all sorts of narratives, we tend to create models in our minds and then to adopt, towards those models, different attitudes. Either we commit ourselves to *believing* what is told, or we engage in the story by adopting an *imaginative attitude* (Matravers 2014, 90). Following this line of thought, and combining it with Suvin's definition of the genre, it can be argued that science fiction narratives provide their recipients with the instructions to build the mental models of worlds that they know have never been enacted at that time. Yet, such worlds are in principle ruled by the same physical laws and share (at least part of) the past of our – the readers' – world.

One crucial reason that is invoked for considering science fiction as sharing its fundamental structure with thought experiments is that science fiction stories demand their readers to imagine that something is the case even though – if they are competent readers – they are well aware that it cannot be the case at the time of the story's creation. Such works assume that their readers or viewers know that the portrayed scenarios were fictional at the time of their creation (Vidmar 2013, 183). Readers and viewers are therefore not asked to *believe* that what they read *is true*, even though – and this is a prerogative of most science fiction works – it is "cognitively validated" in the story (Suvin 1979). The effort put by authors in accounting for the scientific viability of what they recount typically does not aim at *persuading* the audience of any scientific truth. Rather, it is an invitation to imagine scenarios and the related constraints within which plots can develop.

This same attitude toward a mental model – that is, pretending that something is the case while at the same time knowing that it cannot be the case – is purportedly crucial when engaging in thought experiments as well (Davies 2007). For, it is claimed, thought experiments are paradigmatically conceived to allow us to test beliefs, intuitions, and theories that we could not otherwise put to a test. If we believed that what we are invited to imagine by the thought experiment narrative held in the actual world, we would not make the effort of engaging in the thought experiment. As a matter of fact, we may either have direct, empirical access to the described scenario, or at least draw conclusions based on a realistic and logically consistent report. Similarly, if we believed that what we are invited to imagine when attending to a science fiction story were actually true in our own world, then why bother engaging in the story? We would rather turn to a science book or magazine.

In other words, being aware of the fictional nature of – at least part of – the introduced scenario seems to be part of the narrative pact subscribed by science fiction recipients. Once they enter the make-believe game, they are provided information whose reliability can vary widely from work to work. Still, the process of mental model manipulation is such that they can treat such information as if they constituted an experimental procedure leading from a hypothesis, to a proof to some conclusion. As long as – at least part of – the information is true, veridical, reliable, but also reminiscent of our own world, the outcomes of the manipulation can cast new light on actual phenomena.

What Thought Experiments Are Elicited by Science Fiction Works that Stage the Exploration of Outer Space?

Thus, if one is disposed to agree that science fiction narratives typically engage us the way thought experiments do, then we can ask what is specific of imaginings triggered by science fiction stories that involve outer space in the first place. As we have seen, the exploration of outer space is a *topos* in sci-fi literature and cinema. However, it is extremely difficult to isolate something like a subgenre based on the presence of outer space as a scenario or even as a feature that determines the narrative development. *Space opera, space Western, military sci-fi*, and *planetary romance* gather science fiction works set in outer space. Yet, as it is easy to see, they neither ascribe space the same role, nor can be considered monolithic, self-standing categories.

In the light of this manifold nature, however, one can turn to the just-mentioned structure of thought experiments and try to consider the peculiarities exhibited by such a scenario as the universe. This will allow us to assess the specific potential of fictional narratives that exploit outer space as their setting to trigger thought experiment–like imaginings in their audience. Unsurprisingly, one first remark has to do with the relation between science fiction and the scientific domain.

Science fiction works that stage the exploration of outer space often ask their recipients to imagine what might happen if certain scientific or technological advances were to occur in combination with still untested assumptions about astronomy, physics, or biology.

As Harald A. Wiltsche (2021) has shown, a novel like *The Forever War* (1974) by Joe Haldeman, for instance, is particularly effective in making some of the oddest consequences of Einstein's special relativity theory understandable. In the story – a military science fiction narrative – humans are at war with some still unknown alien race. What is particularly relevant against this classical trope is the scenario conveyed by the author: humans can actually reach separate points in space–time through "Einstein–Rosen-bridges", or wormholes. This discovery has apparently allowed them to colonize the entire galaxy. However, these travels in space–time require space vessels to move at such a high speed that the phenomenon known as "time dilation" becomes tangible. In short: time passes much more slowly for those who – like the protagonist – spend most of their life traveling near the speed of light through wormholes. Social and psychological consequences of this de-synchronization between characters are therefore explored by the novel. Affective and psychological consequences of the very same phenomenon are put on screen by award-winning film *Interstellar*, whose protagonists (father and daughter) experience the suffering of a separation made tragic by such a gap between temporal branches. What at the time of the realization of both works could not be empirically tested – namely time's dilation – finds in the creators' and, subsequently, in the audience's imagination a scenario whose consequences can be followed, cognitively validated, visualized, and, thus, better understood.

Thought experiments about astronomical claims are instead elicited by fictional works that deal with the so-called "Fermi Paradox". In short, this paradox questions why, given the apparent vastness of the universe, humans have not yet detected any signs of intelligent extraterrestrial life. By setting up scenarios in which alien life exists and makes contact with the Earth's inhabitants, works such as Carl Sagan's novel *Contact* (1985), Liu Cixin's *The Three-Body Problem* (2006) and its sequel *The Dark Forest* (2008), or Peter Watts's *Blindsight* (2006) explore the possibilities that intelligent civilizations may exist, but be deliberately hiding from each other to avoid being detected and destroyed, or else (as it is the case in Stanisław Lem's *Solaris* (1961)) that intelligent alien life may be sending signals, but too subtle or complex for human comprehension.

As to other branches of science that play a role in science fiction staging interstellar adventures, biology is worth mentioning. First and foremost, health consequences of aerospatial travels are often discussed by these works. Take once again the protagonist of *The Martian* who incurs the physical effects of living for several years using limited resources in a low-gravity environment, including muscle atrophy, hypoxia, and exposure to Mars's radiations. In addition, biological and genetic processes and mechanisms that can partially be observed in real life are often presented in their most extreme outcomes by sci-fi stories. in Oscar-winning *Alien* (1979) by Ridley Scott (drawn by the homonymous novel by Alan Dean Foster) endoparasitoid xenomorphs nest and reproduce in living creatures' bodies, thereby triggering thoughts about the place of humans in the food chain: what if we were no longer on the top? Genetic modification appears instead in *Pandora's Star*, the first book of Peter F. Hamilton's *Commonwealth Saga* (2004). There, inhabitants of the Pandora planet routinely manipulate their own genome so as to survive in its dangerous ecosystem: what advantages and risks might follow from an increasing ability to modify genetic information and enhance them technologically?

Often the scientific assumptions from which many of these works take off are not (fully) reliable. In other words, not all writers and directors ascribe to the scientificity of their products the same value. Scientific theories that are invoked and used to justify (cognitively validate) what happens in novels and films are often just seeming theories, para-scientific assumptions, simplifications, or patent misconceptions. Yet, it is worth noticing that this does not necessarily undermine the power of such narratives to trigger thought experiments. The scopes, results, and possible implications of their outcomes can clearly be discussed and evaluated in the light of the credibility of their premises. Yet the scientific unreliability of a thought experiment's set-up does not necessarily diminish its effectiveness as an understanding device.

It must finally be added that these works not only invite us to perform thought experiments concerning scientific topics, conundrums, and debates, but they also elicit thought experiments and model manipulations related to psychological, political, and ethical issues.

One first ethical domain that is encompassed by many works of this kind is the one of intergenerational ethics. While *Interstellar* shows how space exploration might be pursued in order to save a dying planet, thereby taking charge of the survival of future generation, animated film *Wall-E* (2008), by Andrew Stanton, portrays a future where Earth is uninhabitable due to environmental degradation, and humanity has abandoned the planet to live on a space station. The story raises questions about the ethical implications of a society that prioritizes short-term convenience and consumerism over long-term sustainability.

More specifically, stories about the exploration and, above all, the colonization of the Universe raise questions about the responsibilities of the explorers and the colonizers in front of future generations. Outputs of this kind of thought experiment have an impact not only on the debates about ongoing space exploration programs. They also promise to affect ethical views and opinions about colonization processes that take and have taken place on Earth. If *Avatar* can be seen as a modern version of the Pocahontas story, one where the colonizers are clearly the evil characters, exploiting and destroying indigenous people who live in harmony with nature, the strand of space western born in the 1950s conveys myths about frontiers and settling, thereby reflecting a view of colonization particularly rooted in Western – especially American – society (Abbott 2006; Westfahl 2000).

Connected to the issue of colonization, outer space exploration offers its recipients the opportunity to exercise their thoughts and imaginings about cultural relativism. Encounters with other civilizations, different ways of communication, more or less radical divergences in values and cultural norms are put on stage by many such works of fiction. Consequences of such encounters are depicted, made – so to speak – visible, stressed, magnified, and manipulated so that audiences gain vivid quasi-experience of ethical and cultural trade-offs they could hardly have in real life.

One further family of topics that is often tackled by science fiction set in outer space is represented by environmental issues. Not only such works as *The Expanse* series (2011–2019) by James S.A. Corey invite audiences to imagine and better understand the impact of space exploration on the environment, due for instance to the long-term effects of launching rockets and spacecraft into space and leaving debris in orbit around the Earth, but – maybe more relevantly for the current epoch – they enact scenarios of climatic crises that promise to challenge their audiences (Benenti & Giombini 2023).

Finally, another theme (which undoubtedly requires more space and depth than this tiny paragraph) is utopia, dystopia, and the way in which science fiction set in outer space allows us to reflect on ideal societies. *The Dispossessed* (1974) by Ursula K. Le Guin features twin planets where humans have established two competing governments, one led by a capitalist and patriarchal system, the other by anarcho-syndicalist principles. A political laboratory, the novel casts light on ethical implications, pros, cons, and – above all – ambiguities of different political organizations.

Overall, science fiction works that stage the exploration of outer space can raise a range of ethical questions and spark important discussions that are not limited to our responsibilities as a society as we venture beyond Earth's boundaries, but go as far as to question the responsibilities of any – past, present, and future – society as it ventures beyond its geographical and cultural boundaries.

What can tentatively be concluded about the sorts of thought experiments triggered by science fiction featuring outer space exploration is that they typically rely on the possibility to imagine and visualize scientific and technological advancements (and drifts) that have not been enacted at the time of the writing (or of the shooting). This can be done thanks to the limited reality constraints that are characteristic of science fiction, on the one hand, and to the process of cognitive validation that make these advancements be seen as justified within the story context. If this can be said of most – if not all – science fiction stories (Terrone 2021), however, outer space exploration offers specific opportunities for engaging in thought experiments that are relevant both for science understanding and for ethical, political, and psychological comprehension. As to the former, a crucial role is played by space exploration representing a particularly stimulating scientific endeavor, which is part of popular culture and has produced a widespread imaginary. As to the latter, the hypothesis to be further developed is that outer space provides a framework where, at the same time, imagination can run free from our current real-life conditions, but is not fully detached from reality and realistic projections towards a not-too-distant future.

References

Abbott. C. (2006). *Frontiers Past and Future: Science fiction and the American West*. Lawrence: University Press of Kansas.

Arcangeli, M. (2021). The conceptual nature of imaginative content. *Synthese*, 199(1–2), 3189–3205. doi:10.1007/s11229-020-02930-7.

Benenti, M., Giombini, L. (2023). Climate change, philosophy, and fiction. In: Pellegrino, G., Di Paola, M. (eds) *Handbook of Philosophy of Climate Change*. Cham: Springer. https://doi.org/10.1007/978-3-030-16960-2_123-1.

Brown, J. R., Fehige, Y. (2019). Thought Experiments. In: Zalta, E.N. (ed.), *The Stanford Encyclopedia of Philosophy* (Spring 2022 Edition). https://plato.stanford.edu/archives/spr2022/entries/thought-experiment/.

Clute, J., Nicholls P. (1993). *The Encyclopedia of Science Fiction.* London: Orbit.

Davies, D. (2007). Thought experiments and fictional narratives. *Croatian Journal of Philosophy*, 7(9), 29–45.

Egan, D. (2016). Literature and thought experiments. *The Journal of Aesthetics and Art Criticism*, 74, 139–150. https://doi.org/10.1111/jaac.12270.

Elgin, C. Z. (2007). The Laboratory of the Mind. In: Gibson, J. (ed.), *A Sense of the World: Essays on fiction, narrative and knowledge.* London: Routledge, 43–54.

Elgin, C. Z. (2014). Fiction as thought experiment. *Perspectives on Science*, 22(2), 221–241. https://doi.org/10.1162/POSC_a_00128.

Evnine, S. J. (2015). "But is it science fiction?": Science fiction and a theory of genre. *Midwest Studies in Philosophy*, 39(1), 1–28. https://doi.org/10.1111/misp.12037.

Gendler, T. S. (2004). Thought experiments rethought – and reperceived. *Philosophy of Science*, 71(5), 1152–1163. https://doi.org/10.1086/425239.

Grau, C. (2006). Eternal sunshine of the spotless mind and the morality of memory. *Journal of Aesthetics and Art Criticism*, 64(1), 119–133.

Huemer, W. (2019). Power and limits of a picture: On the notion of thought experiments in the philosophy of literature. In Bornmüller, F., Lessau, M., Franzen, J. (eds), *Literature as Thought Experiment?* Paderborn: Fink, 71–82.

Matravers, D. (2014). *Fiction and Narrative.* Oxford: Oxford University Press.

Nersessian, N. (2018). Cognitive science, mental models, and thought experiments. In Stuart, M. T., *et al.* (eds), *The Routledge Companion to Thought Experiments.* London and New York: Routledge, 309–326.

Suvin, D. (1979). *Metamorphoses of Science Fiction: On the poetics and history of a literary genre.* New Haven: Yale University Press.

Swirski, P. (2007). *Of Literature and Knowledge: Explorations in narrative thought experiments, evolution, and game theory.* London: Routledge.

Terrone, E. (2021). Science fiction as a genre. *Journal of Aesthetics and Art Criticism*, 79 (1), 16–29. https://doi.org/10.1093/jaac/kpaa003.

Vidmar, I. (2013). Thought experiments, hypotheses, and cognitive dimension of literary fiction. *Synthesis Philosophica*, 55–56, 177–193.

Walton, K. (1990). *Mimesis as Make-Believe: On the foundations of the representational arts.* Cambridge: Harvard University Press.

Westfahl, G. (2000). Space and beyond: The frontier theme in science fiction. Contributions to the study of science fiction, number 87. *Utopian Studies*, 12(1), 278–279.

Wiltsche, H. (2021). The forever war: Understanding, science fiction, and thought experiments. *Synthese*, 198, 3675–3698. https://doi.org/10.1007/s11229-019-02306-6.

7

CONSPIRACY THEORIES ABOUT SPACE

Are They Epistemically Special?

Juha Räikkä

Introduction

Conspiracy theories address a variety of issues, including the origin of certain diseases, the causes of death of famous people, and the "real facts" behind tragedies, accidents, and even the outcomes of sporting events. Interestingly, outer space has been the subject of a famous group of conspiracy theories. The theory that the Earth is actually flat and the claim that the Moon landings were faked have been around for some time and still attract many supporters. Other conspiracy theories about space are relatively new, though no less popular than those that have gained considerable traction. For instance, the theory that shape-shifting space lizards in human disguise rule the world has become one of the favorite conspiracy theories, at least in the United States (Abad-Santos 2015).

Conspiracy theories are implausible mainly because they offer relatively little support in defense of what they allege. Usually, they also go against received knowledge and claim something that is commonly thought to be false, for instance, that humans never set foot on the Moon. However, the epistemic implausibility of conspiracy theories does not mean that they must be false, and it is important to note that some of these theories may deserve further investigation, despite their apparent implausibility. This situation can be compared with science (Räikkä 2023, 63–71). When a scientist formulates a hypothesis that clearly conflicts with present established knowledge, the hypothesis is unlikely to receive justification. However, this does not imply that the hypothesis should not be carefully considered. There may be observations that encourage the study of the hypothesis, despite it being apparently implausible. The same is true of conspiracy theories, however unlikely it is that one of them turns out to be warranted or that such a theory rises to the status of a competing explanation of an event.

DOI: 10.4324/9781003374381-7

In this chapter, I will consider whether conspiracy theories about space (CTSs) are *special* in the sense that their epistemic status, as a class, differs from the status of other conspiracy theories. Call this the *specialty thesis*. which can have two meanings. It can be argued that it is epistemically *more inappropriate* to accept CTSs than those addressing other phenomena. After all, we can rather safely assume that space lizards have not plotted against us. CTSs seem to involve especially *extraordinary claims*. However, it can also be argued that it is epistemically *less inappropriate* to accept conspiracy theories that make statements about outer space than those addressing other phenomena.[1] Our knowledge about outer space is limited, and it is very difficult, if not impossible, for non-experts to check experts' claims about outer space. This possibly leaves people greater freedom to choose their views about space.

I intend to show that the arguments I examine do not support the specialty thesis. A popular understanding of CTSs suggests that they are somehow epistemically special, that is, particularly weird or exceptionally interesting. However, I will argue that these conspiracy theories do not seem to differ much from everyday conspiracy theories – alternative explanations of events such as the death of J.F. Kennedy, the destruction of the World Trade Center in 2001, or the origin of SARS-CoV-2 coronavirus. The question whether CTSs are special is interesting, as it is important to evaluate more carefully the epistemic status of the popular understanding of the topic. Possibly, the question may have some practical relevance in the future if space travel becomes more common (and we need to know more about space). Let us begin by looking briefly at what CTSs are.

Conspiracy Theories about Space

It is not completely clear how the notion of a conspiracy theory should be understood (cf. Uscinski & Enders 2022). Here, a "conspiracy theory" is understood as an explanation of an event or phenomenon that (1) refers to an actual or alleged conspiracy or a plot; (2) conflicts with the received explanation of the event (if there is one), providing an alternative to the "official view"; and (3) offers insufficient evidence in support of the alternative explanation so that it is not even considered as a competing scientific theory or anything of the sort (Ichino & Räikkä 2021, 249). In ordinary language, the claim that the first Moon landing was faked is called a "conspiracy theory." According to the definition above, this is correct. The theory refers to a plot, conflicts with the official view of epistemic authorities, such as researchers, and is rather poorly supported by evidence.

The definition is based on the descriptive conceptual analysis of the spoken language (Napolitano & Reuter 2021), which is important if we do not want to change the subject of the discussion. For instance, the idea that we would refer to *all* explanations that refer to a conspiracy as "conspiracy theories" would imply that usual historical explanations (concerning, say, Caesar's murder) would count as conspiracy theories. But commonly accepted historical explanations are not conspiracy theories, whether or not they refer to a conspiracy or plot (cf. Douglas, van Prooijen & Sutton 2021). Notice also that to say that the pharaoh Tutankhamen was killed by conspirators is *not* to support a conspiracy theory, although the claim refers to a conspiracy and is not presently the "official" view of historians. The claim that Tutankhamen was assassinated is (or at least was) a competing historical explanation.

CTSs are conspiracy theories about space. While CTSs often involve weird claims about space, or things that are or happen in space, not all weird claims about space are conspiracy theories. For example, a person who believes that little green men live on Mars need not believe in any conspiracy. The flat Earth theory and the Lunar conspiracy theory about the Moon landings are famous CTSs. However, there are many other interesting theories. As noted earlier, the theory of shape-shifting space lizards in human form is a relatively well-known CTS. The claim that NASA does not really exist is also a popular theory, according to which the function of the so-called NASA institute is not to explore space but to create space-related hoaxes in order to "justifiably" distribute an inflated budget among officials. NASA is merely a cover story that hides administrative corruption. Claims about UFOs are often conspiracy theories, for instance, when aliens are said to have plotted with the U.S. military – which makes use of advanced technology – but not all UFO claims are CTSs (Emerson 2016). The claim that there are many super intelligent alien civilizations around is not a conspiracy theory, although there is little evidence to support this claim. The claim that NASA officials lied when they said that there was no alien life on Mars is a CTS. In 1976, the Viking orbiter took a photograph of part of the Martian surface that resembled a human face, but NASA claimed that it was only because of shadows.[2] Science fiction books and movies include many interesting claims about space, and sometimes, they concern space conspiracies. They are *artistic* CTSs. The fictional and funny claim (of the movie *Iron Sky*) that Nazis escaped to the Moon in 1945 and later conspired there is an example of an artistic CTS. Novels that incorporate messages from a space theme can but need not be artistic CTSs.[3]

It is often said that conspiracy theories attribute "nefarious intentions" to alleged conspirators (Keeley 1999, 116–118). This view is understandable as many conspiracy theories involve moral blaming. However, in general, a conspiracy theorist need not blame anyone and can even appreciate the actions of alleged conspirators. A person who thinks that the first Moon landing was a fabrication need not think that the operation was morally blameworthy and may think that it was a clever move, given the space race between the United States and the Soviet Union. Therefore, it would be a mistake to think that conspiracy theories always accuse someone (cf. Douglas & Sutton 2011). In the context of real historical conspiracies, it is clear that conspirators *themselves* need not think that they are doing anything wrong and may be ready to defend their decision to conspire. President Ronald Reagan surely did not think that the so-called Iran–Contra affair was problematic. In his view, it was patriotic (Räikkä 2009).[4] It is true that there is something morally suspect in conspiring. A group's secret plan to organize a funny birthday party is not a conspiracy as there is nothing morally wrong with the plan. In conspiracies, there *is* something wrong, albeit merely *prima facie* wrong. It is *prima facie* wrong to harm a person, but a conspiracy to displace a dictator, for instance, can be morally acceptable, all things considered.

The above definition (based on three criteria 1–3) does not imply that one can reject a conspiracy theory simply because it is a conspiracy theory. Although conspiracy theories offer insufficient evidence in support of their allegations, there is always a chance that further evidence will be found in support of some theory and that the theory could turn out to be less implausible. Of course, this kind of development is unlikely. Although hundreds of real conspiracies have been revealed, conspiracy theorists have not played a major role in processes. In any case, it is important to keep in mind that the general observation regarding the implausibility of conspiracy theories does not mean that one could safely conclude that some particular theory will always be implausible. What if, someday, it is proven that NASA funds have really been massively deployed for purposes other than space exploration?

Philosophical debates about conspiracy theories often draw a distinction between *generalism* and *particularism*. According to generalism, the acceptability (or rationality) of conspiracy theories can be assessed without considering particular conspiracy theories. Particularism denies this claim (Buenting & Taylor 2010, 568; Dentith 2016, 581; Duetz 2022.)[5] The distinction, however, is imperfect, to say the least. The problem is that the general characterization of conspiracy theories as implausible is based on observations concerning details of individual conspiracy theories (Räikkä 2023). Thus, it is unlikely that anyone is a full-blooded generalist. On the other hand, if generalism is interpreted as a doctrine that allows us to say something general about the acceptability of conspiracy theories, for instance, that they are implausible, then everyone is a "generalist," at least if they adopt the definition above that relies on the ways in which we tend to use the concept. Notice that to identify some claim as a "conspiracy theory" presupposes that some sort of evaluation of its merits has already taken place; otherwise, we would not be able to say that it is a conspiracy theory, that is, a theory that is poorly supported by available evidence.[6] Usually, the evaluation is made by epistemic authorities such as researchers and journalists. Other people (who do not have the relevant data or expertise) then make use of the evaluation. The reason that we know that the claim that humans never set foot on the Moon is a conspiracy theory is that, among other things, epistemic authorities have estimated the merits of the claim and found them poor (Räikkä 2023, 63–71).

It is often said that a cautious attitude toward conspiracy theories disturbs further investigations of individual theories if someone decides to investigate them (Dentith 2016, 581). The claim is that generalism may easily lead to the "inappropriately flippant" rejection of a theory (Hagen 2022, 233–234). It is an empirical question whether this is so, but clearly, it should not be. The fact that hypotheses are known to be implausible does not justify their careless investigation. After all, great achievements in science have often resulted from brave research employing "implausible" hypotheses that are then found to be warranted. Of course, caution may decrease people's willingness to initiate further investigations of the claims of conspiracy theories in the first place (Räikkä 2023). Researchers are perhaps not eager to study the alleged plot of space lizards.[7] However, if claims are not investigated, then they are not (literally) rejected either. They are simply put aside as implausible ideas – which they undoubtedly are. (If a conspiracy theory is rejected after careful assessment, this does not mean that the case is conclusively closed as further evidence may show up, making it reasonable to restart investigations.)

What is true of conspiracy theories in general is true of CTSs. The claim that aliens are plotting with the U.S. military is an implausible theory, and it is advisable to think twice before starting more profound investigations about this issue. It is epistemically inappropriate to accept this theory.

Are CTSs Exceptionally Poor Theories?

Could it be even *more inappropriate* to accept aerospace conspiracy theories than other conspiracy theories? Many of us feel that this is a natural question and tend to think that the reply may well be in the affirmative. Because of science fiction novels, TV series (such as NASA's Unexplained Files), and epic space movies, we are more than familiar with wild claims about space. Conspiracy theories about lizards and conspiring UFOs that are not created for entertainment seem even wilder than fictitious stories about space wars and messages from alien civilizations. Perhaps, the popularity of the view that CTSs are particularly weird can be explained by the long tradition of space baloney. If it is even more inappropriate to accept CTSs than other conspiracy theories, then CTSs are epistemically *special*.

Are they special in the sense of being epistemically exceptionally poor theories? Is it more inappropriate to accept CTSs than other conspiracy theories? A possible argument for the view that CTSs are exceptionally implausible conspiracy theories is based on the doctrine called *the Sagan standard*, named after the cosmologist and astrobiologist Carl Sagan (1934–1996). The Sagan standard (or Sagan's dictum) is the rule that "extraordinary claims require extraordinary evidence." A similar requirement (that extraordinary claims require extraordinary proof) was presented by the sociologist Marcello Truzzi (1978, 11) and is said to have had many early defenders, including the French scholar Pierre-Simon Laplace (1749–1827). The point of the requirement is to say that if an extraordinary claim (concerning, say, astrology) is not supported by extraordinary evidence, then it would be irrational to believe it (Smith 2010, 3).

The argument against CTSs based on the Sagan standard follows this simple reasoning. Extraordinary claims require extraordinary evidence. In comparison to usual scientific theories and most conspiracy theories for that matter, CTSs include very extraordinary claims. Still, supporters of CTSs have not provided us with extraordinary evidence that would support their claims (about NASA's non-existence and so on). Therefore, it is even more inappropriate (or irrational) to believe in CTSs than in most other conspiracy theories.

Whether this argument is interesting at all depends, among other things, on what "extraordinary claims" are supposed to be and what counts as "extraordinary evidence." The astrobiologist Sean McMahon (2020), in his discussion on the Sagan standard, has distinguished several meanings of "extraordinary claim." (1) *Weird-extraordinary* claims are claims that people find strange and bizarre and are tempted to reject them. (2) *Wow-extraordinary* claims (e.g., about extraterrestrial life) refer to claims that are sensational and considered exciting, and many people want to believe them. Both classes of claims are "extraordinary" only psychologically. (3) *Improbable-extraordinary* claims differ in this respect. They are probabilistically extraordinary. In many cases, however, it is difficult to say which claims are in fact improbable as there are disagreements regarding the proper reference class (McMahon 2020, 121). The final class of extraordinary claims is (in McMahon's vocabulary) a set of claims that are (4) *Truzzi-extraordinary*. They are claims that entail falsehoods about fundamentally important established scientific ideas that are well supported by evidence. We could say that Truzzi-extraordinary claims contradict existing scientific paradigms. The claim that there is a "monster" (i.e., a very big animal) in the Loch Ness is psychologically extraordinary and improbable-extraordinary, but it would *not* require major revisions to current understandings of ecology and zoology (McMahon 2020, 122–123). Astrologers' claims are Truzzi-extraordinary. Suppose that it turned out that one could predict the future of one's marriage by interpreting the shapes of the stars. The finding would be truly revolutionary.

According to McMahon, Truzzi-extraordinary claims do require "extraordinary" evidence. Perhaps evidence cannot be "extraordinary" proper (as there are no miracles), but surely, there is a sense in which evidence can be extraordinary. Evidence can be said to be extraordinary when it (1) shows that the new claim is warranted or true *and* when it (2) outweighs or accounts for all the evidence for the traditional view (and explains why we were so wrong) (McMahon 2020, 122). A rational person would believe in an extraordinary claim were she provided with sufficient extraordinary evidence for the truth of that claim.

McMahon's interpretation of "extraordinary claim" and "extraordinary evidence" gives content to the Sagan standard and makes it an understandable requirement. If we accept the interpretation, then we can evaluate the "Sagan argument" for the view that CTSs are exceptionally poor. According to the argument, CTSs include very extraordinary claims, even more extraordinary than other conspiracy theories. This claim is plausible, at least in the sense of weird-extraordinary. Theories about lizards and the Earth as a pancake are strange; there is no question about it. CTSs also include wow-extraordinary claims. It would be great to have distant super intelligent visitors who could help us cure diseases, end all wars, and so on.

However, here we should ask whether CTSs are, as a class, more extra-ordinary than other conspiracy theories in the sense of contradicting funda-mentally important established scientific ideas, either more profoundly or more often than other conspiracy theories. The answer seems to be in the negative. The flat Earth theory is probably extraordinary in the relevant sense, but most CTSs are not. Even the claim that there are lizards that can take on human form is merely weird-extraordinary and improbable-extraordinary. After all, there are many animals that can change their color and outlook, shed their tails, and imitate plants and other animals. If someone found a lizard that was able to imitate humans, that would be really amazing, but not from the point of view of biology.[8] CTSs that concern NASA and the Moon landing are not extraordinary in the relevant sense. They are theories that suggest that officials are being dishonest. However, as lying is a common social phenomenon, there is no need to present extraordinary evidence in support of claims of dishonesty. CTSs concerning UFOs (or aliens who live in Area 51 in Nevada) can but need not be extraordinary in the relevant sense. Our present understanding of reality does not imply that there cannot be extraterrestrial life and other civilizations (that are perhaps very intelligent).[9] Therefore, CTSs about UFOs do not nor-mally require extraordinary evidence.

Those who defend CTSs are unable to provide extraordinary evidence. However, this is not problematic as the claims of CTSs are not usually extra-ordinary in the relevant sense. The problem of CTSs is that their defenders are unable to provide even *ordinary* evidence in support of their theories. In this respect, CTSs resemble other conspiracy theories that go against received knowledge and claim something that is commonly thought to be false, offering insufficient evidence for the alleged conspiracy.

The "Sagan argument" for the view that CTSs are exceptionally poor does not support the specialty thesis. The argument does not show that CTSs are special in the sense that their epistemic status, as a class, differs from that of other conspiracy theories. The popular view that CTSs are particularly ill-advised is understandable, but mostly unjustified.

CTSs and Testimonial Knowledge

Could it be justified to think that CTSs are *less* ill-advised than other con-spiracy theories? Is it epistemically *less* inappropriate to accept conspiracy the-ories that make statements about outer space than it is to accept other conspiracy theories? After all, our knowledge of space is limited, and what we know is not always that easy to understand. The physicist Albert Einstein said in his general theory of relativity that light travels along curved space. This is probably correct, but only a few of us have personally checked it. The philosopher David Lewis (1986) wrote that beyond our actual world, there are countless possible worlds that are as real as the actual one. This is merely philosophical speculation about modalities, but nobody has proven that claim to be false. Keeping in mind these and similar claims about space, one may ask whether CTSs are, after all, that strange. To say that there are conspiring extraterrestrial civilizations sounds odd, but so do the claims that space is curvy (which is true) and that countless possible worlds are real (which is speculation).

One way to defend the view that it is epistemically less inappropriate to accept CTSs than other conspiracy theories is the idea that *testimony* may not be a reliable source of knowledge in certain expertise contexts where it is difficult to make any personal judgment about the plausibility of the testimony. We learn many or most things just because other people kindly inform us, and it is difficult to overestimate the importance of *testimonial knowledge* (Lackey & Sosa 2006; Goldman & Whitcomb 2011; Hawley 2019). But can we trust in an expert opinion presented by a person whom we do not know and that concerns issues (e.g., extraterrestrial life) that we cannot personally evaluate?

The argument in favor of CTSs based on the view that expert testimony can be unreliable goes as follows. What is true of testimony in such core cases as "strangers giving directions" is not true in certain expertise contexts where testimony is the only source of knowledge and non-experts are unable to evaluate the sincerity and motives of experts. Therefore, in expertise contexts, for example, that of astrobiology, a person would need a specific reason to trust in an expert's opinion. Unfortunately, a person often does not have such a reason. Therefore, not accepting an expert's opinion can be rational; it may not be irrational for a person not to believe what an expert says. However, if it is sometimes rational not to believe experts, for example, when they speak about outer space, then CTSs need not conflict with the claims that a rational person would accept. In this respect, they differ from many other conspiracy theories, for other theories tend to conflict with views that would be rationally acceptable. Therefore, it is epistemically less inappropriate to accept CTSs than other conspiracy theories.

The unreliability argument does not claim that it would be rational and appropriate to believe in CTSs. The conclusion is merely that it is less inappropriate to believe in CTSs than in usual conspiracy theories that conflict with the views we should rationally accept. The argument is not overly nihilistic. Although it points out that the experts *can be* insincere – a layman cannot evaluate an expert's motives – it does not suggest that experts *are* insincere. The *possibility* of deceit justifies concern and the requirement of having a specific reason to trust. The argument is not based on the idea that, in some cases, there would *be* no reason to trust in an expert's opinion. The point is that a person who gets an expert's testimony does not necessarily *have* such a reason. Therefore, she is justified in putting aside the testimony.

The claim that an expert's testimony can be unreliable is not uncommon. In his discussion about the reliability of testimony, Alexander Guerrero (2016, 166) defends the view that in contexts of strategic expertise we should be "skeptical of testimony as a source of knowledge – given the many other motivations." In ordinary life, "we make assertions for many reasons other than to simply provide information – we aim to inform, but also recommend, encourage, advise, warn, console, convince, manipulate, and deceive" (Guerrero 2016, 161). All this is true of experts as well, he argues, and their testimonies create special concerns. In non-expert contexts, "much of what is testified to is also supported by our perceptual observations, other background evidence, memories, and so on" (Guerrero 2016, 161). However, it may be difficult for a layman to have "any independent judgment of the plausibility of the testimony offered by the expert Testifier" (Guerrero 2016, 163). Guerrero rejects the thesis, which he calls a *continuity suggestion* – the view that the core cases of testimony (in which strangers give directions) provide valuable insight into the epistemic issues arising in expertise contexts. In core cases, a person may not need a special reason to trust a Testifier's sincerity (as it may suffice that she does not have a special reason to distrust the Testifier), but in expertise contexts, the "hearer ought to obtain independent evidence to confirm a belief that a speaker is trustworthy" (Guerrero 2016, 161, 168). Unfortunately, hearers do not always have such independent evidence.

Guerrero does not write about conspiracy theories or issues pertaining to space; his discussion concerns expert testimony more generally. Nevertheless, the unreliability argument regarding the thesis that it is epistemically less inappropriate to accept CTSs than other conspiracy theories draws on Guerrero's worries. Is the unreliability argument justified?

Probably not. One may object that core cases of testimony do not really differ that much from expertise contexts. This depends partly on what is meant by "core cases" and "expertise contexts," but we seem to know many everyday facts *only* because of testimony. If someone says that she was at the movies yesterday, I may rationally believe it, even though I have not checked her reliability and sincerity from any independent source and do not have background knowledge of her behavior. Similar things happen in expertise contexts. If a doctor tells me that I have a bone fracture in my finger, I may very well rationally believe her (if I do not have a specific reason not to believe her). Perhaps I have inductive evidence pointing me to trust strangers because they have not usually deceived me (cf. Lackey 2011; Simpson 2012; Faulkner & Simpson 2017).

Notice also that if it is true that it is sometimes rational not to believe experts, this is relevant to the plausibility of almost *all* conspiracy theories, not only those relating to space. According to the unreliability argument, CTSs need not conflict with the claims that a rational person would accept. But if it is usually rational not to believe what experts say (e.g., that the World Trade Center destruction was not an "inside job"), then there are plenty of conspiracy theories that do not conflict with views that would be rational to accept. If so, then CTSs are *not* epistemically more plausible than other conspiracy theories.

The main problem with the unreliability argument is that it conflates "an expert's opinion" with "expert opinion." Sometimes, we should not accept an *individual expert's opinion* of a complicated issue if we do not have a specific reason to trust her. Obviously, however, this does not mean that we should not trust *expert opinion* if such opinion exists. If all or almost all experts agree on the shape of the Earth ("it is not flat"), then there is expert opinion on the issue. Expert opinion is the result of experts' collective efforts. If we are rational, then we should accept expert opinion, as we normally of course do (Fricker 2006, 243). As John Hardwig (1985, 343) points out, when a rational layman recognizes that there is expert opinion, he ought not to make up his mind and start "free thinking." Expert agreement provides a good ground to trust in expert opinion – even though errors may sometimes occur.[10] If experts strongly disagree on an issue, a rational layman recognizes that there is no expert opinion and that she should not form a belief for the time being (Hardwig (1985, 343).

CTSs and most other conspiracy theories conflict with expert opinion, that is, an opinion that is widely shared among experts. We should not think that their common testimony is likely to be insincere and false (although a committed conspiracy theorist would disagree).[11] The unreliability argument regarding the view that CTSs, as a class, are not as implausible as other conspiracy theories does not support the specialty thesis. The argument does not show that CTSs are special in the sense that it would be epistemically less inappropriate to accept them than to accept other conspiracy theories. Our knowledge about space is limited – this is true – but this does not help the supporters of aerospace conspiracy theories.

Concluding Remarks

I have criticized the thesis that CTSs are special in the sense that their epistemic status, as a class, differs from that of other conspiracy theories. Popular discussions around conspiracy theories often list the "strangest" or "most interesting" conspiracy theories, and these lists almost always include many conspiracy theories about space. Nevertheless, it seems that, at least epistemically speaking, CTSs are not special but rather similar to everyday conspiracy theories – theories about the death of Princess Diana, the origin of AIDS, and so on.

I discussed two possible arguments for the specialty thesis: (1) an argument that CTSs are especially implausible conspiracy theories and that it is more inappropriate to accept them than other conspiracy theories; and (2) an argument that CTSs are less ill-advised than other conspiracy theories and that it is less inappropriate to accept them than those relating to other phenomena. I found both arguments unconvincing. No doubt, other arguments can be formulated in defense of the specialty thesis. However, their evaluation would require another project. In light of the present discussion, conspiracy theories about space seem to be ordinary conspiracy theories that offer relatively poor evidence in defense of an alleged conspiracy.

Acknowledgments

I would like to thank Oskari Sivula, Susanne Uusitalo, and Jukka Varelius for helpful comments. I am also grateful to the anonymous referee and the Editors. Finally, I would like to thank Maarten Boudry and Brian Keeley for their instructive remarks about conspiracy theories during the informal coffee break discussions at the 2nd International Conference on the Philosophy of Conspiracy Theory (Amsterdam, June 2023).

Notes

1 My discussion concerns the degrees of inappropriateness, not the degrees of appropriateness. When I say that it is "less inappropriate" to accept p, I do not mean that it is "more appropriate" to accept p (as accepting p is not appropriate in the first place).
2 https://airandspace.si.edu/stories/editorial/what-are-your-favorite-aerospace-history-conspiracy-theories (September 1, 2022).
3 An example of a novel that uses the message from the space idea is Stanislaw Lem's 1968 classic *His Master's Voice*.
4 The Iran–Contra affair was a 1980s political scandal in which the Reagan administration sold guns to Iran and gave funds to Nicaraguan right-wing contra guerrillas, both in violation of the law.
5 Dentith (2016, 581) writes that "[a]ccording to generalists, conspiracy theories can be assessed *without considering the particulars of individual conspiracy theories.*" (emphasis added)
6 According to Dentith (2019, 2244), the "*prima facie* suspicion of conspiracy theories *generally*, before assessing the *particulars* of individual theories, gets things back-to-front." However, you cannot suspect a claim because it is a conspiracy theory unless you have identified it as a conspiracy theory, which, in turn, means that it has been assessed, at least to some extent.
7 The requirement that "we" should evaluate conspiracy theories on a case-by-case basis should not be understood as a demand that *all* people should start their own investigations concerning the Lunar conspiracy theory and thousands of other such theories. The requirement that *all* conspiracy theories should be investigated further sounds tricky. It is not reasonable to start further investigations of all implausible claims that we encounter, including claims about alleged conspiracies (cf. Räikkä 2023).
8 There are many versions of the lizard conspiracy theory. Some of them contradict biology.
9 Claims such as "there is life on Mars" presuppose a certain understanding of what life is, but the question of "what is life" is difficult and a source of philosophical debate. A familiar Earth life could represent a single example that may not be characteristic of life. If so, then life on Earth today provides an inadequate basis for theorizing about life generally considered (see Cleland 2012).
10 "It doesn't matter so much if one's peers are biased or operating in bad faith; they will be found out" (Hardwig 1985, 343).
11 Trust, expert opinion, and testimony: for a discussion, see e.g., Hardwig (1985); Lackey & Sosa (2006); Simpson (2012); Levy (2019); Räikkä & Ritola (2020).

References

Abad-Santos, A 2015, 'Lizard People: The Greatest Political Conspiracy Ever Created', *Vox*, February 15.

Buenting, J & Taylor, J 2010, 'Conspiracy Theories and Fortuitous Data', *Philosophy of the Social Sciences*, vol. 40, pp. 567–578.

Cleland, C 2012, 'Life without Definitions', *Synthese*, vol. 185, pp. 125–144.

Dentith, M 2016, 'When Inferring to a Conspiracy Might Be the Best Explanation', *Social Epistemology*, vol. 30, pp. 572–591.

Dentith, M 2019, 'Conspiracy Theories on the Basis of Evidence', *Synthese*, vol. 196, pp. 2243–2261.

Douglas, K & Sutton, R 2011, 'Does It Take One to Know? Endorsement of Conspiracy Theories Is Influenced by Personal Willingness to Conspire', *British Journal of Social Psychology*, vol. 50, pp. 544–552.

Douglas, K, van Prooijen, J & Sutton R 2021, 'Is the Label "Conspiracy Theory" a Cause or a Consequence of Disbelief in Alternative Narratives?', *British Journal of Psychology* (online December).

Duetz, J 2022, 'Conspiracy Theories Are Not Beliefs', *Erkenntnis* (online September).

Emerson, S 2016, 'Some of the Very Best Alien Conspiracy Theories', *Vice*, July 2.

Faulkner, P & Simpson, T (eds.) 2017, *Philosophy of Trust*, Oxford University Press, Oxford.

Fricker, E 2006, 'Testimony and Epistemic Authority', in J Lackey & E Sosa (eds.), *The Epistemology of Testimony*, Clarendon Press, Oxford, pp. 225–253.

Goldman, A & Whitcomb, D (eds.) 2011, *Social Epistemology: Essential Readings*, Oxford University Press, Oxford.

Guerrero, A 2016, 'Living with Ignorance in a World of Experts', in R Peels (ed.), *Perspectives on Ignorance from Moral and Social Philosophy*, Routledge, New York, pp. 156–185.

Hagen, K 2022, *Conspiracy Theories and the Failure of Intellectual Critique*, University of Michigan Press, Ann Arbor.

Hardwig, J 1985, 'Epistemic Dependence', *The Journal of Philosophy*, vol. 82, pp. 335–349.

Hawley, K 2019, *How to Be Trustworthy*, Oxford University Press, Oxford.

Ichino, A & Räikkä, J 2021, 'Non-Doxastic Conspiracy Theories', *Argumenta*, vol. 7, pp. 247–263.

Keeley, B 1999, 'Of Conspiracy Theories', *The Journal of Philosophy*, vol. 96, pp. 109–126.

Lackey, J 2011, 'Acquiring Knowledge from Others' in AI Goldman & D Whitcomb (eds.), *Social Epistemology: Essential Readings*, Oxford University Press, Oxford, pp. 71–91.

Lackey, J & Sosa, E (eds.) 2006, *The Epistemology of Testimony*, Clarendon Press, Oxford.

Levy, N 2019, 'Is Conspiracy Theorising Irrational?' *Social Epistemology Review and Reply Collective*, vol 8, pp. 65–76.

Lewis, D 1986, *On the Plurality of Worlds*, Blackwell, Oxford.

McMahon, S 2020, 'Do Extraordinary Claims Require Extraordinary Evidence?' in KC Smith & C Mariscal (eds.), *Social and Conceptual Issues in Astrobiology*, Oxford University Press, Oxford, pp. 117–129.

Napolitano, MG & Reuter, K 2021, 'What Is a Conspiracy Theory?', *Erkenntnis* (online September 24).

Räikkä, J 2009, 'On Political Conspiracy Theories', *The Journal of Political Philosophy*, vol. 17, pp. 185–201.

Räikkä, J 2023, 'Why a Pejorative Definition of "Conspiracy Theory" Need Not Be Unfair', *Social Epistemology Review and Reply Collective*, vol. 12, pp. 63–71.

Räikkä, J & Ritola, J 2020, 'Philosophy and Conspiracy Theories' in P Knight & M Butter (eds.), *Routledge Handbook of Conspiracy Theories*, Routledge, London, pp. 56–66.

Simpson, T 2012, 'Testimony and Sincerity', *Ratio*, vol. 25, pp. 79–92.

Smith, J 2010, *Pseudoscience and Extraordinary Claims of the Paranormal: A Critical Thinker's Toolkit*, Wiley-Blackwell, Oxford.

Truzzi, M 1978, 'On the Extraordinary: An Attempt to Clarification', *Zetetic Scholar*, vol. 1, pp. 11–19.

Uscinski, J & Enders A 2022, 'What Is a Conspiracy Theory and Why Does It Matter?', *Critical Review* (online October).

8

SUSTAINABILITY AND HUMANITY'S FUTURE IN SPACE

A Conceptual Exploration

Mikko M. Puumala

Introduction

In environmental philosophy and sustainability sciences planet Earth is sometimes presented as a spaceship (e.g., Hargrove 1986) – a closed system travelling in space, where almost nothing but sunlight comes in and almost nothing goes out. This is an important metaphor for sustainability thinking, helping us realize and remember that we are all alone, floating in vast emptiness, able to rely only on ourselves and the scarce resources we have. Planet Earth is like a self-sustaining spaceship, and it is the only vessel we have – thus we also must maintain and take good care of it. In this way, also practical and normative ideas spring from the metaphor.

But certain technological advancements, some older, some new, and some still forthcoming, have made this metaphor less intact, and possibly obsolete. We are not stuck in this vessel, and in the long term this might not be the only possible vessel we could have. Nor is it really a closed system – objects and even persons have been sent out and brought back successfully. Humanity is taking careful but firm first steps into being a truly multiplanetary species. Not only states but also private companies have set their eyes to the sky and ideas that once belonged to the realm of science fiction are becoming reality. We are witnessing what is called a New Space Age, to mark a difference between the more limited state-led space operations of the Cold War era. In the New Space Age, companies and even private citizens are becoming space actors (see Capova 2016).

Sustainability is a fitting framework for assessing humanity's future in space at least in the sense that it has an orientation towards the future, and space research, exploration, exploitation, and development raise issues that match well with sustainability's three-dimensional nature.[1] These different space

DOI: 10.4324/9781003374381-8

activities raise environmental, social, and economic sustainability issues. For instance, the way space settlements are designed can significantly limit the freedom of settlers (e.g., Cockell 2019), raising questions about social sustainability. From an environmental perspective, space activities have raised a concern about the preservation of pristine space environments (Cockell and Horneck 2004). Economically, space can provide new resources and room for new growth, but it is unclear how and from whom one can claim property rights on those resources (Schwartz 2020, ch. 5). Although space activities fit well within the sustainability framework, it has not reached the official list of United Nations Sustainable Development Goals (SDGs) (United Nations 2015). However, the United Nations Committee on the Peaceful Uses of Outer Space recognizes space activities as essential for realizing the SDGs in their 2018 "Guidelines for the Long-term Sustainability of Outer Space Activities", so the relevance of space activities to sustainability is acknowledged.

Many space sustainability issues are practical, including issues like space debris and sustainable use of space in low-Earth orbit (Palmroth et al. 2021) or planetary protection from the risks of back and forward contamination (Rummel and Billings 2004). This chapter, however, focuses on wider and more far-reaching questions about the sustainability of our space future, and how the New Space Age affects our very thinking about sustainability.

The main question is how sustainability thinking is challenged by humanity's increasing space activities. To address the issue, I will first shortly discuss three concepts and ideas closely related and important to sustainability. They are *substitutability, future generations*, and *limits of growth*. They respond to important aspects of the classic definition of sustainable development from *Our Common Future*, which states that "Sustainable development is development that meets the needs of the present without compromising the ability of future generations to meet their own needs" (World Commission on Environment and Development 1987). In this definition, *needs, future generations*, and *development* are the three elements that are particularly important for thinking about sustainability. To satisfy needs, resources are required, and here substitutability is important. To what extent can natural resources be substituted with human-made resources to satisfy human needs? Future generations will be directly addressed in this chapter. What do we owe to the future generations? Finally, the notion of development, especially in its economic sense, is closely tied to the notion of limits of growth. To what extent can human societies be developed, and are there limits to growth?

While the chapter does not argue for any specific position[2] towards space sustainability, it suggests a more cosmic perspective to sustainability (and perhaps environmental ethics in general) and tries to demonstrate the potential shortfalls of not adopting such a perspective. *Homo sapiens* is on its way towards being planet Earth's first multiplanetary species, but technological advancement is not enough – we may need new ethical and conceptual thinking to inhabit outer space safely and sustainably.

For theoretical purposes, I will assume that humanity can and will have a future in space. Thus, space future is taken as a thought experiment that provides a *conceptual stress test* to sustainability thinking: what *if* humans become a multiplanetary species? So, this work is very theoretical and speculative. In the following sections, I will examine how the stress test affects some key ideas and concepts in sustainability thinking, and potential ways that these concepts can be adjusted to survive the stress test. While these concepts work relatively well in the closed system of planet Earth (and the rather short-term timeframe typical of sustainability thinking), introducing the possibility to extend human activities outside the ecological, social, and economic limits on Earth can create some challenges for their typical use.

Substituting Terrestrial Capital with Extraterrestrial Capital

Sustainable development requires that the needs of future generations are taken into account when satisfying the needs of the present generation. To satisfy their needs, people need resources. But not all needs and resources are similar. For instance, people need to eat, and for that they need food. The need to eat is fundamental, which entails that it cannot be satisfied by, say, sleeping. Only edible things, food resources, can satisfy that need (see Thomson 2005). Consequently, not all resources satisfy all needs. A small patch of forest, which can be an economic resource, does not provide much to eat, but if it is cut down and ploughed into a field, it starts to provide food. On the other hand, the economic use of a forest satisfies needs *instrumentally*, because you can cut the trees, make furniture, sell them, and buy food with your earnings. When doing so, something interesting happens. The forest, which is *natural capital*, turns into *human capital*. While natural capital is lost, human capital is gained instead. One form of capital is substituted with another. But if all forests were turned into furniture, that would lead to an ecological catastrophe. This means that there is a limit to how much natural capital can be *substituted* with non-natural capital. To be sustainable, one must also make sure that substituting one form of capital for another does not jeopardize the ability of future generations to satisfy their needs (see Solow 1993). This way, substitutability is a core concept to sustainability.

So-called *weak sustainability* holds that all forms of capital are substitutable with one another; for example, there is no limit to substituting natural capital with human capital such as economic capital or social capital. Weak sustainability acknowledges that loss in natural capital is a loss nevertheless, but if the economic benefits outweigh the natural or environmental costs, one can still be on track with sustainability. *Strong sustainability*, however, holds that there is a limit to substituting natural capital with other forms of capital (Holland 2001, 396).

Apart from substitutability, weak sustainability also seems to entail a strong belief in humanity's ingenuity and capability to substitute natural capital on the one hand, and an assumption that it is morally permissible to use, exploit, and destroy natural capital on the other. For instance, it seems to assume that there is no inherent value in natural resources that would speak against exploiting them. On the other hand, a guiding idea behind strong sustainability seems to be skepticism towards humanity's ability to solve problems with technology, or that there are environmental philosophical, ethical, or aesthetical reasons not to exploit natural resources or that make them irreplaceable.

In theory, if Earth's resources could be substituted with extraterrestrial resources, and if there would be plenty of extraterrestrial resources, Earth could be left entirely depleted and it would still be possible to satisfy the basic needs of the present generation while enabling future generations to satisfy their needs. This is an inconvenient implication for weak sustainability, which places less limits to substitution. A version of weak sustainability that allows limitless substitution of natural capital for human capital becomes problematic. Strong sustainability does not seem to face similar challenges, as it already assumes a limit to substituting natural capital with other forms of capital.

If the nature, origin, or source of capital is irrelevant, it entails that as long as it remains otherwise socially and economically sustainable, we could imagine Earth's resources fully tapped out and all of Earth's surface covered with cities, if food production and the need for other resources could be satisfied with off-planet production. So, in addition to the question of substituting natural capital with human capital, there seems to be a question of *substituting terrestrial capital with extraterrestrial capital*. While this is a highly theoretical scenario, the conceptual stress test reveals unwelcome consequences of weak sustainability and points out a need for finding *some* way to limit substitution.

A proponent of weak sustainability could dispute terrestrial–extraterrestrial substitutability by claiming that there is something special to Earth's resources and thus no terrestrial resources can be substituted with an extraterrestrial resource. This claim seems to suppose some kind of *earthism*, which holds that there is something special, or some additional value, in having an origin on Earth. This underlying earthism prefers Earth's life, resources, or habitats over extraterrestrial ones. Earthism is a similar notion to originism, which gives value to or treats certain beings as superior due to their origin (Cockell 2007). For instance, an originist could prefer Earth-originating life because that life shares a common origin: all life on Earth can be traced back to a single common ancestry, and this shared origin gives an originistic reason to prefer Earth's life to extraterrestrial life (see Mautner 2009). Originism can give reasons for and against holding extraterrestrial lifeforms as inferior, or devoid of deserving respect. However, the kind of originism that treats extraterrestrial life as inferior can also be seen as a form of speciesism. And while treating something differently because of their belonging to different species can be prudent (elephants ought not to be treated similarly to micro-organisms), to treat something systematically as inferior on speciesist grounds is mere prejudice (Cockell 2007, 148, 150–151).

However, one can argue that it hardly counts as a prejudice – at least a morally worrying kind of prejudice – to prefer terrestrial resources like minerals over extraterrestrial ones. The kind of earthism defined here does not only refer to life, but also habitats and resources – or capital. As far as earthism is related to originism, it is not an *evolutionary* originism, but rather a *shared home* originism. However, it is not clear whether earthism is a well-grounded moral principle or merely a bias that puts "Earth first" without any firm justification. Evolutionary originism gains its argumentative strength from a kinship that comes from a shared biological origin, but earthism seems more arbitrary. While people seem to put value in locality, this hardly gives reasons to say that something is objectively more valuable merely because it is local from some perspective. On the cosmic level, earthism might as well be replaced with "solarism" (preferring something because it originates from the Solar System), "milkywaynism", or whatever arbitrarily defined position one deems "local". In fact, a cosmocentric position has been defended to counter these kinds of local perspectives (see Lupisella 2020).

To avoid the depleted Earth scenario, a proponent of weak sustainability could dispute the possibility of substituting terrestrial capital with extraterrestrial capital. However, even if earthism was a well-argued position, it is not clear that such a move could be made easily within the weak sustainability framework. There would seem to be some kind of double standard. Why would weak sustainability be uncomfortable with substituting terrestrial capital with extraterrestrial capital if it is not uncomfortable with substituting natural capital with human capital? From the perspective of weak sustainability, loss of terrestrial capital can surely be defined as an all-things-considered greater loss than loss of extraterrestrial capital, but this does not limit substitution per se. It only amounts to putting a greater value to terrestrial capital, which requires greater increase in other forms of capital to outweigh the loss. If the material basis of the system is maintained, economic growth can continue, and social problems do not occur, the depleted Earth system seems to be – in theory – sustainable in the weak sense.

This way, the conceptual stress test shows that substitutability becomes a key issue in the context of expanding human activities beyond Earth. It should be noted that this is not a practical challenge that proponents of weak sustainability need to address immediately, but rather a theoretical challenge that shows how the weak version can in itself be unsustainable in the long term and in certain circumstances.

Unlimited Growth beyond Earth?

Another key idea for sustainability is that there is a *limit to growth*. Limits of growth are related to the planetary boundaries (see Rockström et al. 2009), so that the economic and social well-being of present generation can only be increased within the ecological limits of planet Earth now and in the future.

This idea is captured by Kate Raworth's (2018) concept of *doughnut economics*. To be sustainable, a system should not overshoot its ecological boundaries nor fall short from a certain minimum level of social well-being on multiple sectors. The area (of the shape of a doughnut) between the ecological and social boundaries is where sustainable development should be pursued (Raworth 2018). A system that fits within these boundaries could, in theory, sustain itself to the end of Earth's habitability.

The idea of limits of growth is impactful in sustainability thinking. To be sustainable, any pursuing of development must be within the ecological boundaries of planet Earth. There is no infinite growth on a finite planet, as the common phrase goes. This limit also creates a tension between social and economic sustainability and environmental sustainability, as human well-being cannot be increased indefinitely and staying within the ecological limits can even require decreasing the level material well-being (see Gough 2017, 33). Expanding human presence beyond Earth, however, seems to bring down the tension between social and environmental sustainability. If nothing limits people to stay on this planet, could growth then continue beyond the terrestrial boundaries? While the idea of limits to growth gains its force from planetary boundaries, space future seems to provide a way to escape these boundaries. At the outset, this seems to undermine the idea of doughnut economics.

However, doughnut economics does not need to necessarily work only in the context of planet Earth. In a very broad sense, some kind of *doughnut thinking* is inescapable, because any set of human settlements and their interplanetary activities forms a closed system consisting of those subsystems. Furthermore, each settlement has its own physical boundaries that depend on the realities of their local environments (e.g., heavy reliance on life support systems on Mars). This is analogous to the current ecological, social, and economic circumstances on Earth: there are the local level systems of countries, municipalities, and such, and at the same time they form a broader, global closed system of planet Earth and its global economy. Just as doughnut thinking reminds us that Earth is a closed system, even with its many subsystems, an interplanetary human presence forms its own closed system, even if on a more cosmic level. Even if Earth, Mars, or any other space settlement must consider and respect the local boundaries, the interplanetary system has to consider and respect its total environmental and physical boundaries.

Thus, the stress test challenges only one fundamental thing about doughnut thinking, and that is the closedness of planet Earth. Doughnut thinking needs to be amended to take this new reality into account – Earth alone cannot be treated as a closed system (a spaceship). The doughnut gets bigger and broader, or perhaps there is a box of doughnuts that forms the whole economic and social reality for future humans. There is an expansion from planetary boundaries to solar system boundaries. While any human society must operate withing the physical limits of its environment, the economic and social boundaries do not any longer have to be adjusted *only* to the ecological boundaries of planet Earth.

In the near future, limits of growth cannot likely be escaped by pursuing new economic benefits from space activities. Apart from the technological challenges that have to be overcome, the availability of extraterrestrial resources is very limited. It seems that at least the known extraterrestrial resources are relatively scarce. They are not enough and in an economically viable way they are not available resources to hold a promise of great economic benefits. Instead, the value of space exploration and utilization of extraterrestrial environments is primarily scientific. (For discussion, see Schwartz 2020, ch. 5.) Even if the limits of growth go beyond the planetary boundaries of Earth, this does not promise an unlimited growth – the limits follow humanity to outer space, even if the boundaries are incrementally shifting.

Outer Space and Future Generations

The third core concept for sustainability is *future generations*, which is also directly mentioned in the definition of sustainable development. Considering the central role of future generations, it is perhaps surprising how short-term-focused much of the sustainability thinking is. Many space-related sustainability issues have a far longer timeframe than usual sustainability issues, for example the ones presented in the SDGs. Sustainability goals are often set for the next following decades, but perhaps less typically beyond the end of the 21st century. Problems linked to issues like climate change and world poverty require immediate action, shifting the focus to putting out fires. Indeed, this kind of *emergency thinking* is characteristic of sustainability.

Yet, space sustainability requires visions extending much further than that, spanning thousands of years to the future. However, even though emergency thinking is fairly short-term, it is not irrelevant for space activities. For instance, space debris is a major space sustainability issue that requires immediate attention, for both short-term and long-term sustainability. Satellites and other objects are launched to space at an increasing pace, of which only 10% during the last 15 years have been successfully maneuvered down. (Frey and Lemmens 2017.) The rest stay there for centuries, with a risk of crashing into other objects, creating more space debris. This may create an effect called the *Kessler syndrome* where the amount of space debris increases exponentially, destroying existing satellites and preventing us from sending new ones in, or otherwise safely leaving Earth for the next few hundred years (Palmroth et al. 2021; Virgili et al. 2016). The problem has a structure of a typical tragedy of the commons (see Hardin 1968) case,[3] where it is in the interest of each party to increase the number of their satellites, while the common-pool resource, for instance the low-Earth orbit, is uncontrollably consumed and eventually depleted so that people now and for some time in the future are not able to benefit from it (Green 2021, 74.)

Space activities that humanity pursues now can have far-reaching consequences, and sustainability requires considering the needs of future generations. The considerations particularly interesting for future generations present in the literature dealing with space ethics include ideas about protecting life or even spreading out life and increasing the number of living beings in the universe.

Space activities can be ethically justified if they lower existential risks ranging from nuclear warfare to life-threatening asteroids, and thus protect life. Indeed, one of the core arguments for space expansionism and development of space technology is that they secure the long-term survival of future generations (e.g., Munevar 2019). For instance, establishing space settlements has been defended because they can secure long-term survival for humans (see Green 2019). Of course, humans also have the capacity to destroy life and, unfortunately, remain probably the greatest existential risk to most of Earth's life, at least in the short term. From the perspective of ecological sustainability, taking humans out of the equation would probably be the most sustainable thing to do. But the ability to protect life from asteroids and other existential threats makes it – in the long term – sustainable to have humans around (see Jebari and Sandberg 2022).

Protecting life can also mean sending it away, so that life in the universe could have a contingency plan if something catastrophic happened to Earth. Intentionally seeding suitable exoplanets with life, also known as directed panspermia, could protect (Earth's) life in the universe (Sivula 2022). Ultimately life could escape before our Sun dies out, giving significantly more time for life. This way, space activities can be ethically justified because they increase the prospects of future generations of humans and non-humans alike. Space activities can increase life, its prospects, and biodiversity. For instance, seeding other planets with life and "greening the universe" have been defended because life itself is valuable, a value that should be increased if possible (see Owe 2023).

If humans gain the technological means to protect life and spread it across the universe, the present generation may gain control over the destinies of countless more generations of humans and non-humans alike. This can be challenging if satisfying the needs of the present generation and developing the space technologies that could protect and spread life are at odds. Sometimes arguments against space activities are raised because there are more pressing problems that should be addressed first (for discussion on this "Earth first" objection, see Haqq-Misra 2023, 10–13). It seems like a waste of resources to send people to the Moon when there are severe problems like climate change on Earth. But if future generations are considered, long-term sustainability may permit or even require advancing space technologies.

Considering future generations in a long-term way can also work in a constructive manner. With *utopian thinking*, sustainability can be seen especially as a normative concept, and the question is, what should we hope to continue, or what is the best outcome for humanity and life as we know it in the next thousand, ten thousand, or even million years, or up until the heat death of the universe? What is the state of humanity we want, and best possible social arrangements that respect the boundaries of their surrounding environments? Here the division between sustainability goals and sustainable processes is important (see Boström 2012). If we focus on sustainability goals, like satisfying basic needs for everyone and pursuing greater equality, space activities could support these goals by providing new resources. A long-term goal could be to end all material human need while respecting the ecological boundaries of the environments that humans inhabit. If we focus on sustainable processes, there are important questions about access to space resources and the chance to participate and influence the space future. Realizing a sustainable space future requires sustainable governance.

Conclusions

Recent developments in space research and technology, and the emergence of new space actors, such as private companies, are shifting the realm of possibility. Some space-related sustainability issues have already materialized, space debris being one of the most discussed topics, but many we have not yet faced. It would be better to think about possible problems *before* they emerge. There are many kinds of issues to consider, and all raise ecological, social, economic, and cultural questions about a sustainable future. These should all be handled with sustainable practices.

Even if some of these issues still belong in the realm of science fiction, they can be treated as a thought experiment to test how some important ideas like sustainability function with long-term questions. In this sense, space is like a mirror: it helps to evaluate our relationship to Earth, and our core sustainability concepts. Including space in concerns about sustainability allows us to shift timeframes, to truly think long-term. Further, it forces us to use concepts less lavishly and to understand their limits – and ours.

It is time to take seriously the notion that Earth is not a closed system; the first Earthlings have already spread their influence outside it, and will soon be bringing new knowledge, materials, resources, and ideas back on Earth. We are not inhabiting a spaceship, but a space station, where things come and go, and hopefully they will do so sustainably.

Acknowledgments

I would like to thank Yasha Rohwer, Keje Boersma, Oskari Sivula, and Laura Puumala for their comments on the chapter, as well as the participants of the ISEE 2022 summer meeting and NSU Nordic Environmental Ethics Summer Session 2022 for comments and discussion. This chapter was written with the support of the Maj and Tor Nessling Foundation and Alfred Kordelin Foundation.

Notes

1 Sustainable development and sustainability are often characterized as three-dimensional or consisting of three mutually supportive "pillars": social, economic, and environmental.

(See e.g., United Nations 1997; WSSD 2002, 2.) The social and environmental aspects of development and human activities are interconnected, and one area of development cannot be sustainably achieved without consideration of the other two.

2 For instance, Andreas Losch (2019) has argued for the need for an "ethics of planetary sustainability" (see Beisbart 2019 for critical discussion).

3 Or rather that of *Tyranny of the Contemporary* scenario, where the present generation makes decisions that affect the future generations without a chance for reciprocity or cooperation (see Gardiner 2011).

References

Beisbart, C. (2019). Do we need an ethics of planetary sustainability? *Global Sustainability*, 2, e22. https://doi.org/10.1017/sus.2019.19.

Boström, M. (2012). A missing pillar? Challenges in theorizing and practicing social sustainability: Introduction to the special issue. *Sustainability: Science, Practice and Policy*, 8 (1), 3–14. doi:10.1080/15487733.2012.11908080.

Capova, K. A. (2016). The New Space Age in the making: Emergence of exo-mining, exo-burials and exo-marketing. *International Journal of Astrobiology*, 15 (4), 307–310.

Cockell, C. S. (2007). Originism: Ethics and extraterrestrial life. *Journal of the British Interplanetary Society*, 60, 147–153.

Cockell, C. S. (2019). Freedom engineering – using engineering to mitigate tyranny in space. *Space Policy*, 49, 101328.

Cockell, C. S. and Horneck, G. (2004). A planetary park system for Mars, *Space Policy*, 20, 291–295.

Fogg, M. (2000). The Ethical Dimensions of Space Settlement, *Space Policy*, 16 (3), 205–211. https://doi.org/10.1016/S0265-9646(00)00024-2.

Frey, S. and Lemmens, S. (2017). Status of the space environment: Current level of adherence to the space debris mitigation policy. In Flohrer, T. and Schmitz, F. (eds.) *Proceedings of the 7th European Conference on Space Debris*. ESA Space Debris Office. https://conference.sdo.esoc.esa.int/proceedings/sdc7/paper/483, accessed 15 August 2023.

Gardiner, S. M. (2011). *A Perfect Moral Storm: The Ethical Tragedy of Climate Change*. Oxford: Oxford University Press.

Gough, I. (2017). *Heat, Greed and Human Need: Climate Change, Capitalism and Sustainable Wellbeing*. Cheltenham: Edward Elgar Publishing.

Green, B. P. (2019). Self-preservation should be humankind's first ethical priority and therefore rapid space settlement is necessary. *Futures*, 110, 35–37.

Green, B. P. (2021). *Space Ethics*. London: Rowman & Littlefield.

Haqq-Misra, Jacob (2023). *Sovereign Mars: Transforming Our Values through Space Settlement*. Lawrence: University Press of Kansas.

Hardin, G. (1968). The Tragedy of the Commons, *Science*, 162 (3859), 1243–1248.

Hargrove, E.C. (ed.) (1986). *Beyond Spaceship Earth: Environmental Ethics and the Solar System*. San Francisco: Sierra Club Books.

Holland, A. (2001). Sustainability. In Jamieson, D. (ed.) *A Companion to Environmental Philosophy*. Oxford: Blackwell.

Jebari, K. and Sandberg, A. (2022). Ecocentrism and biosphere life extension. *Science and Engineering Ethics*, 28, 46. https://doi.org/10.1007/s11948-022-00404-2.

Losch, A (2019). The need of an ethics of planetary sustainability. *International Journal of Astrobiology*, 18 (3), 259–266. https://doi.org/10.1017/S1473550417000490.

Lupisella, M. (2020). Meaning and ethics. In Lupisella, M. (ed.) *Cosmological Theories of Value*. Cham: Springer, 171–194.

MacNiven, D. (1995). Environmental Ethics and Planetary Engineering, *Journal of the British Interplanetary Society*, 48, 441–443.

Mautner, M. N. (2009). Life-centered ethics, and the human future in space. *Bioethics*, 23 (8), 433–440.

Munevar, G. (2019). An obligation to colonize outer space. *Futures*, 110, 38–40.

Owe, A. (2023). Greening the Universe: The Case for Ecocentric Space Expansion. In Schwartz, J. S. J., Billings, L. and Nesvold, E. (eds.) *Reclaiming Space: Progressive and Multicultural Visions of Space Exploration*. Oxford: Oxford University Press.

Palmroth, M., Tapio, J., Soucek, A., Perrels, A., Jah, M., Lönnqvist, M., Nikulainen, M., Piaulokaite, V., Seppälä, T. and Virtanen, J. (2021). Toward sustainable use of space: Economic, technological, and legal perspectives. *Space Policy* 57. 1–12.

Raworth, K. (2018). *Doughnut Economics: Seven Ways to Think Like a 21st-Century Economist*. New York: Random House.

Rockström, J., Steffen, W., Noone, K., Persson, Å., et.al. (2009). A safe operating space for humanity. *Nature* 461 (7263), 472–475. https://doi.org/10.1038/461472a.

Rummel, J. D. and Billings, L. (2004). Issues in planetary protection: Policy, protocol and implementation, *Space Policy*, 20 (1), 49–54.

Schwartz, J. S. (2020). *The Value of Science in Space Exploration*. Oxford: Oxford University Press.

Sivula, O. (2022). The cosmic significance of directed panspermia: Should humanity spread life to other solar systems? *Utilitas*, 1–17. doi:10.1017/S095382082100042X.

Solow, R. M. (1993). Sustainability: An Economist's Perspective. In Dorfman, R. and Dorfman, N. S. (eds.) *Economics of the Environment: Selected Readings* (3rd ed.). New York: Norton, 179–187.

Thomson, G. (2005). Fundamental needs. *Royal Institute of Philosophy Supplement*, 57, 175–186. doi:10.1017/S1358246105057097.

United Nations (1997). *Agenda for Development*. https://digitallibrary.un.org/record/188719, accessed 15 August 2023.

United Nations (2015). *Transforming Our World: the 2030 Agenda for Sustainable Development*. https://sdgs.un.org/2030agenda, accessed 15 August 2023.

United Nations (2018). *Guidelines for the Long-Term Sustainability of Outer Space Activities*. https://www.unoosa.org/res/oosadoc/data/documents/2019/aac_105c_1l/aa c_105c_1l_366_0_html/V1805022.pdf, accessed 15 August 2023.

World Commission on Environment and Development (WCED) (1987). *Our Common Future*. New York: Oxford University Press.

Virgili, B., Dolado, J. C., Lewis, H. G., Radtke, J., Krag, H., Revelin, B., Cazaux, C., Colombo, C., Crowther, R. and Metz, M. (2016). Risk to space sustainability from large constellations of satellites. *Acta Astronautica* 126, 154–162.

WSSD (2002). *Plan of Implementation of the World Summit on Sustainable Development*. https://www.un.org/esa/sustdev/documents/WSSD_POI_PD/English/WSSD_PlanImpl. pdf, accessed 15 August 2023.

9

"IMPROVING" OUTER SPACE

Arden Rowell

On Earth, many people's intuitions about the environment are informed by a profound sense that people are the source of environmental problems. There is an obvious element of truth to this sense. People have done many damaging things to the Earth, and humans are definitively a source of pollution and environmental degradation (Goudie, 2018; IPCC, 2007). Indeed, the anthropogenic impact on Earth's environment is now so great that this epoch of time is increasingly styled as the "Anthropocene" by (Earth) environmentalists (Crutzen & Stoermer, 2000; Purdy, 2015).

Are humans degraders (only)? Improvers (only)? Both? Neither? How we answer this question has fundamental implications for how we think about the relationship between humans and the environment, and thus for the opportunities (and limitations) presented by human behavior and its regulation. Answering these questions will help us determine whether we would do better to adopt policies insulating environments from human-led degradation and ruin; whether policies should encourage environmental change where doing so promotes human opportunity and economic growth; whether we should focus on finding principles to discern when and what to insulate, and when and what to humanize through development. If we start by thinking about these issues on Earth, however, it can be too easy to become entangled in the complexities of how we think about our current relationship with the planet, and to end up retrenching old perspectives and arguments. Perhaps some distance can help.

Environmental Quality from a Distance

Thinking of the human relationship with the environment in outer space pays several dividends. We gain a kind of emotional and analytical distance from our Earthly situation that may help us in better understanding how to more

DOI: 10.4324/9781003374381-9

reflectively conceive of "the environment" and human relationships with it. And from a space-regarding perspective, enriching our conception of the human relationship with outer environments is an important step in developing considerate policy towards humans' environmental impacts in outer space.

Law and policy provide one impactful area in which to look for operationalized intuitions about human–environment interactions. Perhaps unsurprisingly, Earth-based environmental law and policy has not traditionally focused outwards. Rather, environmental law and policy has historically assumed that "the environment" to which humans are exposed is (only on) Earth. After all, all humans lived on Earth until quite recently, and we had little reason to believe that human action had extraterrestrial impact.

Nowadays, however, not (quite) every human lives on the surface of the Earth (as of writing, seven people are living on the International Space Station; National Aeronautics and Space Station 2023), and it seems probable that more future humans will live and be exposed to non-Earth environments – whether in almost purely artificial environments such as space stations or space ships, or on extraterrestrial surfaces such as the Moon or other planets. We are also aware now of a panoply of ways in which human activities already impact extraterrestrial locations, as through space debris (Diaz, 1993), forward-contamination and other exploration impacts (Williamson, 2006), and the purposeful and ancillary emission of electromagnetic signals and light (Farah, 2019).

Given our increasing awareness of – and impact on – outer space, it seems right to recognize that Earth is not the only surrounding in which humans may find themselves, or about which humans may care. As we turn towards thinking and speaking of environmental concerns in outer space, however, a linguistic point presents itself: whether it makes sense to speak of "the" (singular) environment in space, or whether we instead should speak of "environments" in the plural. The point may seem small, but it touches fundamentally on how it is that we conceive of environmental issues and human–environment relationships.

On Earth, it is of course the norm to speak of *the* environment, especially when discussing environmental law and policy. This convention recognizes the overlapping and networked ecological connections on Earth, which create a dense field of causal connections between environmental cause and effect. But while this convention may be valuable in emphasizing ecological interconnections between Alaska and Antarctica, it is an awkward fit for space, where such interconnections between environments are limited (where they exist at all), and where environmental conditions themselves are subject to far greater diversity. This diversity will frequently justify differing standards for what constitutes environmental quality: it does not make sense to measure the quality of environmental conditions on the Moon, the Sun, Pluto, asteroids, protostars, and red giants according to either the same yardstick as Earth, or even the same yardstick as one another. Changes of even a few degrees in mean surface temperature on Earth, such as a 4°C increase from the current mean of 15° to 19°C, will generate catastrophic environmental degradation (IPCC 2014). Yet it would be a non sequitur to conclude that similar levels of temperature change are necessarily degrading to other celestial bodies. Pluto, for instance, undergoes a 14°C shift in mean surface temperature during each of its 248-year orbits of the Sun, but such changes are plausibly either irrelevant to – or perhaps even valuable to – maintaining the unique environmental quality of Pluto. Similarly, conditions on the surface of the Sun, which averages 5,600°C, need not mirror conditions on Pluto. In sum, both the diversity and disconnection of outer space—of countless planets, stars, satellites, celestial bodies, and galaxies, spread across 94 billion light years of vacuum – justify a linguistic shift towards speaking of outer space environments in the plural.

With this shift in mind, let us consider how various models of human–environment interaction may apply to non-Earth environments. As we do so, it is clearly important to consider the possibility that human action can harm an expanding set of environments – as well as the possibility that interacting with outer space environments may generate environmental risk back on Earth (Puumala, 2024). And indeed, the language of the touchstone treaty on outer space, the Outer Space Treaty, recognizes both of these concerns. It provides that:

> State Parties to the Treaty shall pursue studies of outer space, including the moon and other celestial bodies, and conduct exploration of them so as to *avoid their harmful contamination* and also adverse changes in the environment of the Earth resulting from the introduction of extraterrestrial matter and, where necessary, shall adopt appropriate measures for this purpose.
>
> *(Outer Space Treaty, 1966, Art. IX, emphasis added)*

A critical question in interpreting this language is determining what constitutes "harmful contamination" of celestial bodies.

Humans as Agents of Environmental Harm

As noted above, humans are demonstrably capable of harming environments. In considering when human action leads to environmental harm, however, it is worth pausing to recognize that intuitive perceptions of environmental quality are especially susceptible to heuristic-based thinking and to subconscious oversimplification (Rowell & Bilz, 2021). This is because the diffuse, complex, and nonhuman qualities of environmental harm make it especially difficult for people to intuitively recognize, understand, and evaluate. As a result, recognition of humans as *a* source of pollution can subconsciously slip into a simplistic mental model where humans are *only* a source of pollution: what I will call the "humans-as-ruiners" heuristic. In this heuristic model, human are seen as separate from nature (Wiener, 1996); nature – inhuman nature – may be imagined as intrinsically pure (Rowell & Bilz, 2021) or as normatively superior to "artificial" nature (Siipi, 2008); and enormous value may be placed on the preservation of "untouched" (Nelson & Calicott, 2008; Calicott & Nelson, 1998) or "virgin" wildernesses, which have not (yet?) been defiled by human hands. Indeed, the taint of human action may extend to perceptions of technology and technology-based solutions to environmental problems (Douglas & Wildavsky, 1982), and/or may interweave with a social narrative of the mad scientist: a dangerous, unpredictable figure who brings (to him unanticipated, to the teller inevitable) catastrophe because of his arrogant belief that he might do better than God/nature (Haynes, 1999; Tudor, 1989).

The more we slip into thinking of humans as (only) ruiners, or as only a source of environmental harm, the more it will seem tempting to conclude that *any* human involvement in a celestial body is harmful: that mere contact with humans is a kind of ruinous contamination. Exhortations to avoid harmful contamination of celestial bodies would be best served, on this simplified line of thinking, by insulating non-Earth environments from the contaminating presence of humans and human technology. Interpreting the Outer Space Treaty in this way would have dire but clear implications for space exploration and colonization: signatories would be obligated to leave space alone so that they didn't ruin it. Under this view, the appropriate policy to adopt towards space is a "cosmic noninterference doctrine": one that treats the non-Earth universe as a protected wilderness, eternally virgin and pristine (other than where we have mucked it up already), protected from contamination from humans, and which forbids (further) interference of any type.

This approach has the intuitive appeal of simplicity: in equating any human involvement in an environment with ruin, it vitiates – or perhaps obscures? – the need to find answers to difficult ethical questions, such as what affirmative obligations humans might owe to extraterrestrial environments; what makes an environment "good" and worth preserving or "degraded" and worth avoiding; whether some environments or environmental characteristics are better than others, and if so how and how much; how environmental quality should be distributed across disconnected environments; and who gets to decide the answer to any such questions. All such questions are replaced by a simple direction to leave the universe alone.

Yet by adopting a view that human involvement in an environment is absolutely and *only* damaging, such an approach also adopts a set of assumptions about human–environment interactions that are incomplete at best. Human interactions with the Earth provide no shortage of examples of humans degrading the environment, as I have readily conceded. But there are other possible relationships between environmental quality and human involvement that may be worth considering, and which may be neglected if we allow ourselves to be pulled along by intuition alone. These include: (1) the possibility of human irrelevance; (2) the possibility of "pure" human-led improvement without environmental degradation; and (3) the possibility of humans generating a net improvement in environmental quality while generating both environmental benefits and environmental costs. Failing even to consider these human–environment relationships as legitimate possibilities may unreasonably truncate our analysis of environmental quality, may impoverish our understanding of ethical obligations, may lead to undesired outcomes, and in some cases may even serve as a rationalization for human inaction in the face of environmental peril.

The Possibility of Human Irrelevance

To see how these risks may come about, let us start by considering categories of human–environment interaction that are prone to intuitive neglect. First, let us recognize that the quality of many space environments is likely to be indifferent to many human actions, in the sense that human action does not affect them either positively or negatively. This irrelevance might arise from at least three sources: the *de minimus* nature of the action, such as moving a rock on the surface of the Moon three centimeters to the left; from the qualities of resiliency of the environment itself, as if a human-made satellite crashed into the Sun; and/or from the discontinuous quality of space environments.

Recall that space environments are generally separated by (light years of) vacuum and lack the types of ecological connections that are instead characteristic of a single interconnected environment, such as Earth. On Earth, there are plausible arguments to be made for the so-called "butterfly effect" – that even the beat of a butterfly's wings may affect the course of a typhoon on the other side of the planet (Lorenz, 1963) – such that even minimal human actions such as disturbing a butterfly can have important environmental consequences. Deterministic chaos theory of this type relies precisely on the presumption that there are causal interconnections between natural systems, such as atmospheric systems and fluid flow. Such causal interconnections exist on Earth, yet between space environments, years of vacuum break most (perhaps all) such connections. (And what connections may remain – for example, the possibility that all of space–time is quantumly entangled (Bell, 1964) – have yet to be theorized in relation to environmental quality.) Even were every butterfly wing beat relevant to environmental quality on Earth, the same beats must overcome remarkable causal distance to be relevant to the environment on the Moon or the surface of Venus. Their irrelevance becomes still more overwhelmingly likely as we move into more distant space environments – to our neighboring star Proxima Centauri, 40 trillion kilometers or 4.2 light years away. Once we reach the edge of the visible universe, 13.8 billion light years away, the possibility that human actions of almost any kind – much less the disturbance of a single butterfly – can impact the quality of such distant environment seems unimaginable. Indeed, any conviction that humans are so powerful as to affect environments at that distance smacks, if anything, more of arrogance than prudence. To the quality of most space environments, many human actions are almost certainly irrelevant. This does not mean that no human action will ever affect a space environment for good or ill. But it does mean that such effects must be placed in the context in which they unfold: in the extraordinary reaches of space, where the ecological interconnections we may be accustomed to recognizing on Earth are decisively severed.

"Pure" Human-Led Environmental Improvements in Space

Now let us consider the possibility that some human actions may not just impact space environments but do so in a *solely* positive way. Here as well the discontinuity of space environments plays an important role. Unlike on Earth, where any action may generate environmental externalities somewhere on Earth, environmental change in disconnected space environments offers a far greater possibility of "pure" (intra-environmental) improvements, generating environmental benefits absent internalized costs. Indeed, so long as we think of environments as discontinuous in this way, the cost of human action can be borne by one environment while the benefits are borne by another. It is thus quite possible for humans to generate a "pure" environmental improvement in one space environment – by the expediency of paying for that improvement through resources or risks elsewhere. Identifying the possibility of such "pure" improvements can help us recognize the importance of considering if, when, and how such transferences of environmental benefit are ethical, justifiable, or even obligatory.

Recognizing the possibility of human-led environmental improvement can also have important consequences for policy choices – even if those improvements come at environmental cost to other environments, such as Earth. In this vein, imagine a scenario where scientists using an advanced research probe discover a nearby solar system. The solar system holds a planet, "Bios," teeming with millions of forms of indigenous life that have generated a rich tapestry of (on-planet) ecological interconnection. Unfortunately, the probe has also detected a colossal meteor headed on a collision course towards Bios. If the meteor strikes, the planet will be destroyed. The probe has enough power that it can slightly alter the trajectory of the meteor by slamming into it at full thrust. In that case the probe would be destroyed, but Bios would be saved. Should the scientists sacrifice the probe to save the biodiverse Bios?

Unless we adopt the (controversial) view that lifeless pieces of exploded rock constitute a better environment than a biodiverse planet, human intervention is an unalloyed benefit to the environment on Bios. The scientists thus have the opportunity to improve the environment on Bios by taking action to protect it from destruction. True, the improvement is not cosmically free: the reason there is a potential puzzle for the scientists is that costs are being borne via the destruction of the research probe, which was presumably manufactured (with associated environmental externalities) on Earth, and the destruction of which impoverishes future research. If the scientists choose to save Bios, however, Bios will only experience an improvement in environmental quality (without any concomitant costs).

The possibility of humans generating "pure" environmental improvements in outer space environments presents interesting ethical puzzles about when and how much human investment is justified or obligated to secure those improvements. In this case, the question for the scientists should be whether the extent of the improvement on Bios justifies the cost accrued by losing the probe.

Answering this question might be informed by a number of perennially challenging debates in environmental ethics, such as whether the quality of an
environment should be evaluated anthropocentrically – by reference only to
human interests – or biocentrically, by reference to all its living elements
(Taylor, 1981), as well as newer space-based versions of those debates, such as
what role alien life should play in a biocentric analysis, how we should calcu-
late the value of such life to humankind (and whether it should be presumed to
be positive or negative), and what obligations humans owe alien lives and
environments. These are difficult questions subject to substantial disagreement.
For instance, adopting an anthropocentric approach that highly valued the
probe's future research potential, and/or that calculated the human benefit of
preserved alien life to be low or negative (for example, if the life on Bios posed
a threat to human life), might lead the scientists to preserve the probe and
allow Bios to perish. A biocentric view that attached high value to biodiverse
alien life would by contrast support preserving Bios, even at the cost to humans
of the lost probe. Strong views from either perspective might even see such
actions (or inaction) as ethically obligatory. The outcome of reflecting on these
difficult ethical questions would presumably lead, however, either to the preservation of the research probe or to the preservation of the biodiverse planet.

Reaching these questions is only possible, however, if we start by recognizing
that it is possible for human action to improve outer space environments. Here it is
worth contrasting the shape of the ethical and policy analysis if the scientists were
to fail to recognize such a possibility, as by subconsciously adopting a simplified
humans-as-ruiners heuristic, or by purposefully adopting the cosmic noninterference doctrine such a heuristic would encourage for space policy. Under
those approaches, any human interference would be presumed to be definitionally
damaging – so that the scientists would be bound not to interfere, and thus to leave
Bios to its sad fate. Indeed, if any order at all were sent to the probe, it would
presumably be to end the exploration mission to minimize the additional space
environments that the probe contaminates. The result would then be a lose–lose:
both the loss of future research and the destruction of a biodiverse alien planet.
While relying upon intuition in this way would simplify the analysis, it would do
so in a way that would short-circuit engagement with important ethical questions,
in this case with wasteful and perhaps even tragic consequences.

In sum, recognizing the possibility of human-led improvements in space
environments can have important implications for both the direction and depth
of our ethical analyses, as well as for the practical and policy choices that will
be based on those analyses.

Net-Beneficial Human-Led Environmental Improvements

We have now considered situations where human action is irrelevant to (some)
space environments, as well as situations where a particular space environment
may be purely improved via human interaction (albeit presumably at a cost to

some other environment, such as Earth). This takes us to the final form of human–environment interaction that is worth considering, which is where a specific environment experiences both environmental benefit and environmental harm as a result of human action. On this front, terraforming – purposefully making some extraterrestrial surface more "terra-like" – is a helpful example (Sivula, 2024). Many potential options for terraforming exist, ranging from the transportation of some form of Earth-based life (such as bacteria) to another planet (Friedmann & Ocampo-Friedmann, 1995), to creating vast geoengineering projects to fundamentally change extraterrestrial atmospheres and/or surfaces (Fogg, 1995).

Others have considered the ethics of terraforming from a variety of standpoints and in much greater detail than there is space for here (Fogg, 1995, 2000; McKay & Zubrin 2002; Stoner, 2021; Sivula, 2024). For current purposes, it is worth noting that the project of terraforming is necessarily premised upon the presumption that it is possible to create a "better" environment by purposefully changing that environment in some human-desired way, i.e. by changing the extraterrestrial environment from a less Earth-like state to a more Earth-like state, as by increasing oxygen or reducing the temperature to human-survivable levels. Creating such changes, however, necessarily damages the aspects of the terraformed environment that are less Earth-like. In circumstances where there is existing indigenous life, the ethical implications of this are particularly fraught (McKay & Zubrin, 2002); such life would presumably have evolved to the pre-terraformed environment, and would be harmed or even destroyed. But even the terraforming of a lifeless planet has been likened to "vandalism," or a form of aesthetic harm (York, 2002).

Recognizing that terraforming may generate significant environmental costs to extraterrestrial environments does not preclude recognizing that it may also provide significant environmental benefits, both in the form of ecosystem services for humans and in the creation of biodiversity. Whether – and if so, when and how – terraforming is appropriate should therefore turn on a variety of challenging questions, including what it means to make an extraterrestrial environment "better" or "worse," what the qualities of Earth are that are valuable and why, what humans owe extraterrestrial life or environments, and whether humans have obligations – for example to future generations or non-human lifeforms – to terraform and/or expand human habitats. These are challenging ethical puzzles that deserve authentic consideration. Such consideration follows only, however, from the recognition that it is possible for human–environment interactions to generate benefits as well as harm – and that at least on net, such interactions may create environmental improvement.

In sum, human interactions with outer space environments may harm, benefit, or be irrelevant to the quality of those environments. Which type of interaction unfolds will be determined by the specifics of the interaction and the environment, and how we will be navigating the labyrinth of ethical puzzles presented by managing human interactions with multiple environments. To map this labyrinth, the first step is to recognize that all human interactions do not lead the same way: while some pathways will cause environmental harm to outer space environments, some will not matter, and others may actually generate environmental benefits for those environments. Considering the larger set of potential relationships will give us a better chance of recognizing when and how humans should interact with outer space environments.

Looking Back Towards Earth

The prior analysis focused upon human–environment relationships in space. To consider Earth implications, let us return for a few minutes to the concept of the "Anthropocene," a term that elicits a profound sense of loss and sadness in many environmentalists. Taking a space-based perspective may give reason to be (somewhat) more positive about the Anthropocene. First, it may be worth noting that the concept of the Anthropocene is cosmically provincial. Except for our planet and a few messy regions of space next door, human action or inaction is irrelevant to the vast majority of environments in the universe. The more that one thinks of humanity as a vector (only) for ruin, the more encouraging one may find the reflection that the universe remains a pristine wilderness, unpolluted by human hands. Indeed, the universe is so large – at current estimate, about 28 billion light years across – that it seems impossible for humans to affect (contaminate?) more than a tiny fraction of it.

That said, the reflection that most of the universe will never experience an Anthropocene is cool comfort for those who care about the fate of Earth. Yet there may still be hopeful lessons even when thinking only of a more local perspective. More specifically, it may be helpful to recognize that the view of the Anthropocene as depressing is at least partly driven by the assumption that human impacts on the environment are necessarily and exclusively bad. This is a vestige of the humans-as-ruiners heuristic – which as we have seen, at least in space environments, is an oversimplification of the relationship between humans and environments, insofar as it forecloses plausible possibilities both of human irrelevance and of human-led environmental improvement (via pure- or net-positive impacts). If we make mental space for the possibility that humans on Earth can also affect the Earth in positive ways, it makes it more imaginable that an Anthropocene can be made happy, or at least less sad – that an age of humans might involve preservation or even cultivation of what we find good in our Earth environment, even if it also involves degradation and loss.

This (somewhat) happier vision of a manageable Anthropocene may be clarified by transferring reflections on the human–environment relationship from space contexts to Earth ones. There are barriers to simple transfer, however. Chief among these is the critical difference between examining disconnected and discontinuous environments that may be separated by light years of vacuum from both each other and the nearest human, and understanding human relationships with the interconnected environment inside of which billions of humans live.

In this vein, consider again the category of human–environment interaction that is irrelevant to environmental quality. When considering space environments, we imagined *de minimis* actions: actions that had no important effect because of some quality of resiliency in the affected environment, and actions that had no important effect on an environment because the environment was disconnected from the location where the action occurred. All of these categories of irrelevance can at least theoretically occur on Earth: disturbing a butterfly from a flower will not always cause a typhoon; an extra half kilogram of carbon dioxide emissions may truly not affect the state of the Earth's present or future atmosphere; and despite the interconnectedness of ecosystems in Earth's environments, the planting of daffodils in a window box in New Jersey may not in fact affect any quality of the environment in New Delhi. That said, as noted, there are overwhelmingly more interconnections across Earth's ecosystems than exist across the vast majority of outer space environments, and humans are interacting daily, repeatedly, and pervasively with those Earthly ecosystems in ways that they do not – and presumably never will – interact with most outer space environments. An important difference between outer space and Earth environments is therefore that, while there may be some circumstances where human actions are irrelevant to environmental quality in both cases, most human actions fall into this category for most outer space environments, while the category is far rarer when applied to the planet we live on.

Now consider whether there are "pure" improvements in environmental quality that can be created by humans on Earth – that is, whether there are categories of human action that generate environmental benefits (for Earth) without accruing any environmental costs (to Earth). When we considered this category for space environments, we were able to imagine pure improvements by externalizing the cost of action from one discontinuous environment to another – so we imagined being able to, for example, improve the environment inside a spaceship by relying on resources extracted from and manufactured on Earth. This accounting option is only available in discontinuous environments, however; within a single interconnected environment such as Earth, the environmental cost of any action will be borne by Earth. It is true that it is possible to "carve up" Earth environments, as along political borders, and to generate facially disconnected outcomes between domestic and "foreign" harms (Rowell & Wexler, 2014; Rowell, 2015). The United States, for example, can ship its plastic waste to Vietnam, thereby increasing environmental quality in the United States and harming environmental quality in Vietnam. Yet the interconnected nature of the environment on Earth means that the environment in the United States is likely still affected by the exported plastic, via both the atmospheric emissions from transport and the global spread of microplastics. So even within the United States' environment alone, there would be environmental costs to this policy as well as benefits.

Plausibly, however, the future likely holds multiple opportunities for the Earth environment to be improved by externalizing resource and environmental costs to non-Earth environments. For example, environmental quality on Earth might benefit significantly from shifting (highly polluting) extraction activities, such as mining for rare earth minerals, from Earth to asteroids and other celestial bodies. Purposeful externalization of environmental harms to non-Earth environments would take advantage of the discontinuous nature of Earth and extraterrestrial environments to create an on-Earth environmental win – although, much as with the puzzle of whether Earth-based resources should be sacrificed to save the biodiverse planet Bios, such actions should be understood to implicate a series of difficult emerging ethical questions about when it is ethical to shift environmental costs and benefits between environments. My plea here is not to resolve those questions in any particular way, but rather to reach those questions by recognizing the possibility of human-led action generating environmental improvement (somewhere).

Finally, it is worth considering whether human–environment interactions might ever generate net environmental benefits on Earth. Recall that this category of interaction does not require that there be no environmental costs to an interaction; merely that on the whole, the environment is left better off. In space, we imagined this category of human–environment interaction as potentially arising from (some) terraforming, or the purposeful cultivation of some valued Earth-like characteristics in distant environments. Related actions could, of course, be taken in respect of geoengineering the Earth – offering significant potential upside alongside potentially catastrophic risk (Rowell, 2021; Felgenhauer, et al., 2022). At a homier and perhaps less terrifying scale, however, we might also consider the example of the garden. People engage in gardening for many reasons, but those who garden generally believe themselves to be cultivating some quality of the environment that they value, and believe that their activities will on the whole make things better. In this sense, gardens are a kind of hopeful instantiation of the possibility that anthropogenic environmental change can be an improvement rather than a degradation. At a global scale, it is worth serious consideration of when and how geoengineering might accomplish similar goals.

Merely hoping that human activity will generate net-positive environmental changes is not, of course, sufficient to achieve that goal. To have positive impacts on the Earth's environment, we must have an idea of what is good (and bad) in an environment, and our ability to affect our desired ends remains constrained by our knowledge and our choices. Sometimes our views may even change over time; consider, on this front, modern social changes in valuation of wetlands (Vileisis, 1999) and predator species (Ripple & Larsen, 2000). These points present real challenges. But focusing on how to manage the (Earthly) Anthropocene this way—on seeking net improvement even while recognizing and minimizing damage—gives us a very different (and more encouraging) focus than imagining the Earth on a human-led death march to ruin.

So long as we recognize that net environmental improvement is possible, we can focus on more clearly articulating what it would mean for humans to improve the environment on Earth—and by then taking what actions we can to implement that vision. In some cases, of course, different accounts in environmental ethics may generate different priorities. In many other cases, however, the overlapping interests of Earth-based biocentric targets and humans will generate a significant number of commonalities between anthropocentric and biocentric accounts – more, it may be worth noting, than we might expect to see on other planets or in outer (and discrete) environments. Preventing an insect apocalypse on Earth, for example, is obviously an improvement from a biocentric perspective, and is also likely to be an improvement from an anthropocentric perspective because of the various ecosystem services provided by insects (Kehoe, Frago & Sanders, 2021). Managing plastic pollution to avoid all of Earth's marine life being destroyed (United Nations Environmental Programme, 2021) has a similarly overdetermined quality. Any of these actions will use resources on Earth, and will therefore have environmental costs for the Earth as well as benefits. Yet so long as we believe that the positive changes that are wrought are worth the environmental costs, improving *net* environmental quality is possible.

Objections, Counterarguments, and Opportunities for Further Specification

There are several ways to resist the argument that thinking of environments in outer space can help us understand that – and to some degree how – humans can improve the environment on Earth. Here I respond to three.

The first objection I would like to address is that the substantive work of determining when humans "improve" the environment is determined by the definition of improvement. I largely agree with this objection, and hope it is clear that this piece has neither attempted to nor succeeded at specifying a substantive account of improvement. I am more interested here in establishing that human-led environmental improvement is at least theoretically possible, and that there may be interactions between improvement and degradation that have ethical and pragmatic implications. More specifically, I think it is clearly true that the concept of environmental degradation is based upon a conviction – often unexamined – that environments can be better or worse; that it is the progression to a worse state that comprises degradation; and the specification of counts as "better" or "worse" clearly matters to determining whether, when, and how much the environment has degraded. If the environment can go from "better" to "worse," however, it can at least logically go from "worse" to "better" – that is, if degradation is possible, then improvement should be too. What I am adding here is not a specification of what that movement between states looks like, but a recognition that unless the possibility of human-led improvement is definitionally or intuitively excluded, it is possible for human activity to be the source of improvement as well as degradation.

A second way of objecting would be to argue that the point made here is obvious; that humans can obviously improve the environment both extraterrestrially and on Earth. This is likely to be the response of some of my readers, especially those who are not engaged deeply in environmental debates. This is one risk in interdisciplinary work; what is obvious in one field may not be obvious in another. Insofar as it may seem obvious to some that environmental improvement is possible, I would welcome the agreement, and then urge recognition that degradation and irrelevance are also possible, and that thinking about the relationship between these various impacts across environments may still be fruitful.

Finally, a third way to resist my argument would be to insist that space environment(s) are so fundamentally different than the Earth environment that we need entirely different ethics to understand them, or to understand our obligations to them (Owe, 2019). Such an objection could cut logical connections between thinking about Earth and non-Earth environments. Certainly, there are increasingly robust accounts, some articulated in this volume, calling for different ethics in the space age. And this chapter has itself emphasized the important differences that flow from the discontinuity of space environments when compared to the environment on Earth; such discontinuities may put special pressure on the importance of developing ethical accounts of environmental justice, which evaluates the fairness of how environmental costs and benefits are distributed (Shrader-Frechette, 2002). Furthermore, although I have drawn on anthropocentric and biocentric traditions in my analysis, it is worth noting that some environmental ethicists have also suggested that *nonliving* features of an environment, such as rock formations (Marshall, 1993) or geographical diversity (Washington, 2018), have ethical importance; such accounts would make room for evaluating environments by reference to these features as well. Along with aesthetic accounts of environmental good, which do not depend upon the existence of life or potential life for value, these accounts may prove to have special importance throughout the lifeless reaches of space. I am not personally convinced this means we need an entirely new set of ethics, but it does seem right that space-based problems will often implicate certain qualities – like discontinuity of environments, high uncertainty, low immediate impact on humans, likelihood of impacting lifeless environments – that can have ethical weight. Even if this is so, however, I would contend that one key component for environmental ethics – in space or on Earth—is to develop an account of what good environments are that accounts for the possibility that humans may have multiple relationships with the environments they engage with. These relationships may be degrading, it is true – but they may also improving, or even irrelevant. The best ethical accounts – and the best policies built upon those accounts – will address each of these possibilities.

Conclusion

It is clear that human actions often cause environmental harm on Earth. Reflecting on human–environmental interactions in space, however, may help clarify that such interactions are not inevitably harmful. In fact, it is possible for humans to impact their environments in positive as well as negative ways – and thus to generate environmental improvement as well as environmental degradation. There are a number of benefits to recognizing the possibility of human-led improvements to environmental quality. One of these is that such a recognition invites engagement with important ethical questions, such as what it means to make an environment better or worse, if/how to make tradeoffs across environments, and when and whether obligations to terrestrial and extraterrestrial life vary with distance and causal connection. Such ethical engagement may help, in turn, in generating ethical and effective environmental law and policy on Earth as well as in space.

References

Aronson, E. (1969). The theory of cognitive dissonance: A current perspective, in *Advances in Experimental Social Psychology*, Vol. 4. (ed. L. Berkowitz).

Bell, J. S. (1964). On the Einstein Podolsky Rosen Paradox. *Physics*, 1, 195–290.

Calicott, J. B., & Nelson, M. P. (eds) (1998). *The Great New Wilderness Debate*. University of Georgia Press.

Coffey, Y., Bhullar, N., Durkin, J., Islam, M. S. & Usher, K. (2021). Understanding Eco-anxiety: A systemic scoping review of current literature and identified knowledge gaps. *The Journal of Climate Change and Health*, 3, 1000047.

Crutzen, P. J., & Stoermer, E. F. (2000). The "Anthropocene." *Global Change Newsletter*, 41, 17–18.

Danaher, J. (2022). Techno-optimism: An analysis, an evaluation and a modest defence. *Philosophy & Technology*, 35(54), 8.

Diaz, D. (1993). Trashing the final frontier: An examination of space debris from a legal perspective. *Tulane Environmental Law Journal*, 6, 369–395.

Doherty, T. J., & Clayton, S. (2011). The psychological impacts of global climate change. *American Psychologist*, 66(4), 265–276.

Douglas, M. (1966). *Purity and Danger: An analysis of concepts of pollution and taboo.* Routledge & Kegan Paul.

Douglas, M., & Wildavsky, A. (1982). *Risk and Culture: An essay on the selection of technical and environmental dangers.* University of California Press.

Farah, T. (2019). Light pollution from satellites will get worse. But how much? *Astronomy.* https://www.astronomy.com/news/2019/06/light-pollution-from-satellites-will-get-worse-but-how-much.

Felgenhauer, T., Govindasamy, B., Borsuk, M. E., Brune, M., Camilloni, I., Wiener, J. B., et al. (2022). *Solar Radiation Modification: A risk-risk analysis.* Carnegie Climate Governance Initiative C2G. www.c2g2.net.

Fogg, M. (1995). *Terraforming: Engineering planetary environments.* Society of Automotive Engineers.

Friedmann, E., & Ocampo-Friedmann, R. (1995). A primitive cyanobacterium as pioneer microorganism for terraforming Mars. *Advances in Space Research*, 15(3), 243–246.

Gawronski, B., & Strack, F. (eds). (2012). *Cognitive Consistency: A fundamental principle in social cognition.* Guilford Press.

Gilovich, T., Griffin, D. & Kahneman, D. (eds). (2002). *Heuristics and Biases: The psychology of intuitive judgment.* Cambridge University Press.

Goudie, A. (2018). *The Human Impact on the Natural Environment*, 8th edition. MIT Press.

Hamilton, C. (2021). Space and existential risk: The need for global coordination and caution in space development. *Duke Law and Technology Review*, 21, 1–60.

Haynes, R. D. (1999). *From Faust to Strangelove: Representations of scientists in Western literature.* The Johns Hopkins University Press.

Hegerl, G. C., *et al.* (2007). Understanding and attributing climate change, in *Climate Change 2007: The Physical science basis. Contribution of Working Group I to the Fourth Assessment Report of the Intergovernmental Panel on Climate Change* (eds Solomon, S.*et al.*). Cambridge University Press.

IPCC (2007). *Climate Change 2007: Synthesis Report. Contribution of Working Groups I, II and III to the Fourth Assessment Report of the Intergovernmental Panel on Climate Change* [Core Writing Team, Pachauri, R. K., & Reisinger, A. (eds)].

IPCC (2014). *Climate Change 2014: Synthesis Report. Contribution of Working Groups I, II and III to the Fifth Assessment Report of the Intergovernmental Panel on Climate Change* [Core Writing Team, Pachauri, R. K., & Meyer, L. A. (eds)].

Kehoe, R., Frago, E. & Sanders, D. (2021). Cascading extinctions as a hidden driver of insect decline. *Ecological Entomology*, 46, 743–756.

Launius, S., & Boyce, G. A. (2020). More than metaphor: Settler colonialism, frontier logic, and the continuities of racialized dispossession in a southwest U.S. city. *Annals of the American Association of Geographers*, 111(1), 157–174.

Lorenz, E. (1963). Deterministic nonperiodic flow. *Journal of the Atmospheric Sciences*, 20, 130–141.

McKay, C., & Zubrin, R. (2002). Do indigenous martian bacteria have precedence over human exploration?, in *On to Mars: Colonizing a new world.* Apogee Books.

McKibben, B. (1989). *The End of Nature.* Random House.

Marshall, A. (1993). Ethics and the extraterrestrial environment. *Journal of Applied Philosophy*, 10(2), 227–236.

Morales, A. C., & Fitzsimons, G. J. (2007). Product contagion: Changing consumer evaluations through physical contact with "disgusting" products. *Journal of Marketing Research*, 44(2), 272–283.

National Aeronautics and Space Station (2023). *International Space Station: Crews & expeditions.* https://www.nasa.gov/mission_pages/station/expeditions/index.html.

Nelson, M. P., & Calicott, J. B. (eds). (2008). *The Wilderness Debate Rages On: Continuing the great new wilderness debate.* University of Georgia Press.

Outer Space Treaty (1966). *Treaty on Principles Governing the Activities of States in the Exploration and Use of Outer Space, including the Moon and Other Celestial Bodies.* https://www.unoosa.org/oosa/en/ourwork/spacelaw/treaties/introouterspacetreaty.html.

Owe, A. (2019). *Environmental Ethics in Outer Space: A macrostrategic space journey through cosmism, posthumanism and moral enhancement* (Master's thesis). https://www.duo.uio.no/bitstream/handle/10852/69331/1/Owe-Andrea-15-05-2019-Environmental-Ethics-in-Outer-Space-MAthesis-.pdf.

Potthast, T. (2014). The values of biodiversity: Philosophical considerations connecting theory and practice, in *Concepts and Values in Biodiversity.* Routledge.

Purdy, J. (2015). *After Nature: A politics for the Anthropocene.* Harvard University Press.

Puumala, M. (2024). Sustainability and humanity's future in space: A conceptual exploration (this volume).

Ripple, W. J., & Larsen, R. A. (2000). Historic aspen recruitment, elk, and wolves in northern Yellowstone National Park, USA. *Biological Conservation*, 95, 361–371.

Rowell, A. (2015). Foreign impacts and climate change. *Harvard Environmental Law Review*, 39, 371–421.

Rowell, A. (2021). Regulating best-case scenarios. *Environmental Law*, 50, 1105–1172.

Rowell, A., & Bilz, K. (2021). *The Psychology of Environmental Law*. New York University Press.

Rowell, A., & Wexler, L. (2014). *Valuing Foreign Lives. Georgia Law Review*, 48, 499–578.

Rowell, A., & Wexler, L. (forthcoming). *The Environment is Not a Woman*.

Rozin, P. (2005). The meaning of "natural": Process more important than content. *Psychological Science*, 16(8), 652–658.

Rozin, P., Milliman, L. & Nemeroff, C. (1986). Operation of the laws of sympathetic magic in disgust and other domains. *Journal of Personality and Social Psychology*, 50(4), 703–712.

Rozin, P., & Royzman, E. B. (2001). Negativity bias, negativity dominance, and contagion. *Personality and Social Psychology Review*, 5(4), 296–320.

Shrader-Frechette, K. (2002). *Environmental Justice: Creating equity, reclaiming democracy*. Oxford University Press.

Siipi, H. (2004). Naturalness in biological conservation. *Journal of Agricultural and Environmental Ethics*, 17(6), 457–477.

Simon, J. (1983). *The Ultimate Resource*. Princeton University Press.

Sivula, O. (2024). Faking biosphere (this volume).

Stoner, I. (2021). The ethics of terraforming: A critical survey of six arguments, in *Terraforming Mars* (eds Beech, M., Seckbach, J. & Gordon, R.). Wiley.

Taylor, P. W. (1981). The ethics of respect for nature. *Environmental Ethics*, 3(3), 197–218.

Taylor, P. W. (1986). *Respect for Nature*. Princeton University Press.

Tudor, A. (1989). *Monsters and Mad Scientists: A cultural history of the horror movie*. Wiley, 133–157.

United Nations Environmental Programme (2021). *From Pollution to Solution: A global assessment of marine litter and plastic pollution*. https://wedocs.unep.org/handle/20.500.11822/36963.

Veracini, L. (2010). *Settler Colonialism: A theoretical overview*. Palgrave Macmillan.

Vileisis, A. (1999). *Discovering the Unknown Landscape: A history of America's wetlands*. Island Press.

Wiener, N. (1996). Beyond the balance of nature: environmental law faces the new ecology. *Duke Environmental Law and Policy Forum*, 1: 1–24.

Williamson, M. (2006). *Space: The fragile frontier*. American Institute of Aeronautics and Astronautics.

York, P. (2002). The ethics of terraforming. *Philosophy Now*. https://philosophynow.org/issues/38/The_Ethics_of_Terraforming.

10

UNEARTHING GLOBAL JUSTICE

From Space to Inter-Planetary Ethics

Derek Matravers, Alessandra Marino and Natalie Treviño

Introduction

Space ethics, being concerned with matters extra-terrestrial, has often been
deemed to be free of considerations of global justice. However, this chapter
deals with the interdependence of historical and technological processes on
Earth and beyond, to show that such presumed freedom needs to be unpicked.
The proliferation of actors and activities in space that characterizes the New
Space Age has pushed the boundaries of traditional understandings of the
global and, as discussed below, it has enabled new injustices.[1] In this context,
space ethics can reconfigure the reach and limits of global justice debates, providing a fresh perspective. This chapter tackles three issues related to space
exploration: the ramifications of global injustice in space; issues that arise from
the classification of space as a 'global commons'; and the implications of satellite observations for global justice. We use the phrase 'space exploration' in an
expansive way, meaning all activity connected with geostationary orbit, low
Earth orbit, medium Earth orbit, and beyond, including inter-planetary
exploration. The focus on justice connects seemingly different topics, such as
the proliferation of satellites (including so-called 'megaconstellations' – systems
that use thousands of individual satellites), missions including landers on the
moon and other planets, and deep space probes.

Space Exploration and Earthly Injustice

Current earthly distributions of wealth and power exhibit marked inequalities.
The root cause of much of this inequality has been the parceling up of resources
into ownership, whether by states or individuals. The question of the historical
sedimentation of these inequalities raises the question of what, if anything,

DOI: 10.4324/9781003374381-10

could justify the appropriation of resources held in common. Western philosophy has, traditionally, argued that two steps would be necessary for this. First, the move from no ownership to ownership would have to be just, and second, any subsequent changes in ownership would have to be just. A classic statement of how the first step could be just is due to John Locke: 'Nor was this *appropriation* of any parcel of *land*, by improving it, any prejudice to any other man, since there was still enough, and as good left' (Locke, 1997, p. 33). That is, one can only 'acquire' something (take ownership of it) if one leaves 'enough and as good' for others. One can (temporarily at least) acquire lungfuls of air because, in doing so, one leaves enough air of the same quality for others. However, most worldly resources are not like air. Land for example is culturally and affectively marked, and its use, appropriation, and exploitation affect both its availability and quality. So the first test is failed. The second step would imply that all exchanges of wealth would be transfers such as gifts or fair exchange. Instead, both primary acquisition of resources and subsequent changes have depended upon expropriation with violence and the establishment of colonial relations that disproportionately enriched the Global North at the expense of people and environments in the Global South. Hence, the second justice test has not been satisfied.

Colonialism structurally exploited peoples, claimed lands, and attempted to destroy pre-existing ways of being and thinking, creating an unjust distribution of resources that has a bearing on the possible futures in space (Redfield, 2002). If thought about as an extension of the current status quo on Earth, the distribution of burdens and benefits brought about by space exploration will inevitably inherit, and could even amplify, these injustices. In fact, in dialogue with critical scholarship of space studies, we argue that space exploration does not simply inherit historical wrongs, but it continues to be made possible through mass injustice. Examples of these injustices are stolen lands still used as launch sites (Redfield, 2000), companies offering consumers to launch the ashes of the deceased to the moon despite Indigenous peoples' objections,[2] and the many ways in which polluting activities such as rocket launches impact negatively on the Earth.

Aspiring to Redistribution

This unpromising background of earthly inequalities has been used as an argument to propose space exploration as a way to rectify past wrongs. Entrepreneurs of the New Space Age have justified their interplanetary enterprises by highlighting the utopian aspect of space activities. The increase in human population and reduction of resources on Earth, depleted of its richness by centuries of anthropogenic exploitation, are cited as reasons for increasing space exploration and enhancing existing capabilities for supporting life in space. This argument underpins both commercial activities and their scholarly justifications. For example, studies about space mining for sustainable development on Earth suggest that an increase in resource availability could, with the right international agreements in place, end up benefiting humanity as a whole (Dallas et al., 2020).

The plausibility of this justification rests on two claims. The first is that the environmental costs of extractive activities, through mining celestial bodies for example, can be offloaded onto space. Although this is an empirical matter, there is reason to be pessimistic. These claims usually do not fully consider the multiple forms of pollution that such activities generate: from the use of fuel for flying rockets to the possible contamination and cluttering of space debris. The second claim is that any new abundance of resources will be used or distributed in a just manner. Once again, looking at Earth means approaching this claim with caution. Existing models of resource use are predicated upon extraction until exhaustion, and inherently discard other modes of living sustainably with the environment. Moreover, these models are biased towards those responsible for the extraction, who either own the resources outright or are compensated for their work.

If such a model were carried over to space activities, the expansion into space could be understood as the new spatial 'fix' of capitalism. In other words, as highlighted by Dickens and Ormrod (2007), space exploration would fulfil the need of capitalism to simply extend its reach over new territories and claim access to resources and materials. Near Earth orbit has already been used as a fix for capitalism as satellites have come to play an important economic and militaristic role in the current world order (Dickens, 2023). It is in this sense that space constitutes a new 'rare Earth frontier' (Klinger, 2017). Space emerges as a utopian promise of richness for those in charge of extraction. One result of this is that extractive capitalism has been questioned for its injustices and has seen mounting resistance. Such resistance has opened new ground in scholarship and public opinion around conservation policy, and reconfigured debates around space exploration as a new battleground for competing ideas of justice. Humanity would need to adopt an entirely different approach if any resources that did flow from space exploration were either to be distributed equitably or used to compensate people for past injustice.

Distribution of Benefits and Burdens

The massive disparities in available resources to commit to space exploration, together with different levels of technology, mean that the sector is dominated by a small number of states. Hence, the benefits of space exploration (which includes, as we shall discuss below, dominating the most desirable locations for orbits) have not been distributed by some principle of justice and equity, but rather have accrued to those states that most participate in the space economy, through technology development and deployment. The burdens, however, have a global reach that is not commensurate with the enjoyment of space benefits. A global justice lens is useful to foreground 'the systemic and transnational nature of political and economic forces that produce injustices' (Martin, 2013). Specific space injustices come in various sorts, of which we shall mention space debris and multiple ways in which damages to the environment can occur.

First, there are the dangers from space debris. Figures vary, but there are currently around 30,000 pieces of space debris that are larger than 10cm in orbit around the Earth (and 128 million larger than 1mm).[3] The potential injustice here is that, as the amount of space debris increases, it becomes more difficult and costly for those who have not yet developed a space program to find safe ways of flying satellites and spacecraft (Klinger, 2019). Those that by virtue of having longer histories of space exploitation have caused the problem of space debris benefit from technologies in orbit, while those who have least been responsible of orbital cluttering are faced with an increasingly congested space environment. Second is the complex nature of damages to the environment and the ways in which they are experienced by communities on Earth. For example, the light pollution caused by satellites and mega-constellations has a different, and greater, effect on Indigenous groups with ancestral cultural ties to the dark sky, than it has on those for whom the night sky is simply the backdrop to their urban life (Committee on the Peaceful Uses of Outer Space, 2021; Vidaurri et al., 2020).

In the examples above, those who are outside the group who dominate space exploration have been disproportionately affected by the increase in orbital technologies, while simultaneously being less served by their use. As Munamato Chemhuru (2019) argues, nations in the Global South have mostly endured the burdens of environmental damage and policies that have benefited mostly those in the Global North. This unequal distribution of resources on our planet is foundational for the creation of interstellar futures. The use of land for space infrastructure, such as the telescope to be built on Indigenous land in Hawaii and the radio-telescope in South Africa, which interferes with the local farming economy (Chinigò and Walker, 2020), is paradigmatic of the interconnections between environmental injustices on Earth and in space. The debris and light pollution caused by satellites owned by a handful of space actors point to their extension into the orbital environments.

The 'Global Commons'

So far, space injustices have appeared as both worldly, that is, entangled with world histories, and extra-terrestrial, by virtue of their effects on space environments. However, in law and ethics, when space is addressed as a 'global' domain, the attribute 'global' often refers to the ways in which its governance relies on international cooperation despite contested norms, including its main international instrument: the Treaty on Principles Governing the Activities of States in the Exploration and Use of Outer Space, also known as the 'Outer Space Treaty' (OST). The first two Articles of the OST run as follows:

Article 1: The exploration and use of outer space, including the moon and other celestial bodies, shall be carried out for the benefit and in the interests of all countries, irrespective of their degree of economic or scientific development, and shall be the province of all mankind.

Outer space, including the moon and other celestial bodies, shall be free for exploration and use by all States without discrimination of any kind, on a basis of equality and in accordance with international law, and there shall be free access to all areas of celestial bodies.

There shall be freedom of scientific investigation in outer space, including the moon and other celestial bodies, and States shall facilitate and encourage international co-operation in such investigation.

Article 2: Outer space, including the moon and other celestial bodies, is not subject to national appropriation by claim of sovereignty, by means of use or occupation, or by any other means.

Thinking through issues of justice in space exploration needs to be done against this background, which can be summarized as the claim that space (like the non-territorial sea and seabed, the atmosphere, and Antarctica) is a 'global commons'. At first glance, the OST seems to guarantee justice in space: activities should be 'carried out for the benefit and in the interests of all countries'; 'shall be the province of all mankind'; and 'not subject to national appropriation'. However, as we shall see, the notion of the 'global commons' is at the center of conflicting interpretations, and states have used this lack of clarity to act in ways contrary to at least the egalitarian spirit (if not the letter) of the OST.

The Global Commons as an 'Enabling Concept'

The fact that all are allowed equal access to the high seas enables passage between various parts of the world. This is important for, perhaps even a necessary condition for, international communication and trade and other forms of co-operation. If a state owned, say, the Atlantic Ocean, they could prevent other states from traveling across it. Hence, one conception of 'the global commons' is that protecting a global commons enables benefits, which, like other public goods, are non-excludable and non-rivalrous: that is, users cannot be barred from them and use by one party does not prevent use by another party (Goehring, 2021, p. 1303). Article 1 of the OST would seem to make 'outer space' a public good in this respect in that 'it shall be free for exploration and use by all states'.

Although space might in principle be open to all (in practice it depends, of course, on the availability of resources), some of the available space resources are positional; this means that if one person has them, others cannot have them. A good example of this are satellite orbits. The fact that one nation owns a satellite at a particular place means that another nation cannot have their satellite at that place – and not all places are of equal value. In an analysis of the geostationary orbit and conflicts around allocations of slots, geographer Christy Collis looks at the issue of position as being integral to the desirability of what she defines the 'most valuable real estate' (Collis, 2009). That one nation could use its resources to occupy the prime spaces (at the moment, the US owns more than 90% of the satellites in orbit) before others get a chance raises a question of justice. This effectively obviates claims to be non-excludable and non-rivalrous.

The Global Commons as a 'Constraining Concept'

Article 2 of the OST claims that outer space is 'not subject to national appropriation'. That is, the commitment to space being a global commons is a commitment by states to constrain their behavior by not appropriating it. This is naturally interpreted as not claiming it as national property, or not exploiting it for national advantage. Once again, the OST would seem to serve global justice by leaving space and its resources as the common property of all.

Despite these aspirations, the constraint set by regarding space as a global commons is not all that it seems. Marino and Cheney (2022), borrowing from Lauren Benton's description of ships as 'islands of sovereignty' on the high seas (Benton, 2001, p. 112), show that a similar concept works for human-made objects in outer space. Ships are 'islands of sovereignty' because states have 'exclusive jurisdiction' and control over ships flying their flags on the high seas (UN Convention on the Law of the Sea, Art. 92/94). In the same way, Article VIII of the OST stipulates that the state of registry retains jurisdiction and control over any space object and its personnel. Jurisdiction and state authority in outer space, like on the high seas, is exercised over persons and objects, not territory. However, there is insufficient concern for the impact of these proliferating objects on the space environment and the inequalities brought about by the *de facto* occupation of considerable swathes of the space commons (Boley and Byers, 2021). As opposed to individual space objects, which can be seen as 'islands of sovereignty', Marino and Cheney present megaconstellations as 'archipelagos of sovereignty' because of their extension. Under the technocratic rules of space governance there is no issue with Starlink's 42,000 proposed satellites;[4] however, this would represent 42,000 areas of space that fall under the jurisdiction of a single state.

Regarding objects that travel in space as national property explicitly conforms to the OST, but the same cannot be said for a second development: namely, the exploitation of space resources by companies or states. The line of argument presented by the United States, which is geared towards allowing and incentivizing use of space resources (including for commercial purposes), explicitly rejects the view that space is a global commons. The Executive Order 13914, signed by US President Trump in 2020, says:

> Americans should have the right to engage in commercial exploration, recovery, and use of resources in outer space, consistent with applicable

law. Outer space is a legally and physically unique domain of human activity, and the United States does not view it as a global commons. Accordingly, it shall be the policy of the United States to encourage international support for the public and private recovery and use of resources in outer space, consistent with applicable law.

(Quoted in Goehring, 2021, 582–583)

How can the exploitation of space resources (which is 'not subject to national appropriation') be compatible with the 'public and private recovery of resources'? According to John S. Goehring, this is because the USA interprets the OST in terms of what has been called an 'enabling concept': anyone can travel there. This interpretation is independent of the 'constraining concept' claim, as to who owns the resources. There is nothing inconsistent in holding the former and not the latter; the question is whether it is a reasonable interpretation of the OST. Prima facie, it is difficult to see that it is a reasonable interpretation of the legal obligation to share space benefits. Having 'due regard' for the interests of other states and their nationals places upon space actors an ethical, if not a legal, responsibility to consider the possible impact of space activities on the environments and beyond national jurisdiction.[5]

Moreover, if the 'public and private recovery of resources' in outer space is to be allowed, then it will face the same questions of justification as the public and private recovery of resources on Earth. That is, the same justifications for appropriation of common property will apply. If one is skeptical of the Lockean justification of appropriation on Earth, there is reason to be skeptical of it in space. Indeed, in space the problem is exacerbated as the accumulation of space power by dominant actors relies on wealth and power acquired through unjust earthly exploitation of peoples and lands. It is this position of technological advantage that will allow space resources to be extracted, appropriated, and accumulated (if, indeed, there is wealth and power to be accumulated). Thus, there is a double injustice; those with the capacity to commit the second injustice only have that capacity as they are the beneficiaries of the first.

The All-Seeing Eye

As seen in the previous sections, the recent increase in orbital satellites engenders crucial considerations about pollution beyond the atmosphere and exacerbated geopolitical inequalities. There are currently around 1,000 Earth observation satellites, split between geostationary orbit and low Earth orbit. Every part of the Earth's landmass is photographed several times each day. Satellite data can be used for mapping, monitoring the weather, finding your dream house, or plotting a course to the shops. The role of satellites as an 'all seeing eye' raises questions about surveillance and the reach of military powers literally attempting to gain and retain higher grounds (MacDonald, 2008). This consideration about occupying higher points in the vertical hierarchy of the planet is not new: Werhner von Braun's first attempt to persuade the US to focus on space came from his assertation that having the higher ground of space, or establishing space superiority, would be militaristically advantageous (Neufeld, 2007). This idea is reiterated in the US Space Force's motto: 'semper supra' ('always above') and has been criticized as the creation of 'atmospheric enclosures' (Shaw, 2017). Satellites play both a visible and material role in establishing this dominance, through their position, but they are also vehicles for less visible processes taking place through new data and knowledge flows. Data are resources that can be used in multiple ways: from strengthening military dominance to increasing open knowledge about the status of environmental change on Earth. In fact, the role of space data in tracking climate change is often discussed as one of the major benefits of space technologies. Below, we look critically at how references to climate change are useful to highlight that knowledge itself, and its potential to bring about justice, are constrained if accumulated in the hands of a few.

Knowledge and Combating Injustice

Satellite remote sensing (SRS) is the leading research tool in tracking climate change: it can detect (among other things) changing sea temperatures, changing ice flows, deforestation, the release of large amounts of carbon into the atmosphere, and sea level change. In a global order that is still grappling with the steps needed to combat climate change, one of the arguments given for states not acting on curbing their own 'greenhouse gas' emissions is an absence of trust that others will truthfully act on their own commitments. In this context, information from satellites can be crucial for the international monitoring of agreed actions. If data is transparently shared among states with different space capabilities, and methods of interpretation are appropriately scrutinized, states will be held accountable for failing to act to curb emissions. This has the potential to effectively combat 'free-riding'; a common and egregious form of injustice. Free-riding is a state of affairs in which someone does not contribute to a common good (in that case combating climate change) while benefiting from the fact that everyone else is doing so. The existence of SRS makes free-riding, at least where it concerns combating climate change, more difficult.

However, existing inequalities in space capabilities extend to access to and possibility to interpret satellites data. In the space sector, there is a strong push to include and work with emerging space nations to incentivize the use of space data; but technology distribution and the possibilities of equal access to open data remain open questions. First of all, because of rising private ownership of satellites and the advanced technical skills needed for data processing, knowledge is largely in the hands of a small number of actors (among non-state actors, the largest number of Earth observation satellites are owned by a US company, Planet Labs). Once again, the dividend of space activity, this time knowledge, is not spread equally to the benefit of all, but concentrated in the hands of those states that have historically benefited from huge asymmetries of wealth and power.

Accountability and Reparations

Attempts to combat climate change centrally concern justice, and similarly to space and its governance, climate justice can only be achieved if it is attended to at a global level. Moreover, taking steps to ensure the future of Earth as fit for human habitation means tackling accountability for polluting activities and compensation for states more severely affected by climate change. Climate change, like space-related pollution, is the result of a handful of countries' longer history of resource extraction and exploitation. If space ethics must be reformulated, taking account of existing space inequalities and around a more deliberative idea of justice, this brings to the fore two interrelated concepts: redistribution and reparations. While separate ideas with different rationales, they are interconnected. Recognizing injustices leads to accountability, which can take place through repairing past wrongs and creating new models of distribution. While it may be tempting to think of these things strictly in financial terms, in the context of space reparations can enable new discussions on environment and worldmaking, or remaking.

Traditionally understood, reparations are repayments for historical injustices. For example, they refer to compensation to be given to descendants of enslaved people, forcibly taken to the United States (Smith, 2021). The harm and damages caused to countries, cultures, and peoples by the exploration of space and those who do not benefit from space should lead to compensation for their losses and for their exclusion from receiving what is due to them as part of 'humankind'. Given that those nations and beneficiaries of the global injustices have not been held to account and the very idea of reparations has been contested from its creation, how could bringing space into this conversation to foster justice? While a study of reparations is beyond the scope of this paper, rethinking what reparations are and how they function may be key to connecting the idea to space.

For Táíwò, because the relations of injustice were not (are not) static, reparations cannot be reduced to a one-time payment or compensation. Rather, reparations are varied, in motion, and constant because injustices are varied, in motion, and constant. We suggest that a different conception of reparations, one that focuses on the future rather than the past or present, can posit reparations as a worldmaking activity (Táíwò, 2022). In this, reparations are direct engagement with injustices as they exist. As Táíwò frames it: 'Since the injustice that reparations respond to is global and distributive, the constructive view helps explain what reparations needs to accomplish: building a more just planetary future' (Táíwò, 2022, p. 11). Thus, holding those responsible for space-related global injustices does not simplistically mean the establishment of punitive methods to deal with harm, but rather that reparations can function as a reorganization of the current world system.

This radical re-thinking could include a redistribution of low Earth orbits, as part of a move away from claims of property and a focus on wealth accumulation. Rejecting double injustices and endorsing the planetary benefits of space allows us to trace a path back to space as a global commons, in the very spirit of the OST. This includes asking: what would it look like for peoples to access knowledge produced through satellite data without having to overcome issues of distribution? Could this not be a way to help local, Indigenous, or marginalized communities benefit from space even if they do not have direct access?

Conclusion: Inter-Planetary Ethics

This chapter has looked at how benefits and burdens of space exploration are unequally distributed across the globe. The definition of space as a global commons, as in the OST, while important to the pivotal role of space for human activities on Earth, is insufficient to enshrine into law an obligation for all countries and actors to uphold principles of fair access and respect for finite environmental resources, from orbital slots to minerals. Technologies in outer space have also been seen as tools enabling a better distribution of another resource: knowledge about Earth and its health. However, a proprietary regime over tangible and intangible goods restricts the availability of satellite data and the knowledge they enable. In brief, as well as being the product of the unjust distribution of space benefits, the cluttered orbits and the resulting light pollution are also a sobering reminder of the physical closeness and historical interconnection that shaped Earth and space. This interdependence underpins an ethical obligation to reimagine more just space futures.

It is not enough to extend global justice to space; space can effectively help rethink global justice. A new vocabulary may help signal this change. Recently, 'planetary' justice has been used to point to the intersection of social and ecological justice that constitute the conditions of the Anthropocene (Hickey and Robeyns, 2020, p. 1). The use of the adjective 'planetary' was first popularized by Gayatri Spivak, who in *Death of a Discipline* maintained that the abstraction of globalization is a mode of mastery over the totality of life – one that betrays the privilege of Western colonial subjectivity. Financial, information flows, and other forms of connectivity enable the totalizing logics of the global movement of capital. Instead, the obstructed movements of people and migratory flows, together with other modes of inhabiting the planet, can be ascribed to a different domain, one that is concerned with alterity and lack of control. She wrote:

> The globe is on our computers. No one lives there. It allows us to think that we can aim to control it. The planet is in the species of alterity, belonging to another system; and yet we inhabit it, on loan.
>
> *(Spivak, 2003, p. 72)*

Spivak proposed to embrace 'planetarity' as a critique of the smooth, technologically mediated representation of the globe. Planetarity provided a figuration of a defamiliarized planet as home – one that is open to unexpected ways of being with otherness.

With this critique in mind, the smooth narrative of space as an infinite possibility of technological gains and extraction covers the reliance of space activities on a double injustice, one that nests current space inequalities upon historical Earth-based injustices. This critique fundamentally addresses the shortcomings of 'global justice', which has been unable to produce new imaginations for worlds to come. For Hickey and Robeyns,

> 'global justice' needs to be reconfigured not as a colonising logic of a 'royal' kind stipulating how and under what conditions justice will be produced across the myriad differential spaces of human existence, but as a praxis orientated towards valorising the unruliness that disrupts logics of all kinds and thus that creates spaces in which 'justice' becomes open to negotiation.
>
> *(Hickey and Robeyns, 2020, p. 1407)*

Listening to advocates of reparations and redistribution of space benefits is a possible starting point to realize an agenda for an inter-planetary ethics to come.

Notes

1 New Space Age refers to the current increase in space activities resulting from the increase in commercial actors participating in the space economy.
2 https://pages.celestis.com/memorial; https://www.spokesman.com/stories/1998/jan/15/navajos-upset-after-ashes-sent-to-moon-nasa/
3 See https://www.nhm.ac.uk/discover/what-is-space-junk-and-why-is-it-a-problem.html
4 Caleb Henry, SpaceX Submits Paperwork for 30,000 more Starlink Satellites, Space-News, 15 October 2019, available at: https://spacenews.com/spacex-submits-paperwork-for-30000-more-starlink-satellites/
5 These issues are explored in Gangale (2009).

References

Benton, L. (2001), *Law and Colonial Cultures: Legal Regimes in World History, 1400–1900*, 1st edition, Cambridge University Press, doi:10.1017/CBO9780511512117.
Boley, A.C. and Byers, M. (2021), "Satellite mega-constellations create risks in low Earth orbit, the atmosphere and on Earth", *Scientific Reports*, Vol. 11 No. 1, p. 10642, doi:10.1038/s41598-021-89909-7.
Chemhuru, M. (2019), "The paradox of global environmental justice: Appealing to the distributive justice framework for the Global South", *South African Journal of Philosophy*, Vol. 38 No. 1, pp. 30–39, doi:10.1080/02580136.2019.1570712.
Chinigò, D. and Walker, C. (2020), "Science, astronomy, and sacrifice zones: Development trade-offs, and the Square Kilometre Array (SKA) radio telescope project in South Africa", *Social Dynamics*, Vol. 46 No. 3, pp. 391–413, doi:10.1080/02533952.2020.1850626.
Collis, C. (2009), "The geostationary orbit: A critical legal geography of space's most valuable real estate", *The Sociological Review*, Vol. 57 No. 1, pp. 47–65, doi:10.1111/j.1467-954X.2009.01816.x.

Committee on the Peaceful Uses of Outer Space (2021), "Recommendations to keep dark and quiet skies for science and society. Paper submitted by Chile, Ethiopia, Jordan, Slovakia, Spain and the International Astronomical Union", 19 April.

Dallas, J.A., Raval, S., Gaitan, J.P.A., Saydam, S., and Dempster, A.G. (2020), "Mining beyond Earth for sustainable development: Will humanity benefit from resource extraction in outer space?", *Acta Astronautica*, Vol. 167, pp. 181–188, doi:10.1016/j.actaastro.2019.11.006.

Dickens, P. (2023), *Capital and the Cosmos*, Palgrave.

Dickens, P. and Ormrod, J.S. (2007), *Cosmic Society: Towards a Sociology of the Universe*, Routledge.

Gangale, Thomas. (2009), *The Development of Outer Space: Sovereignty and Property Rights in International Space Law*, ABC-CLIO.

Goehring, J.S. (2021), "Why isn't outer space a global commons?", *Journal of National Security Law & Policy*, Vol. 11, pp. 573–590.

Hickey, C. and Robeyns, I. (2020), "Planetary justice: What can we learn from ethics and political philosophy?", *Exploring Planetary Justice*, Vol. 6, p. 100045, doi:10.1016/j.esg.2020.100045.

Klinger, J.M. (2017), *Rare Earth Frontiers: From Terrestrial Subsoils to Lunar Landscapes*, Cornell University Press.

Klinger, J.M. (2019), "Environmental geopolitics and outer space", *Geopolitics*, pp. 1–38, doi:10.1080/14650045.2019.1590340.

Locke, J. (1997), "Second treatise of government", in Cahn, S.M. (Ed.), *Classics of Modern Political Theory: Machiavelli to Mill*, Oxford University Press, pp. 292–297.

MacDonald, B. W. (2008). *China, Space Weapons, and U.S. Security*, Council on Foreign Relations.

Marino, A. and Cheney, T. (2022), "Centring environmentalism in space governance: Interrogating dominance and authority through a critical legal geography of outer space", *Space Policy*, p. 101521, doi:10.1016/j.spacepol.2022.101521.

Martin, A. (2013), "Global environmental in/justice, in practice: Introduction", *The Geographical Journal*, Vol. 179 No. 2, pp. 98–104, doi:10.1111/geoj.12021.

Neufeld, M.J. (2007), "Wernher von Braun's ultimate weapon", *Bulletin of the Atomic Scientists*, Vol. 63 No. 4, pp. 50–57, 78, doi:10.2968/063004019.

Redfield, P. (2000), *Space in the Tropics: From Convicts to Rockets in French Guiana*, University of California Press.

Redfield, P. (2002), "The half-life of empire in outer space", *Social Studies of Science*, Vol. 32 No. 5–6, pp. 791–825.

Shaw, I.G.R. (2017), "The great war of enclosure: Securing the Skies", *Antipode*, Vol. 49 No. 4, pp. 883–906, doi:10.1111/anti.12309.

Smith, R.C. (2021), "Reparations", *Encyclopedia of African-American Politics*, 3rd edition, Infobase Publishing.

Spivak, G.C. (2003), *Death of a Discipline*, Columbia University Press.

Táíwò, O.O. (2022), *Reconsidering Reparations*, 1st edition, Oxford University Press, doi:10.1093/oso/9780197508893.001.0001.

Vidaurri, M., Wofford, A., Brande, J., Black-Planas, G., Domagal-Goldman, S., and Haqq-Misra, J. (2020), "Absolute prioritization of planetary protection, safety, and avoiding imperialism in all future science missions: A policy perspective", *Space Policy*, Vol. 51, p. 101345, doi:10.1016/j.spacepol.2019.101345.

11

SPACE ADAPTATION

How Life Can Be Shaped by Space Travel

Matteo Cerri

Introduction

Adaptation is the critical feature of life. Wherever life evolved, and by which-ever means, it had to possess the ability to adapt not just to the environment of the birthplace but also to all the forthcoming changes in future environments. A life without such a key feature will be limited to the native habitat and die out of the inability to adapt to the always-evolving environment.

The complexity of the relationship between the environment and life extends through multiple layers and can be described from disciplines ranging from genetics to ecology. All of these disciplines have a different layer of interest, a "habitat" in some sort of a wordplay. Still, there is one layer that may hold an advantageous position: the layer of physiology.

Since physiology studies the functioning of a living organism, it can condense the results of changes in the more "micro" layers, such as genetics, with the ones from a "macro" layer, such as ecology. After all, even if it may sound self-evident, life can only proceed if life forms can survive; in other words, the vector of life is the organism, and from the organism, we should start.

To be honest, any environment in which life exists already threatens its existence. Environments are subject to changes in physical conditions, such as light intensity, temperature, pressure, radiation, and, generally, exposure to the elements. Planets are, after all, evolving celestial bodies, and for life to develop on them, a certain degree of complexity is a prerequisite. The result is that a highly stable environment, such as it could be intergalactic space, does not host the necessary complexity for life to evolve; on the contrary, a changing envir-onment, such as a planet, may pose too much of a challenge to the adaptation capability of life. Nevertheless, an environment with suitable complexity and stability will also require life to adapt to its changes.

DOI: 10.4324/9781003374381-11

Homeostasis

The ability to adapt is often referred to as homeostasis. Claude Bernard and Walter B. Cannon first proposed the principle of homeostasis (Bernard, 1865; Cannon, 1932). It is a guiding principle of physiology and the core feature of life. Homeostasis is the set of automated processes by which an organism can maintain internal stability while adjusting to changing external conditions. In other words, life has to develop a mechanism to counteract environmental changes. Those mechanisms ensure that the tool at the base of life continues to work. In a *gedankenexperiment*, imagining a life form living outside any environment, in a stable vacuum, could be possible. We could ask ourselves if such a life form requires the principle of homeostasis. Even if we could be tempted to respond negatively to such a question, we will quickly realize that life, by its mere existence, changes the environment surrounding it. By doing that, a "stable vacuum hosting life" will rapidly become no more stable.

Moreover, it is essential to notice that although the idea of homeostasis focuses on the external environment as the source of changes, it is also the internal environment that is subject to changes. The concept of homeostasis has later been declined with more complexity under other names, like allostasis (Sterling & Eyer, 1981). While homeostasis refers to the actions taken by the body to compensate for a change in parameters key to preserving cellular function, such as pH, pO_2, pCO_2, temperature, allostasis refers to a more complex system of regulation that tends to predict changes in the environments that could lead to potential changes in the key parameters and activate a compensatory mechanism before these changes actually occur. A wider and integrated description of allostatic regulations was later provided under the name of rheostasis (Mrosovsky, 1990). Although these theoretical frames of physiology differ in the description of dynamics, all these interpretations of the basal mechanism of life presuppose the idea of changes as brought about by constant actions, interactions, and counteractions.

Single Cell Organisms and Multicellular Organisms

If we then think of a primordial life form, a single cell, we can imagine the work such a cell must do to maintain its internal mechanism in a changing environment. It has to find a way to take in nutrients to fuel its metabolism and a way to excrete the waste. This gives the cell an advantage: it can move in the surrounding environment to position itself in the most favorable conditions. However, what happens in the evolution from a single cell to a multicellular organism? While the advantage might seem obvious – teamwork may make it easier to reach the goal of surviving – we should also pay attention to the disadvantage. When the size of the multicellular organism increases, it may be that some of its cells find themselves deep inside the organism, with no more access to the external environment. Even worse, the environment of these internal cells will become rapidly flooded with the waste product of the surrounding cells. To solve this problem, the multicellular organism requires its cells to adapt to new functions that can maintain the environment of all the cells fit for life. This is the primordial push toward the appearance of organs and systems.

A complex life form like ours requires the work of thousands of different cell types organized in multiple organs, each carrying a workload necessary for the survival of the whole. With this increase in complexity, it is clear that any change in the work balance of an organ will evoke changes in the activity of other organs, and the wave of changes will reverberate through the entire organism. Most commonly, these waves of changes are well tolerated by the organism and sometimes are even encouraged. The circadian rhythm, for instance, is a way to prepare the organism for changes that we are confident will come, such as the succession of day and night. Other times, the change in an organ function may be the consequence of a malfunction, and the rest of the organism may not be able to compensate for it: this is what we call disease and, in the end, death.

Free Evolutionary Energy: How the Environment May Push the Adaptation

So, how does adaptation come along? After all, evolution is a blind process that reaches long-term aims with very short-term goals. We know how mutations are generated randomly and how natural selection filters the results of those mutations, up to Richard Dawkins's idea of the selfish gene (Dawkins, 1976). In this gene-centric view of evolution, life forms are vessels used by genes to pass from one generation to the next. Although very reductionistic, the idea can be considered valid, especially if we consider life as a whole, but it does not help predict how, let's say, a single species of interest will be shaped in the future by a changing environment. Besides the bottom-up source of variation that goes from genes to the organism, there is an equally important top-down one, from the environment to the genes, that is key for the organism's adaptation and survival (Noble, 2016). In practical terms, the possibilities of evolution are limitless, but we could find a principle that can, at least in some cases, give us a clue of where to expect a new adaptation to take place more easily.

If we go back to the idea of homeostasis and the waves of reverberating adaptations organs go through to maintain the organism working correctly, we can make two interesting observations: 1) not all the organs work all the time at their maximum activity; 2) the maximum activity of some organs cannot be reduced because of their periodic utility. For instance, our lungs can hold quite a large volume of air, called vital capacity, but typically, we use only a tiny fraction of it when we breathe "at rest" (eupneic breathing). Why are we not always breathing at our maximum capacity? We do not need it, but, more importantly, the respiratory system cannot hold such a workload for too long. Why didn't evolution then get rid of such large lungs if we would not need them? We may need them in critical conditions, for instance, when a lion is chasing us or hunting prey. The activity of our lungs is therefore modulated by our brain and adapted to the request of the environment.

Still, there may be more to this story. The fact that our large vital capacity is not in use most of the time leaves this resource open to new possibilities. In other words, we have a functional reserve that may be seen, under evolution's eye, as a type of "free physiological energy" to use and mold to our needs. So, it may not come as a surprise that vocalization is a function that "parasitize" the respiratory system to a function that nothing has to do with the original function of gas exchange. Vocalization uses the mechanical force of air during expiration so much that, in humans, speaking is the principal regulator of breathing, using the large vital capacity for a new aim. Singing brings this to a level of virtuosity.

On these bases, if we ask ourselves how we may adapt to a very different environment, such as outer space, we may have a guiding principle and start imagining how the *Homo sapiens* may become the *Homo coelestis* (Ghidini, 2021) – that is, becoming a different species.

Space – the Challenges

Our planet has many hostile environments, and surprisingly, life has managed to emerge and affirm itself even in the most inhospitable contexts (from the deserts to the Poles), but outer space takes the challenges to a new level. The degree of the hostility of space can also be weighted according to different parameters: a brief stay on the International Space Station in low Earth orbit poses different challenges than a decade-long journey to the asteroid belt. So, what are the main challenges for the human body in a long-term mission?

Muscles

The lack of gravity in a long-term space mission can cause a number of detrimental effects on the muscles, including muscle atrophy and a reduction in muscle mass, due to the body's decreased need for physical activity (Juhl et al., 2021). Muscle loss may also lead to an increased risk of bone loss and fractures. Over time, astronauts may also experience a decrease in their overall strength and coordination, as well as decreased range of motion in their joints. In space, it is possible for astronauts to maintain their muscle strength and prevent, at least partially, muscle atrophy. On board the International Space Station, astronauts exercise for up to 2 1/2 hours each day using cardiovascular and resistance training equipment to maintain muscle mass and prevent muscle atrophy.

Bones

The detrimental effects on bones of a long-term stay in outer space are increased bone loss and weakened bonds due to weightlessness. Astronauts experience a decrease in their bone density, which puts them at a higher risk of fractures and other bone-related health problems. Long-term stays in space can disrupt the body's balance between bone formation and bone breakdown. The bone loss experienced in space is similar to the bone loss caused by osteoporosis, making it critical for astronauts to receive adequate calcium and vitamin D to prevent further bone loss. Additionally, evidence suggests that radiation in space further contributes to bone fragility by inhibiting the ability of the body to produce new bone material.

Eyes

Human eyes can also suffer from multiple challenges in outer space, including alterations in the eyes' shape due to fluid shifts, vision changes, increased risk of cataracts, and neuro-ocular syndrome. One consequence, mainly seen in astronauts, is increased intraocular pressure, which increases the risk of damage to the optic nerve, leading to permanent vision loss or even blindness. Astronauts may also be prone to developing myopia. Long-term space travel and exposure to radiation from solar flares may also increase the risk of developing cataracts, a clouding of the eyes' clear lenses leading to blurry or reduced vision.

Heart

Cardiovascular deconditioning is the most significant detrimental effect on the heart deriving from a long-term stay in space. The heart does not have to work as hard in space to maintain its normal functioning due to the lack of gravity, but this can lead to a decreased heart rate and reduced cardiac output, resulting in a lowered cardiovascular fitness level. Muscle atrophy can also contribute to a decreased cardiac output, reducing aerobic capacity. Additionally, a lack of exercise while in outer space can lead to an increase in body fat, which increases the risk of cardiovascular disease. Finally, radiation exposure in space increases the risk of coronary artery disease.

Brain

The adverse effects of a long-term stay in space on the brain can range from impaired cognitive abilities, vision disturbances, and increased risk of neurological disorders such as depression, sleep dysregulation, and irritability, to long-term physical impairments such as muscular and skeletal degeneration (Roy-O'Reilly et al., 2021). These effects have been seen in astronauts who have spent extended periods of time in a microgravity environment, such as the International Space Station. Other possible physiological effects of long-term space travel may include impaired balance. Additionally, the extreme environmental changes that astronauts experience during space travel, such as alterations in lighting, reduced gravity, and isolation, can lead to psychological conditions such as increased stress, anxiety, and depression.

Sleep

Sleep in a long-term space journey can be affected by several different factors. The space environment is vastly different from that of Earth, meaning astronauts must adjust their sleeping habits to accommodate their surroundings. Long-term space missions often result in disruption to circadian rhythms. The interruption to normal sleeping patterns may be caused by noise, debris, flickering lights from passing objects, different sleeping patterns from fellow astronauts, and circadian misalignment. In order to get better quality sleep, astronauts typically wear eye masks, try to stick to a defined sleep routine, and use muscle relaxation techniques.

Radiation

Radiation is one of the most significant risks of long-term space travel. Humans are particularly vulnerable to radiation, including cosmic radiation, solar particle events, and solar flares. In deep space, astronauts would be exposed to higher radiation levels than here on Earth for longer periods, potentially increasing their risk of developing cancer, acute radiation syndrome, neurological damage, and other long-term, life-threatening diseases.

Thermoregulation

All mammals, including humans, are bound to maintain a constant body temperature of around 37°C. In space, the lack of air convective movement compromises the ability of the body to dissipate heat. The result is that astronauts' body temperatures are higher than normal, which generates discomfort. Recently, it has also been shown that the lack of thermal dissipation might not be sufficient to explain the higher body temperature and that metabolic causes may also be involved. Altered thermoregulation may also compromise sleep effectiveness and misalign the physiological variables' circadian oscillation.

Two Kinds of Changes in Space: Adaptative and Reactive

Space evokes a great variety of changes in a living organism, but we can try to frame those changes according to their physiological value. This is important because it will help us understand what the more severe and complex adverse effects are. Some changes, such as the ones induced in the muscle, can be framed as "adaptative" changes. The organism adapts to the new environment following the general principle of economy. Adaptive changes are an organism's hidden resources that allow that organism to "colonize" a new environment.

Nevertheless, the frame of adaptation is not the only one activated by space. Whereas the adaptation frame predicates minimizing the use of energy pro function, we can see responses characterized by an increase in the energy usage of some systems or organs. We can frame this last category of responses as "reactive." Reactive responses use the functional reserve of the organism to maintain homeostasis in a challenging environment. For instance, the lack of air convection that increases body temperature by reducing the effectiveness of thermal dispersion forces the brain to try to compensate by altering heat production through metabolic changes. In this case, the reaction of the organism may also become a challenge that will need countermeasures to be designed as a treatment.

Generally speaking, adaptative changes, although severe, are making optimal use of the resources of the organism, while reactive changes indicate that the organism is fighting to preserve one or multiple vital physiological parameters. Because of its nature, adaptative changes may therefore be considered less dangerous until a new change in environment presents itself (i.e., when after a long period in space, it is necessary to land on a planet).

Can Life Continue in Space?

It is not very long since humanity took some of its members into space, and since the beginning of that enterprise it feels like space science has rapidly progressed. This is generally true for all the activities related to physics and engineering, but little advancement has been seen in the field of space life science. After all, only the dozen astronauts of the Apollo program were truly in open space, behind low Earth orbit. Among the numerous things we still do not know much about in respect of space adaptation, some questions are worth asking ourselves – because they are critical for making (or not) our species a space species – such as: can we reproduce in space? Very little is known about this crucial issue. Can fertilization happen in space? Moreover, can a pregnancy be carried to term in outer space? And what about the development of the child? A popular TV show called "The Expanse" depicts humans born and raised on the asteroid belt as very tall and thin, with long arms and legs, unable to sustain their own weight in a planetary gravity field. This vision, although seductive and apparently logical – the lack of gravity should allow the body to grow longer – is probably also very wrong. The lack of gravity will be foremost suffered by the bones lacking the directional force necessary for their correct development. So, more likely, a child growing up in space may have severe leg and arm deficiencies similar to what can be observed in a child with osteomalacia. Legs will be bent and unable to sustain the weight of the body, but also to provide locomotion. It is highly possible that a child raised in space may never be able to walk when on the surface of a planet.

Space Life Science within the Frame of the Vulnerable World Hypothesis

In 2019, Nick Bostrom introduced the idea of the Vulnerable World Hypothesis (VWH) (Bostrom, 2019). The concept behind Bostrom's reflection could provide an explanation for the famous Fermi paradox. Briefly, the argument for this paradox is that it is odd that we haven't yet come in contact with another civilization. Given the wide dimension of the universe, it seems likely that within the uncountable existing star systems, some should be well suited for developing life and hosting a civilization. So, why haven't we seen any? The three hypotheses commonly used to justify this paradox are: 1) we are the first; 2) life is a unique event; 3) the great filter hypothesis. Bostrom's idea could provide an explanation for this latter one. According to the VWH, every civilization encounters in its development some technology that necessarily leads to a societal collapse, and this is the essence of the filter. Bostrom describes scientific advancement, intended in a very broad sense and not limited to hard science, as a jar full of white marbles, each marble representing a technology. So far, we have unthinkingly picked marbles from the jar, supporting the progressive development of our civilization, implicitly implying that all the marbles are positive in their effects on society. But what if black marbles existed? What if some technology could lead to societal collapse just by simply being discovered? Among the examples reported by Bostrom, the "easy nuke" scenario well illustrated the idea: if a nuclear bomb were very easy to build, the discovery of nuclear fission might have led to the collapse of our society.

Within this frame, I'd like to propose the existence of "lightening" or "darkening" marbles: marbles that can attenuate or increase the "societal-disruptive" potential of other discoveries. Among the "lightening" marbles, I believe we can safely count the potential findings emerging from space life science, particularly from the study of space adaptations. The ability for our species to become a multi-planetary species can make us more resilient to the potential for societal disruption from other discoveries, especially if, besides other planets, we can effectively develop self-sustained space habitats. Therefore, the changes that our species may encounter and the technology that could ease our adaptation can be an optimal marble to search for. In ethical terms, it could be argued that we would have to search for this specific marble since we are aware not just of its positive value but also of its positivizing effects on other technologies.

The question of whether space colonization, in itself, could yield negative consequences must be carefully examined. It is plausible that accessing the vast physical resources of the solar system may lead to the development of highly advanced military capabilities, thereby presenting a potential threat to civilization greater than existing ones. Additionally, the presence of multiple habitable planets may instill a false sense of security, potentially reducing concerns about environmental exploitation or encouraging a more liberal use of weapons of mass destruction.

Nevertheless, we must also consider the alternative viewpoint that space colonization could foster greater cohesion among humanity, functioning as a unifying force. The challenges and adversity faced in becoming a multi-planetary species may instill a deep appreciation for the remarkable significance of this accomplishment. Instances of international collaboration, such as astronauts and cosmonauts working together on space missions aboard the ISS, have demonstrated the formation of a strong sense of community and inclusion among individuals from diverse nations. This intrinsic human behavior, the need to come together in the face of environmental adversity, offers a glimpse of optimism.

Cooperative behaviors may indeed serve as pivotal advantages in the context of space colonization. If this proves to be the case, future human societies in space may gravitate towards more altruistic tendencies, leaving behind individuals on Earth without this trait.

Conclusion

In conclusion, the multifaceted implications of space colonization warrant meticulous evaluation. While concerns about potential darkening consequences persist, the prospect of enhanced unity and cooperation among humans in space presents a promising counterbalance. Careful consideration of both perspectives is imperative as we navigate the path towards our extraterrestrial future.

What should we do to increase our knowledge of space life science? Significantly, the one thing we are sure about it in space life science is the depth of our ignorance. To tackle this issue, a vast scientific program should be launched and sponsored by national space agencies. A permanent space animal facility should be put on the priority list to allow scientists to study how space adaptation takes place generation after generation and to design adequate countermeasures. Although it would not be an easy structure to design, assemble and run, we should not forget that similar enterprises were already undertaken in other fields, for instance, building a very powerful space telescope for deep space observation.

Another field of investigation could be found in nature itself since some animals display features that are natural countermeasures to many health issues in space, such as hibernation (Cerri et al., 2021).

In conclusion, space pharmacology, space medicine, and space surgery, today in their infancy, will rapidly have to develop if we want to follow our exploration instinct; building a permanent animal facility in space would allow whoever realizes it first a significant strategic advantage over the development of a mature space life science.

References

Bernard, C. (1865) *Introduction a L'étude de la Médecine Expérimentale*. Flammarion, Paris.

Bostrom, N. (2019) The Vulnerable World Hypothesis. *Global Policy*, 10, 455–475.

Cannon, W.B. (1932) *The Wisdom of the Body*. W.W. Norton & Company, New York.

Cerri, M., Hitrec, T., Luppi, M. & Amici, R. (2021) Be cool to be far: Exploiting hibernation for space exploration. *Neurosci Biobehav Rev*, 128, 218–232.

Dawkins, R. (1976) *The Selfish Gene*. Oxford University Press, New York.

Durante, M. (2014) Space radiation protection: Destination Mars. *Life Sci Space Res (Amst)*, 1, 2–9.

Durante, M. & Cucinotta, F.A. (2008) Heavy ion carcinogenesis and human space exploration. *Nat Rev Cancer*, 8, 465–472.

Flynn-Evans, E.E., Barger, L.K., Kubey, A.A., Sullivan, J.P. & Czeisler, C.A. (2016) Circadian misalignment affects sleep and medication use before and during spaceflight. *NPJ Microgravity*, 2, 15019.

Ghidini, T. (2021) *Homo Caelestis*. Longanesi, Milano.

Hughson, R.L., Helm, A. & Durante, M. (2018) Heart in space: Effect of the extra-terrestrial environment on the cardiovascular system. *Nat Rev Cardiol*, 15, 167–180.

Juhl, O.J.T., Buettmann, E.G., Friedman, M.A., DeNapoli, R.C., Hoppock, G.A. & Donahue, H.J. (2021) Update on the effects of microgravity on the musculoskeletal system. *NPJ Microgravity*, 7, 28.

Man, J., Graham, T., Squires-Donelly, G. & Laslett, A.L. (2022) The effects of micro-gravity on bone structure and function. *NPJ Microgravity*, 8, 9.

Mrosovsky, N. (1990) *Rheostasis*. Oxford University Press, New York.

Noble, D. (2016) *Dance to the Tune of Life: Biological Relativity*. Cambridge University Press, Cambridge.

Patel, Z.S., Brunstetter, T.J., Tarver, W.J., Whitmire, A.M., Zwart, S.R., Smith, S.M. & Huff, J.L. (2020) Red risks for a journey to the red planet: The highest priority human health risks for a mission to Mars. *NPJ Microgravity*, 6, 33.

Proshchina, A., Gulimova, V., Kharlamova, A., Krivova, Y., Besova, N., Berdiev, R. & Saveliev, S. (2021) Reproduction and the early development of vertebrates in space: Problems, results, opportunities. *Life (Basel)*, 11.

Roy-O'Reilly, M., Mulavara, A. & Williams, T. (2021) A review of alterations to the brain during spaceflight and the potential relevance to crew in long-duration space exploration. *NPJ Microgravity*, 7, 5.

Stahn, A.C., Werner, A., Opatz, O., Maggioni, M.A., Steinach, M., von Ahlefeld, V.W., Moore, A., Crucian, B.E., Smith, S.M., Zwart, S.R., Schlabs, T., Mendt, S., Trippel, T., Koralewski, E., Koch, J., Chouker, A., Reitz, G., Shang, P., Rocker, L., Kirsch, K. A. & Gunga, H.C. (2017) Increased core body temperature in astronauts during long-duration space missions. *Sci Rep*, 7, 16180.

Sterling, P. & Eyer, J. (1981) Biological basis of stress-related mortality. *Soc Sci Med*, 15E, 39.

12

THE ETHICAL CONSIDERATIONS OF PANTROPY IN THE COLONIZATION OF MARS

Karim Jebari

Introduction

Plans to send humans to and build a permanent settlement on Mars have captured the public's imagination and are once again gaining political momentum. Researchers, entrepreneurs, and public intellectuals (Bostrom 2003; Solon 2018; Worland 2016, Munevar 2019, Szocik 2020, Green 2019) have debated the risks and benefits of such an endeavor, with some claiming that "making humanity a multiplanetary species" would reduce overall existential risk (Musk 2017). If Earth were struck by an asteroid, for instance, or if runaway global warming leads to societal collapse, a permanent and self-sustaining Mars settlement may become "plan B," it is argued. Both Elon Musk and Stephen Hawking have voiced the need for humanity to expand to other celestial bodies to reduce the risk of human extinction.

Humans, however, are not well suited to the Martian environment. The terraforming of Mars (i.e., re-engineering the atmosphere and hydrosphere of Mars to be more Earth-like) cannot be achieved in the near future; even the most optimistic assessments range from a few centuries to a millennium (Steigerwald 2018). Moreover, even when complete, it will still likely result in a planet whose mean temperature, air pressure, and CO_2 levels are far less hospitable to humans than those of Earth (Jakosky and Edwards 2018).[1] This study, therefore, considers the concept of *pantropy* as a complement to existing ideas and plans for the colonizing of Mars. By "colonizing" I mean building a settlement for permanent intergenerational human habitation, i.e., not merely permanent structures with a rotating crew as the research bases in Antarctica, for example, or the International Space Station.

Pantropy, a term coined by American science fiction author James Blish, is a hypothetical process in which humans are modified (for example, via genetic

DOI: 10.4324/9781003374381-12

engineering) to be able to survive in an alien environment, such as that of another planet (Ketterer 1983, Blish 1959). It should first be noted that no amount of human bioengineering is likely to create a person who can thrive in the existing conditions on Mars without environmental support systems; as such, "true" pantropy will not be possible for the foreseeable future. The ideas proposed here are not intended as an alternative to terraforming, or as an alternative to using technological means for shielding habitats against the harsh Martian environment, but as a complement to these efforts that might reduce their risks and costs. The study also considers the ethical concerns of bioengineering humans for this purpose. To be clear, human pantropy would not be a coerced or mandatory activity but something that Martian settlers could choose to provide for their offspring, possibly supported by financial incentives. A similar idea has been discussed by Szocik et al. (2018). While Szocik et al.'s article focuses on reproduction on Mars, and on how social norms about reproduction should be adapted to a fundamentally hostile environment, this chapter focuses more on the aspects of the Martian environment that could be partly adapted to, and the ethical concerns with such adaptations.

One prominent reason for colonizing Mars is to create an "Ark" for humanity to survive a global catastrophe on Earth. The costs and benefits of colonizing Mars have been extensively explored (Baum 2009; Nair et al. 2008). The strength of the "Ark" argument is debatable, however. I have argued elsewhere that a far more cost-effective alternative would be to build such an "Ark" on Earth, and to equip it with the means to restart civilization (Jebari 2014). My skepticism remains, but for the purpose of this chapter it is assumed that permanent human settlement on Mars – whatever the reason, and despite the associated risks and costs – is desirable. Given this assumption, we need to examine some concerns for the long term, chief among which is how the health of Martian colonists could be properly maintained.

The Environmental Hazards of Mars

Mars is a very inhospitable planet to humans.[2] Although humans have shown considerable adaptability to hostile environments on Earth, harnessing technology to settle every major landmass permanently (with the exception of Antarctica), the challenges of conditions on Mars are of another magnitude entirely. For one, the average temperature on Mars is considerably below that which is conducive to human survival: even in its equatorial regions, the climate is approximately as cold as that of Antarctica.

Mars lacks a magnetosphere that could protect its inhabitants from charged cosmic rays (CRs) from the Sun and interstellar space. CRs consist mostly of protons (87%), and alpha particles (12%) (Kennedy 2014). These massive particles travel at a substantial fraction of the speed of light and are therefore very energetic, causing distinct biological damage compared to other forms of radiation, such as X-rays and alpha radiation.[3] Even limited exposure to CRs can cause lasting tissue damage (Stewart et al. 2012). Such damage affects the lymphocytes, cells crucial to the immune system, which leads to lowered immunity (Sanzari et al. 2013). Cherry et al. (2012) show that CRs may harm the brain, accelerate the onset of Alzheimer's disease, and cause cognitive impairment. Long-term exposure to CRs, moreover, significantly increases the risk of cancer and birth defects (Kennedy and Wan 2011).

The Martian atmosphere is very thin compared to that of Earth: 0.6% as dense on average. Indeed, such low pressure levels are typically described as a vacuum on Earth. Since the boiling point (the point at which liquid changes into vapor) for water depends on the atmospheric pressure, a near vacuum condition is hazardous for humans, even when equipped with oxygen masks. Even at the lowest elevations, the Martian atmosphere is so thin that a full pressure suit would be needed to prevent fluids in the lungs from boiling and thus causing considerable tissue damage. This means that the pressure differential between a human habitat and the Martian environment would need to be considerable, which places high demands on building standards and materials. Similarly, the thin Martian atmosphere and lack of an ozone layer affords little protection from ultraviolet (UV) radiation from the Sun; while UV radiation is relatively easy to block with protective filters and clothing, it nevertheless adds another layer of complexity and hazard to any outdoor mission or activity (Schimmerling 2012).

Mars is a relatively energy-poor environment. Due to its relative remoteness from the Sun, the potential for solar power on Mars is modest at best. During frequent sandstorms, the Sun can remain obscured for days or weeks, exacerbating the intermittency problem of solar power. And while Martian winds can reach impressive speeds, and tectonic activity is present on the planet, the potential for wind or geothermal power, respectively, is still less than that of Earth. As a result, the significant amounts of energy that would be required to heat a Martian settlement, including its facilities for crops, are likely to be costly.

In summary, therefore, the environmental hazards of Mars are considerable, and would require multiple technological support systems that are complex, costly, and have many potential points of failure.

Pantropy

While certain obstacles to Martian settlement could in theory be addressed by technological support systems, such systems are costly and, in many respects, currently insufficient. Technology may insulate a fragile system from potential hazard, but such solutions are inherently risky. As Hansson (2008) argues, when reducing risk, we should always aim to eliminate the source of the risk rather than contain it: for example, in a building exposed to a fire hazard, non-flammable materials should be chosen rather than flammable materials treated with flame-retardant chemicals. The more dependent a Martian habitat is on complex technical infrastructure, the greater the likelihood of faults that endanger the lives of the settlers. Engineering systems need rigorous testing in realistic conditions to assess proper maintenance requirements and correct usage, especially in the face of unpredictable environmental challenges. Such conditions cannot be tested easily here on Earth as they are difficult to recreate.

As Szocik et al. (2018) argue, one of the most important issues with a long-term settlement on Mars is survival and reproduction. They discuss various challenges to this, as well as some interesting potential solutions. The suggestions presented here, with an emphasis on genetic interventions that are likely to be feasible in the medium-term future, are meant to be seen as a complement to that discussion.

Any serious plan to create a permanent settlement on Mars should therefore consider the potential use of technology to adapt human settlers or their offspring to Martian conditions, rather than focusing solely on technical infrastructure. Here, I discuss several genetic traits that could in theory be combined with genetic engineering techniques to bioengineer humans who would be more likely to survive the harsh conditions on Mars and/or be less dependent on a complex and fragile technological support system.

I refer to these interventions as "pantropy" since their intended aim is to provide specific remedies that aim to improve health and/or quality of life for extraterrestrial settlers. Pantropy differs from genetic enhancement in the sense that genetic enhancement often refers to interventions that make a person "better than normal." An intervention that improves adaptation to a hostile environment is not an enhancement, as it only allows a person to be not as vulnerable as they would have otherwise been.

Radiation

To take the example of UV radiation, an environmental hazard present on Earth, some humans have already evolved adaptations that could be helpful on Mars: melanin-rich (i.e., dark) skin, which provides some protection against UV radiation. The genes that code for increased melanin production are well known and widely spread among the human population and would thus be of great value to Martian settlers.

Genetic adaptations seen in the animal kingdom offer numerous examples of how humans could be adapted to Martian conditions. While no large animals have evolved mechanisms for coping with the distinct biological damage caused by CRs, research in Ukraine has shown evidence consistent with adaptation to an elevated radiation environment in birds living close to the Chernobyl reactor. These birds have evolved the ability to produce more of the antioxidant glutathione that can mitigate some of the harm caused by ionizing radiation (Møller and Mousseau 2016). Elsewhere, tentative evidence indicates that those animals that are more resistant to dehydration can tolerate much greater levels of radiation than similar animals that are less resistant to dehydration. It would appear that some of the tissue damage caused by dehydration is similar to that caused by radiation, and that existing mechanisms that repair the former have some effect in repairing the latter (Jönsson 2003). However, while some technological countermeasures have been proposed, biological adaptations to prevent the harm caused by CRs remain an unsolved problem (Kennedy 2014).

Low Atmospheric Pressure

Were humans able to live and work under low-pressure conditions, the pressure differential between the habitat environment and the Martian environment could be reduced, allowing for cheaper materials, less structural complexity, and reduced risk of catastrophic decompression. While it is not very difficult to maintain a pressure differential on smaller habitats, this challenge would increase if a settlement opted to construct domes or greenhouses over larger areas. Moreover, standard space suits are typically pressurized at about one third of standard Earth air pressure to allow for mobility (Hsu 2009). On Earth, Tibetan populations have demonstrated heritable adaptations to high-altitude, hypoxic (low-oxygen) environments. For example, the *EPAS1* allele is associated with fewer red blood cells, and correspondingly lower hemoglobin levels. Since elevated red blood cell production is a common response to hypoxic stress, it may be that carriers of *EPAS1* are able to maintain sufficient oxygenation of tissues at high altitude without the need for increased erythrocyte levels (Yi et al. 2010). In the Andes, high-altitude natives have adapted differently to their environment compared to their Tibetan counterparts, as indicated by divergences in the physiological traits that underpin the oxygen delivery process. These findings suggest that evolutionary processes have been different in the two populations; there would thus appear to be at least two different routes to the same outcome of successful oxygen delivery at high altitudes (Beall 2007). Since these adaptations are genetically and functionally distinct, some of them could in theory be combined to create individuals with even greater abilities to tolerate low air pressure.

High CO_2 Concentrations

Managing the right mix of gases in a sealed container, such as a Martian habitat, is difficult and the levels of CO_2 can fluctuate to levels that can be harmful. This was for example the case with the Biosphere 2 project, one of whose aims was to test the viability of closed ecological systems in space (Alling et al. 2020). Here, CO_2 levels fluctuated with 500–600 ppm between night and day. CO_2 is toxic to humans even in relatively low concentrations (Satish et al. 2012). Adaptations to increase CO_2 tolerance may therefore reduce the risk of catastrophic failure. Ilardo et al. (2018) have shown that the Bajau, a small group of "sea nomads" in Maritime Southeast Asia who have earned a living for centuries as divers, have evolved adaptations to tolerate higher concentrations of CO_2 in the blood. Exposure to high concentrations of CO_2 in the blood causes a contraction of the spleen, an organ that acts as an emergency reserve of oxygenated red blood cells, so that an increased supply of these cells is released into the bloodstream. Scans showed that the Bajau's spleens were on average 50% larger than those of a nearby land-living population. Another mutation was also found in a gene responsible for the production of carbonic anhydrase, an enzyme that slows the buildup of CO_2 in the blood (Ilardo et al. 2018). These adaptations could significantly reduce the hazards associated with sudden fluctuations in CO_2 levels.

Low Temperature

Warming up habitats to the point where human and plant life could persist is likely to absorb much energy. If Martian settlers could tolerate low average temperatures, the temperature differential between a Martian settlement and its environment could be reduced significantly, allowing for other uses of the available energy. Human populations seem to follow "Allen's rule", which states that animal populations in cold environments have a smaller body surface-to-volume ratio, allowing them to preserve body heat more efficiently (Katzmarzyk and Leonard 1998; Steegmann and Platner 1968). Genes that code for such morphological features in human populations (shorter extremities, for example) could be incorporated to make settlers more resilient to cold (Fumagalli et al. 2015). In addition, Eskimo and Aleut populations have facial features that are beneficial when breathing cold air, such as narrow nasal passages; likewise, the large, protruding noses with which Neanderthals were able to warm and humidify cold, dry air (Wroe et al. 2018) have been found in modern-day northeastern Asian populations (Azevedo et al. 2017).

Brown adipose tissue (fat) has evolved as an adaptation in humans and some other animals that live in cold climates. Brown fat differs from the more common white fat in that a large amount of lipids can be stored in the cells. Moreover, brown fat can be "burned" to produce heat upon adrenergic stimulation from the central nervous system. This, in combination with a highly developed vascular system to deliver heat rapidly to vital organs, can greatly increase tolerance of extreme cold. Research has found that Inuit populations display a gene variation that helps them to build more brown adipose tissue. This specific pattern of gene variation matched very closely with the equivalent genome portion of the Denisova hominins, an extinct subspecies of archaic humans, suggesting that Denisovan ancestors might be the source of this evolutionary adaptation (Fumagalli et al. 2015; Racimo et al. 2016).

This short review of genetic adaptations is not meant to be exhaustive or definitive, and much of it is based on only tentative research. Nonetheless, it provides useful insight into the kinds of interventions that could be of interest to Martian settlers. It should be noted that some scholars who participate in this discourse have speculated about very radical and sometimes disturbing modifications, often in arguments seeking to discredit extraterrestrial colonization (Tachibana 2020). This review has opted to focus on relatively plausible and realistic modifications that to some extent already exist in the human and/or mammalian gene pool. This heuristic is similar to that employed in Jebari (2015), to avoid suggestions that are too implausible to be relevant to discuss.

The Ethics of Pantropy

Medical Risks

As with all biomedical treatments, including those routinely prescribed by medical professionals, pantropy carries inherent risks. The type and severity of risk will vary from procedure to procedure, and some traits may have undesirable side effects. For example, while dark skin pigmentation protects against UV radiation, it also reduces the skin's ability to produce vitamin D (Bonilla et al. 2014). To bioengineer humans is currently very risky, even with CRISPR. These risks include unintended mutations in genes, which can cause disease and/or disability (Davies 2019). While we may expect the risks of, for example, off-target mutations to be reduced over time, we do not know if this or some other technique may become sufficiently safe to use for the purposes of pantropy. Other, less effective but less risky techniques could instead be considered. For example, artificial insemination of gametes from individuals with the desired traits in combination with embryonic screening could be an alternative to spread certain traits among Martian settlers. While hardly risk-free, embryonic screening is widely used.

It is important not to fall prey to the tendency to exaggerate the risks of unfamiliar technologies. It should be noted that, in other contexts, modern societies have been willing to make biomedical interventions on a population-wide scale. For example, during the 2009 swine flu pandemic, a mass vaccination campaign was carried out in several countries, including Canada, Japan, and the US. While this campaign was considered controversial by some, it demonstrated that population-scale biomedical interventions are considered permissible by most bioethicists and the larger public when there are clear and substantial benefits. Generalizing this principle would imply that pantropy could be considered in a context where it can provide a similar benefit.

However, it can be objected that the analogy between vaccination and pantropy is misplaced, as the former could be seen as a treatment and the latter as an enhancement or augmentation. Whether or not pantropy ought to be seen as enhancement or a (preventive) treatment for environmental hazards depends on the definition of what counts as enhancement. In general, biomedical interventions are considered enhancements if they provide a person with an enhanced bodily function. Vaccines are, according to this definition, not enhancements, because they do not cause super health, but rather prevent illness. Vaccines can in some sense enhance general well-being since vaccinated people can engage in activities that they enjoy, for example going to the cinema during a pandemic, without the risk of (severe) illness. However, this is also the case for the suggested pantropy interventions. People with these modifications would not be "super-humans" nor would they likely be more healthy, happy, or fit here on Earth. They are only enhanced relative to an environment that is otherwise hazardous (in fact, they could possibly be worse off than ordinary humans on Earth, something that will be discussed below). Likewise, vaccinated people are only enhanced relative to an otherwise hazardous environment, and arguably (slightly) worse off in an environment where the pathogen they were vaccinated against does not exist.

As this chapter has illustrated, the risks associated with living on Mars are substantial, and it is therefore reasonable that the additional risks of pantropy should be considered in light of this, as with any biomedical intervention. Being a Martian settler is likely to be associated with a very high risk of premature death and severe morbidity. Giving birth on Mars is likewise a very dangerous proposition. If these actions and choices are themselves acceptable, we should be willing to consider biomedical interventions that could make life on Mars less hazardous. In other precarious scenarios here on Earth, we have accepted subjecting some individuals to biomedical interventions that would not have been acceptable under normal circumstances, on the proviso that such interventions reduce overall risk. For example, during the Persian Gulf War, amphetamine became the drug of choice (on a voluntary basis) for roughly half of U.S. Air Force pilots (Miller 2003), the use of which could be justified on the basis that it would reduce operational risk. While it can be argued that genetic modification is more hazardous than taking amphetamines, the example seeks to illustrate the principle that the risk of an intervention needs to be evaluated in the actual context, and the risks of non-intervention need to be considered as well.

Prenatal Autonomy

While some pantropy interventions could involve individuals choosing to modify themselves, some would involve engineering gametes or embryos to create genetically modified children. However, this poses an ethical complication: unlike adults, unborn children cannot consent to being subjected to potentially risky medical procedures. One of the four ethical criteria that is often considered crucial in medical ethics is autonomy (Beauchamp and Childress 2019). One aspect of respecting autonomy is that an intervention should not limit or unduly influence the life choices of individuals (Sandel 2007). It would be an unacceptable violation of autonomy if the state or a corporation chose to bioengineer embryos to "produce" human settlers adapted to Martian conditions for the purpose of sending them to Mars. Even if these bioengineered humans were given the opportunity to remain on Earth, the mere fact that they would be designed for a specific purpose would place such expectations that it would effectively limit their life choices. Moreover, were these individuals to remain on Earth, the interventions could not be justified with regard to their medical benefits. Note here that while we can expect current methods of bioengineering to become less hazardous in the future, it is not realistic to expect such interventions to become risk-free.

On the other hand, it is widely accepted that the limits of parental authority are less stringent than those of the state (Liao 2005). Parents influence the lives of their offspring not only through explicit choices, such as which school they attend and what norms they learn, but also through indirect choices, such as choosing where and how to live. This would be the case if some people choose to settle on Mars and wish for their offspring to be better adapted to Martian conditions. Modern liberal democracies seem to accept that parents have discretion regarding the language, religion, and skills of their children. Moreover, we also accept that parents make health-related choices about their children, such as whether to abstain from vaccinations or undergo circumcision. According to Savulescu (2001), when parents make such decisions, they have a duty to choose what is best for their child and their life prospects. In this way, Martian parents would have a moral obligation to modify their prospective children if such intervention would improve their prospects of survival on Mars. It is worth noting here that some interventions that change the life prospects of future children are by no means controversial: if a pregnant woman voluntarily takes vitamin supplements and avoids alcohol during pregnancy, for instance, her choices could (positively) affect the biological properties of the child.

In the literature on human enhancement, some have argued that – however controversial a technology may be – parents have the right to modify their children socially and biologically as long as it would promote their children's general well-being, and as long as no better means of achieving such an end is available (Savulescu 2001). Granted, it may be ethically problematic for Martian settlers to conceive at all without first knowing the full extent of the health risks involved in gestation in the Martian environment. However, whether or not those children should be modified to withstand the risks more effectively is a separate question. Given the harshness of the Martian environment and the probable lack of alternative solutions, we might conclude that if a pantropic intervention would on the whole promote a child's future well-being, then parents should have the right to implement such an intervention.

Whether genetically engineered Martians would be able to return to Earth safely is also morally relevant. If the genetic modifications would make Earth-life impossible, then such interventions would pose significant limits on the autonomy of the children, in ways that may be seen as unacceptable even for parents. However, the interventions listed above, such as dark skin, the ability to tolerate low air pressures, the ability to tolerate CO_2 buildup, more prevalent brown adipose tissue, etc., would probably not be so onerous if Martians would prefer to live on Earth. By contrast, other environmental effects caused by growing up on Mars may be more crippling. For example, growing up in Martian gravity (38% that of Earth) is likely to change the body in ways that will hinder adaptation to Terran conditions, such as lower bone density and less muscle mass. Moreover, Martian-born children would be unlikely to have had the same level of diversity in their microbial exposure, making them more vulnerable to microbial infection on Earth. In sum, even if some of the proposed genetic modifications could make life on Earth more complicated to Martian-born people, it is very likely that they would be maladapted for Terran conditions due to reasons inherent in the experience of living one's first years on Mars.

Do Martians Matter?

Bioengineered speciation as a part of extraplanetary settlement raises some specific ethical concerns regarding the value of the persistence of human life. According to Bostrom (2003), intelligent life has the potential to attain a state known as "technological maturity," whose value (in terms of happiness, self-realization, etc.) is immense (see also Ord 2020). Human extinction would delay or possibly even prevent such a state.[4] From this perspective, if there were other sapient creatures that could take on the task of converting available energy into happiness (or some other similar value), then that would be just as desirable according to Bostrom's view as human survival. Consequently, it would not matter if a human successor species on Mars were to become (over time) so different that they could no longer interbreed with terrestrial humans.

Other reasons may persist for wanting human existence to continue, reasons that are more bound to the actual human condition. One such idea is the notion that what matters is the continuation of *our* species. Francis Fukuyama (2002), for example, has argued that humans have a common essence that differentiate us, in a normative sense, from other non-human animals. He argues that "the sum of the behavior and characteristics that are typical of the human species, [arise] from genetics rather than environmental factors" (Fukuyama 2002, p. 130). On Fukuyama's narrow definition of what it means to be human, then, Martian settlers that have non-typical behaviors and characteristics would be non-human, if not in the near future, then at least in a few hundred generations. Were Mars to be inhabited by a Martian successor species, it would no longer serve the purpose of being an "Ark," since their survival would not imply the survival of the human species. However, a more common species concept is the phylogenetic view, or the "species as individuals" – view (Sterelny and Griffiths 1999). Here, instead of two animals being of the same species by virtue of having similar traits, an animal relates to its species as a part to a whole. This means that an animal X belongs to a species S if X has a certain spatiotemporal relation to other members of X. This spatiotemporal relation may differ between species. For example, an animal is a *human* animal if it is the result of a fusion of gametes that originated from other human bodies. In other words, according to the phylogenetic view, an animal relates to a species in the same way as a body part relates to a body. Just as my hand is part of my body by virtue of physical connectedness, rather than similarity, only organisms with the right spatio-temporal relation to the collective are properly considered to be members (or parts) of the species (Ghiselin 1974; Jebari 2015). On this view, Martians would be as human as the people surviving on Earth would, regardless of whether they had bioengineered or evolved non-typical traits. Ultimately, in this view, it is not similarity nor the potential of genetic flow between populations that matters, but that these populations share a common origin.

Another reason for preventing human extinction concerns the perpetuation of human culture, ideas, and projects (Scheffler 2018). In this view, Martian persistence may suffice to preserve at least some of the cultural heritage of humanity, if some aspects of human culture are continued among Martians. Given that data storage is already relatively cheap, it would be relatively straightforward to guarantee that a Martian successor civilization would have access to much of the human art, literature, and music of its Terran ancestry. And while a Martian civilization is likely to become very different over time from Terran civilization due to its unique environmental conditions and will hence consider human history and culture from a somewhat alien perspective to our own, it is not this difference that matters; as espoused by Scheffler, what does matter is that a hypothetical Martian civilization would be able to trace its cultural lineage back to ours.

Transitional Settlers

Koji Tachibana argues that it may require several generations before genetic modifications reach their full potential in a target population (Tachibana 2020). People in "intermediate generations," i.e., persons who have only been partly modified to extraterrestrial environments, may feel that they are being used as mere means. This is an important concern. It is therefore crucial that any effort at genetic modification be carried out in the best interests of the prospective child, and not only of people in the future generations that would be its descendants. Unless a modification can be motivated by the expected welfare of the person who is to be modified, it cannot be justified. Are such modifications possible? They might not be technically feasible at this moment, but it is certainly plausible that they could be. Consider, for example, the above-mentioned genetic mutation that allows a person to function normally in a low-pressure environment. There is no inherent reason to believe that such modifications could not be carried out in an embryo in vitro. Perhaps an initial effort could only change a few genes, allowing the prospective person to attain some, but not all of the capabilities of human populations with this ability. But as long as the modification improves the prospects of Martian settlers, they may be justified, just as an equivalent modification for other purposes may be justified.

An Outlandish Idea?

Perhaps the most immediate objection to the suggestion of pantropy is that it is an absurd idea. Of course, I recognize that creating a human subspecies for the purposes of interplanetary settlement is prima facie outlandish. Nonetheless, exploring such apparently drastic ideas can be a formative learning experience, while failing to do so could result in missed opportunities to address issues that may prove critical to future generations.

First, we should note that the reaction of disgust from some to the prospect of pantropic intervention does not in itself imply that such interventions are immoral. Many life choices that the majority consider repugnant are nevertheless tolerated in most high-income countries. Consider, for example, genital piercing or religiously motivated self-flagellation.

Second, popular attitudes about what may be appalling today may not be so tomorrow. For example, opinions on same-sex marriage have changed considerably in recent times. People's attitudes towards pantropy may undergo a similar change if its effects on the probability of surviving on Mars were to become more widely known.

Third, we should be aware of the ubiquity of status quo bias, whereby people are disposed to favor the current situation even when a new situation is measurably better (Bostrom and Ord 2006). Being aware of this common bias, we should adjust our intuition to seemingly absurd ideas accordingly.

Finally, if we think that pantropy is too absurd to consider, then perhaps we ought to reconsider the plausibility of colonizing Mars in the first place.

Conclusions

Once mere figments of the science-fiction imagination, a manned mission to Mars and the establishment of the first human settlement in outer space are now the subjects of serious consideration. This chapter has argued that humans are woefully incapable of surviving a normal human lifetime (let alone flourishing) in the Martian environment, even when supported by technological means. As a result, if we are serious about making humanity (in the broad sense) a multiplanetary species, we need to consider both the physical possibility and moral justifiability of the pantropic creation of a subspecies that is better adapted to the harsh conditions on Mars. This chapter has explored some potential adaptations that already exist in human and animal gene pools and that would be advantageous to Martians. Finally, I have also argued that, in most respects, the fact that a Martian colony would be settled by individuals bioengineered for this purpose does not reduce the normative value of such an endeavor for the purposes of creating an "Ark."

Notes

1 Unless very radical and costly measures are taken, such as crashing thousands of comets and nitrogen-rich dwarf planets, importing billions of tons of ammonia, etc. (Jakosky and Edwards 2018).
2 Here, I describe the environmental hazards of living on Mars, and exclude those associated with the journey to Mars and the potential risks in landing and takeoff. These are also substantial.

3 Alpha radiation from nuclear decay consists of much slower particles than those in CRs, and thus do not penetrate the skin.
4 Technological maturity could be attained if there were intelligent species other than humans.

References

Alling, A., Nelson, M., and Silverstone, S. (2020). *Life Under Glass* (2nd ed.). Santa Fe: Synergetic Press.

Azevedo, S. D., *et al.* (2017). Nasal airflow simulations suggest convergent adaptation in Neanderthals and modern humans. *Proceedings of the National Academy of Sciences*, 114(47), 12442–12447. doi:10.1073/pnas.1703790114.

Baum, S. D. (2009). Cost–benefit analysis of space exploration: Some ethical considerations. *Space Policy*, 25(2), 75–80. doi:10.1016/j.spacepol.2009.02.008.

Beall, C. M. (2007). Two routes to functional adaptation: Tibetan and Andean high-altitude natives. *Proceedings of the National Academy of Sciences of the United States of America*, 104(Suppl 1), 8655–8660. doi:10.1073/pnas.0701985104.

Beauchamp, T., and Childress, J. (2019). Principles of biomedical ethics: Marking its fortieth anniversary. *The American Journal of Bioethics: AJOB*, 19(11), 9–12. doi:10.1080/15265161.2019.1665402.

Blish, J. (1959). *The Seedling Stars*. New York: New American Library.

Bonilla, C., *et al.* (2014). Skin pigmentation, sun exposure, and vitamin D levels in children of the Avon Longitudinal Study of Parents and Children. *BMC Public Health*, 14, 597. doi:10.1186/1471-2458-14-597.

Bostrom, N. (2003a). Astronomical waste: The opportunity cost of delayed technological development. *Utilitas*, 15(3), 308–314.

Bostrom, N. (2003b). When machines outsmart humans. *Futures*, 35(7), 759–764.

Bostrom, N., and Ord, T. (2006). The reversal test: Eliminating status quo bias in applied ethics. *Ethics*, 116(4), 656–679. doi:10.1086/505233.

Cherry, J. D., *et al.* (2012). Galactic cosmic radiation leads to cognitive impairment and increased Aβ plaque accumulation in a mouse model of Alzheimer's disease. *PLoS ONE*, 7(12). doi:10.1371/journal.pone.0053275.

Davies, B. (2019). The technical risks of human gene editing. *Human Reproduction (Oxford, England)*, 34(11), 2104–2111. doi:10.1093/humrep/dez162.

Fukuyama, F. (2002). *Our Posthuman Future*. New York: Picador.

Fumagalli, M., et al. (2015). Greenlandic Inuit Show genetic signatures of diet and climate adaptation. *Science*, 349(6254), 1343–1347. doi:10.1126/science.aab2319.

Ghiselin, M. T. (1974). A radical solution to the species problem. *Systematic Zoology*, 23, 536–544.

Green, B. P. (2019). Self-preservation should be humankind's first ethical priority and therefore rapid space settlement is necessary. *Futures*, 110, 35–37. doi:10.1016/j.futures.2019.02.006.

Greenfield, A., *et al.* (2016). *Genome Editing: An Ethical Review*. London: Nuffield Council on Bioethics.

Hansson, S. O. (2008). From the casino to the jungle. *Synthese*, 168(3), 423–432. doi:10.1007/s11229-008-9444-1.

Hsu, J. (2009, July 17). *What Will NASA's Next Spacesuit Look Like?* Scientific American. Retrieved from https://www.scientificamerican.com/article/spacesuits-moonwalk-apollo/.

Ilardo, M. A., et al. (2018). Physiological and genetic adaptations to diving in sea nomads. *Cell*, 173(3), 569–580. doi:10.1016/j.cell.2018.03.054.

Jakosky, B. M., and Edwards, C. S. (2018). Inventory of CO_2 available for terraforming Mars. *Nature Astronomy*, 2(8), 634–639. doi:10.1038/s41550-018-0529-6.

Jebari, K. (2014). Existential risks: Exploring a robust risk reduction. *Science & Engineering Ethics*, 21, 541. doi:10.1007/s11948-014-9559-3.

Jebari, K. (2015). Sensory enhancement. In J. Clausen and N. Levy (Eds.), *Handbook of Neuroethics* (pp. 827–838). Heidelberg: Springer Netherlands. doi:10.1007/978-94-007-4707-4_106.

Jebari, K. (2016). Should extinction be forever? *Philosophy and Technology*, 29, 211–222.

Jönsson, K. I. (2003). Causes and consequences of excess resistance in cryptobiotic metazoans. *Physiological and Biochemical Zoology*, 76(4), 429–435. doi:10.1086/377743.

Katzmarzyk, P. T., and Leonard, W. R. (1998). Climatic influences on human body size and proportions: Ecological adaptations and secular trends. *American Journal of Physical Anthropology*, 106(4), 483–503. doi:10.1002/(sici)1096-8644(199808)106:4-483:aid-ajpa4-3.0.co;2-k.

Kennedy, A. R. (2014). Biological effects of space radiation and development of effective countermeasures. *Life Sciences in Space Research*, 1, 10–43. doi:10.1016/j.lssr.2014.02.004.

Kennedy, A. R., and Wan, X. S. (2011). Countermeasures for space radiation induced adverse biologic effects. *Advances in Space Research*, 48(9), 1460–1479. doi:10.1016/j.asr.2011.07.007.

Ketterer, D. (1983). Pantropy, polyploidy, and tectogenesis in the fiction of James Blish and Norman L. Knight. *Science Fiction Studies*, 10(2), 199–218.

Martin, P. K. (2015). *NASA's Efforts to Manage Health and Human Performance Risks for Space Exploration*. Office of Inspector General, Report IG-16-003, p. 15.

Miller, G. (2003, January 4). "Go" pills for F-16 pilots get close look/amphetamines prescribed in mission that killed Canadians. *SFGate*. Retrieved from https://www.sfgate.com/news/article/Go-pills-for-F-16-pilots-get-close-look-2687644.php.

Møller, A. P., and Mousseau, T. A. (2016). Are organisms adapting to ionizing radiation at Chernobyl? *Trends in Ecology & Evolution*, 31(4), 281–289. doi:10.1016/j.tree.2016.01.005.

Munevar, G. (2019). An Obligation to Colonize Outer Space. *Futures*, 110, 38–40. doi:10.1016/j.futures.2019.02.009.

Musk, E. (2017). Making humans a multiplanetary species. *New Space*, 5(2). doi:10.1089/space.2017.29009.emu.

Nair, G. M., et al. (2008). Strategic, technological and ethical aspects of establishing colonies on Moon and Mars. *Acta Astronautica*, 63(11–12), 1337–1342. doi:10.1016/j.actaastro.2008.05.012.

Ord, T. (2020). *The Precipice: Existential Risk and the Future Of Humanity*. Hachette Books.

Perez, J. (2016, March 30). The human body in space. *NASA*. Retrieved from http://www.nasa.gov/hrp/bodyinspace.

Racimo, F., et al. (2016). Archaic adaptive introgression in TBX15/WARS2. *Molecular Biology and Evolution*, 34(3). doi:10.1093/molbev/msw283.

Sandel, M. J. (2007). *The Case against Perfection: Ethics in the Age of Genetic Engineering*. Cambridge, Mass.: Belknap Press of Harvard University Press.

Sanzari, J. K., et al. (2013). Leukocyte activity is altered in a ground-based murine model of microgravity and proton radiation exposure. *PLoS ONE*, 8(8). doi:10.1371/journal.pone.0071757.

Satish, U., *et al.* (2012). Is CO_2 an indoor pollutant? Direct effects of low-to-moderate CO_2 concentrations on human decision-making performance. *Environmental Health Perspectives*, 120(12), 1671–1677. doi:10.1289/ehp.1104789.

Savulescu, J. (2001). Procreative beneficence: Why we should select the best children. *Bioethics*, 15(5–6), 413–426. doi:10.1111/1467-8519.00251.

Scheffler, S. (2018). *Why Worry about Future Generations?* Oxford: Oxford University Press.

Schimmerling, W. (2012). The space radiation environment: An introduction. *WayBack Machine*. Retrieved from https://web.archive.org/web/20120426022341/http:/three.usra.edu/concepts/SpaceRadiationEnviron.pdf.

Solon, O. (2018, March 11). Elon Musk: We must colonise Mars to preserve our species in a third world war. *The Guardian*. Retrieved from https://www.theguardian.com/technology/2018/mar/11/elon-musk-colonise-mars-third-world-war.

Steegmann, A. T., and Platner, W. S. (1968). Experimental cold modification of craniofacial morphology. *American Journal of Physical Anthropology*, 28(1), 17–30. doi:10.1002/ajpa.1330280111.

Steigerwald, B. (2018, July 25). Mars terraforming not possible using present-day technology. *NASA*. Retrieved from http://www.nasa.gov/press-release/goddard/2018/mars-terraforming.

Sterelny, K., and Griffith, P. E. (1999). *Sex and Death*. The University of Chicago Press.

Stewart, F. A., *et al.* (2012). ICRP PUBLICATION 118: ICRP statement on tissue reactions and early and late effects of radiation in normal tissues and organs – threshold doses for tissue reactions in a radiation protection context. *Annals of the ICRP*, 41(1–2), 1–322. doi:10.1016/j.icrp.2012.02.001.

Szocik, K. (2020). Is human enhancement in space a moral duty? Missions to Mars, advanced AI and genome editing in space. *The International Journal of Healthcare Ethics Committees*, 29(1), 122–130. doi:10.1017/S0963180119000859.

Szocik, K., *et al.* (2018). Biological and social challenges of human reproduction in a long-term Mars base. *Futures*, 100, 56–62. doi:10.1016/j.futures.2018.04.006.

Tachibana, K. (2020). Virtue ethics and the value of saving humanity. In K. Szocik (Ed.), *Human Enhancements for Space Missions: Lunar, Martian, and Future Missions to the Outer Planets* (pp. 169–181). Cham: Springer International Publishing. doi:10.1007/978-3-030-42036-9_12.

The Editors (2002). Melanins in fungal pathogens. *Journal of Medical Microbiology*, 51(3), 189–191. doi:10.1099/0022-1317-51-3-189.

Torres, P. (2018). Space colonization and suffering risks: Reassessing the "Maxipok Rule". *Futures*, 100, 74–85. doi:10.1016/j.futures.2018.04.008.

Vazquez, M. E. (1998). Neurobiological problems in long-term deep space flights. *Advances in Space Research*, 22(2), 171–183. doi:10.1016/s0273-1177(98)80009-4.

Worland, J. (2016, November 17). Stephen Hawking gives humans a deadline for finding a new planet. *Time*. Retrieved from https://time.com/4575054/stephen-hawking-humans-new-planet/.

Wroe, S., *et al.* (2018). Computer simulations show that Neanderthal facial morphology represents adaptation to cold and high energy demands, but not heavy biting. *Proceedings of the Royal Society B: Biological Sciences*, 285(1876), 20180085. doi:10.1098/rspb.2018.0085.

Yi, X., *et al.* (2010). Sequencing of 50 human exomes reveals adaptation to high altitude. *Science*, 329(5987), 75–78. doi:10.1126/science.1190371.

13

FAKING BIOSPHERE

Oskari Sivula

Introduction

Mars is a cold, dry planet with a thin atmosphere. It provides an extremely hostile environment for life. The average temperature on Mars is −60°C and the atmospheric pressure is over a hundred times less than on Earth. Because of this, there is no liquid water to be found on its surface. Moreover, the Red Planet receives strong ultraviolet radiation because Mars does not have a planetary magnetic field or a thick atmosphere (McKay & Marinova 2001, 89). To put it bluntly, the conditions on Mars are hellish.

Despite the conditions on Mars, humans have already for quite some time dreamed of settling the Red Planet. Many have envisioned Mars as a habitable planet suitable for terrestrial life without the need for life-support systems. Part of this is because Mars was not always as gloomy. There is evidence that Mars used to have considerable amounts of liquid water and a warmer climate (McKay et al. 1991, 489). Mars also has some considerable similarities to Earth. Both are rocky planets with similar obliquity, they receive enough sunlight for photosynthesis (though Mars receives only 43% of the amount of sunlight that Earth does), and the day length on Mars is remarkably close to that of Earth (24 hours and 37 minutes) (McKay & Marinova 2001, 90). In addition to this, we have realized that humans are effectively, albeit unintentionally, making drastic changes to the climate of Earth by emitting vast amounts of greenhouse gases (GHGs) into the atmosphere. This all suggests that the conditions on Mars could be engineered and made friendly for terrestrial life (McKay 2009, 245–246; McKay & Marinova 2001, 90). This idea of making an astronomical body habitable is known as terraforming or planetary ecosynthesis.

Terraforming presents an interesting case of an artificial biosphere, that is, a planet-wide ecosystem that is unnatural at least in the sense of being human-

DOI: 10.4324/9781003374381-13

made. Moreover, (un)naturalness is a major concept in environmental ethics. Therefore, in this chapter, I examine human-made biospheres and planetary engineering from the perspective of the concept of (un)naturalness using terraformed Mars as a case study.

I start with a cursory description of the hypothetical process of terraforming Mars. It should be noted that the relevance of this inquiry is not washed away if it turns out that terraforming Mars is not technologically feasible any time soon. This is because the idea of terraforming provides a useful thought experiment that can be used to clarify the notion of (un)naturalness. Therefore, the aim of this chapter is both to provide new insights into the (un)naturalness discussion and to learn about environmental ethics beyond Earth. In the third section, I present the concept of (un)naturalness in environmental ethics. Following that, I analyze in what sense the biosphere of terraformed Mars would be unnatural. Finally, in the fifth section, I discuss whether this unnaturalness undermines the value of an artificial biosphere, and thus gives an important criterion for deciding about planetary ecosynthesis.

For the purpose of this text, I assume that there is no indigenous life on Mars. I also assume that Mars would be rigorously studied in its pristine condition before terraforming so that most scientific value that can be expected to be discovered would be gained, and that humanity has good reasons to create a biosphere on Mars. With these assumptions in mind, I can better narrow my focus on the (un)naturalness of a possible Martian biosphere along with its normative implications, and the contribution of this inquiry to discussions about (un)naturalness in environmental philosophy.

Terraforming Mars

It is suggested that the atmospheric pressure and temperature of the Red Planet could be increased so that water would remain liquid there, it would become more hospital for terrestrial life, and humans could operate there without pressure suits. To achieve this, a significant number of gases should be added to the present Martian atmosphere. GHGs, while harmful on Earth, would be beneficial on Mars. CO_2 reservoirs can be found on the surface of Mars. Most of it is either frozen in the polar caps or absorbed in the regolith (McKay et al. 1991, 492; McKay & Marinova 2001, 95–98). Releasing these inventories into the atmosphere and triggering a runaway GHG effect by increasing surface temperature is one suggested strategy to increase the temperature and pressure on Mars. Initial heating will release the frozen and absorbed CO_2 into the air. This will increase the capture of solar heat, which will in turn release more of the CO_2 reservoirs into the atmosphere, and so on (McKay & Marinova 2001, 100). The initial warming could be done in various ways. It is proposed that Mars could be heated, for instance, with giant mirrors, or by producing super GHGs on Mars via in-situ resource utilization. This latter approach is considered to be the most promising technique for warming Mars. Also, a

combination of techniques may be used. It is estimated that shifting Mars to a
new warmer state could be achieved in about 100 to 500 years (ibid., 99–101).

After changing the conditions, lifeforms from Earth could be introduced to
Mars. First, pioneering microbial communities such as cyanobacteria could be
introduced. They do not require oxygen and are very resistant to freezing,
drying, and UV radiation (Graham 2004, 176–177). Through photosynthesis,
cyanobacteria could create oxygen on Mars. Later, more complex life could be
introduced there such as plants, fungi, and eventually even animals. This life
would interact with itself and the Martian environment and eventually create a
(hopefully) stable biosphere.

As we have seen above, the process of terraforming would basically be ecological engineering on a planetary scale. Of course, talking about *ecological*
engineering in the context of Mars is problematic because Mars is purportedly
inanimate. Ecological engineering refers to the design and modification of ecosystems, whereas ecosystems refer to both the biotic and abiotic components
that interact with each other in a given area, and for now it is assumed that
Mars lacks these biotic components.

Planetary scientist Christopher McKay (2009, 257) goes further, claiming that
planetary ecosynthesis on Mars can also be interpreted "as a type of 'restoration ecology'" if Mars had a biosphere in its primaeval times that it has since
lost. After all, we would be restoring the warmer earlier state of the planet.
Despite being an interesting idea, this interpretation of ecological restoration
bends the notion perhaps too far. Typically, what is meant by ecological
restoration is a situation where an ecosystem that has been damaged by *humans*
is restored to its *previous condition* or its *recovering process* is assisted. On
Mars, these conditions do not hold; the damage a possible Martian biosphere
has faced is certainly not human-caused; the conditions the restoration aims to
restore are from the very distant past, which we have limited knowledge of, and
there currently seems to be no recovering process going on that could be assisted. At most, terraforming Mars could only present an extreme borderline case
of ecological restoration.

As a final remark on this section, the feasibility of terraforming Mars is
speculative. Recent studies suggest that there might not be enough accessible
CO_2 remaining on Mars for the aforementioned process to work (Jakosky &
Edwards 2018). Yet, for this chapter, a possibility that in the future (with
technology beyond today's capability) humans could make Mars or some
other celestial body habitable is enough. In fact, only the idea of terraforming
is interesting enough, as noted in the introduction; the basic idea of planetary
ecosynthesis can be used to examine and re-evaluate our traditional theories,
concepts, and intuitions in environmental ethics. Hence, the inquiry of this
chapter is equally motivated by the aim of using space ethics to test our theories and concepts about naturalness, and through that gain new insight – to
say something useful about terraforming extraterrestrial environments.

(Un)naturalness in Environmental Ethics

The concepts of natural and unnatural are central to many arguments in environmental ethics. Many environmentalists tend to value human-independent processes of nature and ecological entities considered to be natural. It has been suggested that the value of an ecosystem is (at least partly) dependent upon its history – it being natural of origin. On these grounds, the value of ecosystem restoration and engineering has been questioned by Robert Elliot (1982) and Eric Katz (1992, 2012). Both Elliot and Katz argue that we should not fool ourselves; the value of a restored ecosystem is less than a natural one. According to them, artificial environments necessarily lack values that natural environments have. In Katz's (1991, 90–91) words:

> I am outraged by the idea that a technologically created "nature" will be passed off as reality. ... The recreated natural environment ... is nothing more than an artifact created for human use. The problem for an applied environmental ethic is the determination of the moral value of this artifact.

Also, Keekok Lee (1999, 119) argues that turning nature into artifacts leads to "ontological impoverishment" and loss of the value of nature as an independent other. Furthermore, geoengineering – the Earth counterpart to terraforming – faces a presumptive argument against it among environmental ethicists. This presumptive argument is at least partly motivated by considerations about (un)naturalness (Preston 2011, 461–464).

Considering this, the possibility of establishing an ecosphere on Mars opens up an intriguing case: an unnatural biosphere. The imagined future Martian ecological system would be, so to speak, "artificial" and "designed". Indeed, Lee (1994, 97) states that "[t]he project [terraforming] embodies the ultimate philosophy of transforming Nature into Artefact". Tony Milligan (2014, 40) also identifies this – what might be referred to as the *unnaturalness objection to terraforming*. According to Milligan, 'there is a concern that terraforming on a planet such as Mars would result in something second-rate, *un-natural* or otherwise faked up" (ibid.).

In the same vein as Elliot and Katz criticize ecosystem restoration and engineering, this chapter explores whether the same applies on a planetary scale. Are we fooling ourselves when we ponder about bringing extraterrestrial biospheres into existence? Are we simply "faking biosphere" and thus not achieving as much as we were hoping to (axiologically speaking)?

The uneasiness related to terraforming is easy to understand. The sheer scale (spatial and temporal) of the engineering is daunting. However, this may be a reason to be skeptical about our initial moral intuitions about it. That is because planetary ecosynthesis presents an unfamiliar problem. According to Joshua Greene (2014, 714), in cases where we lack adequate evolutionary, cultural, or personal experience, our intuitions may be untrustworthy. Hence, we have a good reason to carefully examine our immediate intuitions about terraforming.

(Un)naturalness discussion has centered around two questions in philosophical literature (Siipi 2008, 72). First, is naturalness morally relevant or should it otherwise affect decision-making? Second, how can naturalness be understood in different cases? In what follows, I address both questions in relation to terraforming. First, I analyze in what sense terraformed Mars and its biosphere would be unnatural. Second, I examine whether its unnaturalness undermines the value of the biosphere, and thus give an important criterion for deciding whether humans should aim to terraform extraterrestrial environments or not.

The Unnaturalness of Terraformed Mars

The term natural is notoriously ambiguous. There are various ways how one can understand and use the concept. Due to this complexity, an argument from naturalness needs an amplification of the term 'natural' in play to be convincing (Siipi 2004). Therefore, in this section, I analyze, in what sense terraformed Mars could be deemed unnatural.

Helena Siipi (2008) identifies and distinguishes three forms of (un)naturalness which are 1) *History-based*, 2) *Property-based* and 3) *Relation-based* forms of (un)naturalness. Next, I examine how these different forms of (un)naturalness apply to the hypothetical case of engineering a biosphere on Mars.

History-Based (Un)naturalness

History-based forms of (un)naturalness are interested in the history and origin of an entity (Siipi 2008, 75). A relevant kind of interference in an entity's origin or history implies unnaturalness, while the lack of it indicates naturalness. Thus, if the genesis of an entity involves strong human involvement, then the entity is unnatural. A human-made dune is an example of an ecological entity that is unnatural according to history-based understanding. Even though an artificial dune might be almost identical to natural dunes, its history is different. It would not exist without humans.

Under the history-based understanding of (un)naturalness, a Martian biosphere after terraforming is clearly unnatural. Its origin involves a heavy-handed influence of humans; Mars would not have such an ecosphere at that time without the involvement of humans.

It should be noted that history-based (un)naturalness can be understood in at least two different ways depending on whether naturalness is seen as an all-or-nothing affair or as a continuous gradient (ibid., 78–83). In the context of history-based (un)naturalness, the all-or-nothing reading can be interpreted as total independence of humans. Thus, anything that is affected by human agency is unnatural. This understanding of (un)naturalness is not very useful for decision-making on Earth as almost everything would be unnatural according to it. On Earth, most, if not everything, is affected by humans to some extent, at least through pollution and climate change. Of course, outer space would still largely be natural as humans have not yet reached their influence there. Having that said, given that there are landers and rovers on the Martian surface, even Mars could not be labeled as natural according to a definition of (un) naturalness based on the total independence of humans.

The history-based (un)naturalness as an all-or-nothing affair can also be understood to refer to certain types of human interference in the history of an entity (ibid., 80). This means that not all human influence causes an entity to be unnatural. However, this interpretation does not tell us what kind of human interference contributes to something being (un)natural. Nevertheless, in the case of Mars, it seems reasonable to claim that when the first artificial object landed on Mars it did not turn its environment unnatural as this activity was not invasive enough. But terraforming would certainly be the type of human activity that would make the Martian environment unnatural. The scale of intervention is much larger with terraforming, and it also involves a sense of design to satisfy a human goal. Additionally, few landers or rovers do not fundamentally change the Martian environment, while terraforming would substantially do so.

If history-based (un)naturalness is interpreted as a continuous gradient, then it is accepted that the concept of (un)natural is not absolute. Instead, it exists along a continuum, where gradations of the concept can be observed (ibid.). According to this reading, we can say that an old-growth forest is more natural than a plantation forest. Similarly, we can argue that the current Martian environment is more natural than it would be after planetary ecosynthesis. This seems convincing and shows that in many cases (un)naturalness needs to be understood along a spectrum.

Property-Based (Un)naturalness

Property-based interpretation of (un)naturalness focuses on the current proper-ties of entities. For example, a genetically modified glow-in-the-dark rabbit is unnatural according to this understanding because it has features that rabbits do not normally have. With the property-based form of (un)naturalness, the history of an entity does not matter. To illustrate, imagine palm trees in a typical Finnish boreal forest. This forest patch would be unnatural regarding its properties because it has trees that are usually foreign to such forests, despite how they ended up there.

The relevant issue about the property-based interpretation of (un)naturalness is that it is always a question of comparison (Siipi 2008, 86). To determine whether an entity is natural, its current properties need to be compared with the properties of some entities considered to be ideally natural. This obviously raises the important question of what the ideal or relevant target of comparison in different cases is.

The same applies to terraformed Mars; what to compare it to? To Mars before planetary ecosynthesis? But Mars presumably does not currently have a biosphere so there is nothing to compare to. We could think about the whole planet Mars and say, compared to pre-terraformed Mars, features such as average temperature and atmospheric pressure have changed. But there is nothing unnatural about these higher temperatures and atmospheric pressures, as early Mars possibly had similar conditions. And most properties of Mars have not changed, such as its mass, rotation rate, obliquity, and location in the planetary system. So, should we compare it to the old warm and wetter Mars? The problem with this is that we do not know a lot about these early conditions. Thus, we encounter an impasse here, too.

One possibility is to compare to Earth's biosphere, as terraforming literally translates to *Earth shaping*. But why should we think that Earth's biosphere is in some sense ideally natural? It could be an ideally natural biosphere for Earth but from this, it does not follow that it is an ideally natural biosphere for Mars. The two planets are dissimilar at least concerning the amount of sunlight they receive and their gravity. These two properties are enough to affect the way life adapts to them, meaning that what is natural on Earth (in terms of biological adaptiveness) might not be natural on Mars (cf. ibid., 90).

Finally, we may try to compare the post-terraformed Martian biosphere to an imagined ideally natural Martian biosphere. However, this approach seems to beg the question of what a natural Martian biosphere looks like. Thus, I conclude that because of the planetary scale we are discussing, and because there is only one planet Mars, the property-based interpretation is not suitable for estimating the (un)naturalness of terraformed Mars. That is, the uniqueness of Mars renders statements about the unnaturalness of a Martian biosphere with respect to its properties nonsensical.

Relation-Based (Un)naturalness

Relation-based forms of (un)naturalness locate (un)naturalness in the relation between entities. A case in point is if someone finds an entity repugnant or they are unfamiliar with it and thus consider it unnatural. The repulsiveness or unfamiliarity is not a feature of the entity but rather a relation between it and the person (Siipi 2008, 76).

Robert Streiffer (2003) argues that unnaturalness can be understood in terms of a "yuck factor". The "yuck factor" refers to an experience of disgust and obnoxiousness raised by an entity. Even though we sometimes understand unnaturalness in terms of the emotions it raises in us, I believe we cannot consider terraformed Mars to be unnatural with respect to the "yuck factor". I suspect that on average people would not find the new Mars repugnant. On the other hand, one could be disgusted by the *activity* of terraforming. Perhaps terraforming exemplifies domination, disrespect, and other despicable attitudes towards nature, and hence the act of terraforming can be seen as unnatural.

Either way, I find it improbable that someone would find the final product of terraforming repugnant.

Unnaturalness can also be associated with unfamiliarity (Siipi 2008, 92). People often consider those entities natural that they are familiar with and accustomed to. According to this understanding, an entity is unnatural if those relevant to the case are unfamiliar with it. For example, some can find eating insect larvae unnatural because for them it is something odd while for others it might be perfectly natural because they are used to it.

Now the question is, would people find a terraformed Mars unnatural in this sense? We are indeed used to Mars as a cold, dusty, red planet, and thus the Martian biosphere could be unnatural according to this interpretation. Nevertheless, the process of terraforming would likely take so long that by the time it would be somewhat ready most people would be familiar with the idea of a terraformed Mars. And, to be honest, the Martian environment is something current humans are not familiar with in a more phenomenological sense.[1] Therefore, I doubt that unnaturalness as unfamiliarity is a strong candidate for the possible unnaturalness of terraformed Mars.

Interestingly, Mars after planetary ecosynthesis can be seen as more natural for humans compared to the current Martian environment according to the relation-based (un)naturalness. To see this, consider food. We might say that grass is natural food for cows, but it is unnatural for humans as we do not get necessary nutrients from it. Similarly, the Martian environment is hostile to human health, meaning it is unnatural. In contrast, terraformed Mars would be more natural for humans because we could operate there without pressure suits, using only oxygen masks. With enough time, we could possibly even give up oxygen masks when an adequate amount of oxygen has accumulated in the atmosphere. This reading of (un)naturalness relates to a third understanding of relation-based (un)naturalness: something is natural if it is good for beings relevant to the case (i.e., satisfies their needs or makes them flourish) and something is unnatural if it is bad for them (ibid., 93–95).

Commonly, things can be unnatural in more than one way. However, according to my analysis, a terraformed Mars and its biosphere are unnatural mainly in the history-based interpretation of (un)naturalness, with the exception that the *act* of terraforming can possibly be seen as unnatural according to relation-based (un)naturalness. In the following section, I discuss the normative implications of these findings.

Is an Unnatural Biosphere Any Less Valuable?

History-based naturalness can be a normatively important concept and sometimes we have reasons to value, in reference to the history of an entity, natural entities over unnatural ones. Origin stories and the history of an entity give meaning and thus bring value to us. The same applies to naturalness in environmental ethics. Indeed, the causal genesis of boglands, erratic boulders, fjords, and such can be significant in establishing their value. Therefore, we may be skeptical towards ecological restoration and engineering because often we are *replacing* natural ecological systems with artificial ones and thus losing something in between.

Despite all of this, naturalness does not always have the normative punch it is hoped to have. In many cases, it does not matter (normatively speaking) whether something is natural or unnatural. For example, in vitro fertilization may be considered to be an unnatural aspect in the history of a child, thus implicating that a "test-tube baby" is unnatural. Even though such newborns can be considered unnatural according to some superficial understanding, it does not mean that we have any good reasons to disvalue this child over some other child conceived through coitus.

Now we turn to another example closer to the case of terraforming. It has been suggested that abiogenesis did not occur on Earth but instead primordial life could have been deliberately transmitted to Earth by an early extra-terrestrial civilization. This *directed panspermia hypothesis* was originally presented by Francis Crick and Leslie Orgel (1973). According to this hypothesis, there is a possibility that early life was sent to Earth by ancient extraterrestrials. In theory, this is possible because our galaxy is old enough that civilizations capable of directed panspermia could have existed at the time when Earth was still in formation.[2] Taking inspiration from this hypothesis, suppose we discover that primordial life, which led to the terrestrial biosphere we know today, was seeded by intelligent aliens. Then, we would have to conclude that our biosphere is unnatural in the history-based understanding of the notion.[3] Would this also mean that the value of Earth's biosphere is less? I presume not. The immense value of our living planet would at best be only trivially diminished by the fact that Earth's biosphere did not originate from spontaneous evolution alone. This intuition is echoed even by Elliot (1982, 87), who is a critic of ecological restoration. Elliot writes:

> Artificially transforming an utterly barren, ecologically bankrupt landscape into something richer and more subtle may be a good thing. That is a view quite compatible with the belief that replacing a rich natural environment with a rich artificial one is a bad thing.

As a further point, let me call attention to the fact that many considered colonized lands as primitive wilderness, i.e., natural. In reality, those lands were the home of someone else. Indigenous people in places like America and Australia had been managing and impacting nature for millennia before Europeans landed there. Related to this, John O'Neill et al. (2008, 134) have pointed out that:

> the appropriate response to a recognition of the role of indigenous peoples in shaping the US and Australasian landscapes is surely not to infer that these landscapes do not have the value that we thought they had. Rather it should be to develop a different account of the value that they do have.

That said, even though an artificial biosphere would lack the value of having living systems that originate from evolution alone and without any human modification, still many other sources of value do remain: the value of the creatures living there, the value of intact ecosystems, the many sources of instrumental value, and so on (cf. Attfield 1994, 53). Also, natural spontaneity, creativity, and wildness would emerge if the organisms and ecosystems on Mars would at some point be left to interact with themselves without strong human management. The goals for planetary engineering could be general and rather vague. Then even on terraformed Mars plenty of wildness and forces of nature beyond human control could be found (cf. Vogel 2003, 159–163). McKay and Margarita Marinova (2001, 105) argue similarly:

> While lifeforms from Earth might be introduced to Mars in a controlled and prescribed way, this does not imply that the resulting ecological systems will develop as predicted. In fact, they are unlikely to do so. As life on Mars interacts with itself and the changing Martian environment, it will follow an independent evolutionary trajectory that will be difficult or impossible to control. This is not a problem and, in fact, should be considered an asset.

But do our goals for terraforming make any significant difference? At least one interesting difference can be linked to Katz's (1993, 223–224) statement that not all intentional creations are artifacts, such as children and friendship. Building on this claim, Steve Vogel (2003, 158–159) suggests that restoration projects can be grouped into the same category as human infants. For him, they both are entities that, despite being intentionally created, have their own internal nature, and they do not exist for the sake of their creators but instead to follow themselves as self-directing systems. Katz's (2012, 81) response to this argument is that the comparison is untruthful. According to him, restoration projects tend to have very specific goals in mind and concrete ideas of the type of ecosystems intended to be created. The same is not true for parents planning to have children. According to Katz (ibid., 83), if parents have any goals for their children, "they are quite general and rather vague: may they be healthy, happy, and productive, perhaps". Hence, Vogel's comparison fails in Katz's eyes. Yet, even if the comparison between restoration projects and children is not convincing in Katz's terms, it looks like a comparison between planetary ecosynthesis and children may pass. Our goals for planetary engineering could be more general and vaguer compared to restoration projects. Perhaps our goal could be something like *may Mars have a biosphere that sustains complex life*. Then post-terraformed biospheres would be less of an artifact compared to many restored ecosystems, and similarly, its value would be harder to question.

On Earth, ecological engineering can be the cause of "ontological impoverishment" because natural nature is replaced with an artificial one, and thus a connection to the long natural history regarding that entity is lost.[4] By contrast, in the Martian environment (supposedly abiotic), planetary engineering could be better described as "ontological enrichment". Consider a thought experiment in the form of an analogy between the Red Planet and a lifeless rock. Suppose we place moss spores on a sterile rock and the spores grow into moss habiting the surface of the rock. Have we now lost or destroyed something? Or is the value of the rock now less? It is not obviously so. The rock and its natural history are still there; how it ended up in that location and how it got its geological properties. We have simply added a layer of life that after its genesis forms its own history in a connection with the rock. The discussion in this section and the thought experiment is aimed to show how our conception of nature is deeply terrestrial and tied to the understanding of nature as something living. But our intuitions about (un)naturalness get challenged in outer space and environments completely devoid of life.

What I claim here is that it seems that in the case of establishing a biosphere on Mars the concept of unnaturalness cannot *by itself* play a significant normative role (even though it can be a factor among others in ethical deliberation). Instead, when considering terraforming we must ask other (difficult) questions such as, what value does the abiotic nature of Mars have? Would terraforming ruin this value? Should we value biotic and abiotic nature on par? What is lost in the process of terraforming and how does that balance with what is gained in it? There is no room to investigate these questions here, but what this chapter has done was to pinpoint the relevant and crucial questions when it comes to ecological engineering beyond Earth.

There is still to consider the possibility of seeing the *act* of terraforming as unnatural. Recall that in the previous section I argued that someone could be disgusted by terraforming because it possibly demonstrates negative domination and other objectionable attitudes towards nature. The idea of domination and disrespect hints toward a plausibly strong argument against terraforming: planetary engineering is wrong because in doing so we fail to respect nature. However, even if we assume that there is a duty to respect nature, it remains unclear whether the same duty extends to inanimate nature, and in the case of Mars to its landscapes. The question then is: can lifeless nature be negatively dominated or disrespected? I believe the answer to this is yes. If someone blows a mountain or the Moon up into pieces, it seems clear that they have dominated and disrespected nature. Nevertheless, there is still room to question whether terraforming is necessarily an equivalent case. After all, terraforming does not destroy Mars or its landscape in a very concrete sense. Instead, it alters the atmospheric conditions and introduces life to the planet. Once again, we reach similar questions about the value and place of abiotic nature in our ethical thinking.

There may be many good reasons why we should not terraform Mars any time soon, or perhaps ever. The pristine environment of Mars has significant scientific value. This alone gives us strong reasons not to spoil the Martian environment, at least for long enough to have sufficiently studied it (e.g., Schwartz 2019). Furthermore, the Martian environment may have noteworthy intrinsic value in its current state that terraforming would ruin (e.g., Lee 1994; Lindquist 2022). But, as we have seen, establishing this is challenging due to Mars being abiotic. That said, I do not support terraforming plans for now. However, what I do argue is that the unnaturalness related to terraformed Mars does not remarkably discount the value of its biosphere. Hence, naturalness *in itself* cannot provide a strong argument against planetary ecosynthesis.

Conclusion

In this chapter, I have explored planetary engineering from the perspective of the concept of (un)naturalness using terraformed Mars as an example. First, I have argued that a Martian biosphere would be unnatural mainly in the history-based sense of (un)naturalness where (un)naturalness is seen on a continuum. In addition, I pointed out that perhaps the *act* of terraforming could be considered unnatural according to the relation-based understanding of (un)naturalness if terraforming is seen as repulsive. Following this, I discussed whether this unnaturalness provides grounds to value the artificial biosphere less and thus reasons against terraforming. I argued that on closer inspection the concept of unnaturalness *in itself* does not have a strong normative force because Mars is supposedly abiotic, and the origin of the biosphere is largely irrelevant regarding its value. Instead, the crucial questions related to planetary ecosynthesis were found to culminate in the value of abiotic nature and to the fate of this value after terraforming.

Acknowledgements

I thank Helena Siipi, Christopher J. Preston, Mikko M. Puumala, Olivia Mörck, Kirsi Lehto and those who offered helpful comments at the 4th biannual meeting of The Society for Social and Conceptual Issues in Astrobiology (SSoCIA) at the University of Mississippi and at the Nordic Environmental Ethics NSU Summer Symposium 2021. I am also grateful to the editors. This chapter was written with the support of the Maj and Tor Nessling Foundation.

Notes

1 There may be a possibility to gain experiential knowledge about the Martian environment without traveling there. This could be done through images, videos, audio, or virtual reality mediating experiences of the Red Planet. However, it seems that current experiences are not immersive and vivid enough to provide rich and authentic experiential knowledge. Whether in the future such experiences can be provided, so that they would make Mars feel unfamiliar after terraforming, remains an open question.
2 This theory has generated discussion about how interstellar planetary seeding could be carried out in practice and whether humanity should engage in such an effort. On the question of whether humanity should spread life to other star systems, see Sivula (2022).
3 One could claim that in the directed panspermia case, Earth's biosphere would be *natural* because its genesis does not involve *human* interference and it is specifically human interference in the origin of an entity that makes it unnatural. I am not convinced with this response because it seems *ad hoc*. What is it about humans particularly that needs to be so sharply separated from the rest of nature? I suspect it is not our biology but sophisticated technology or a high level of intentionality and design that is relevant. Thus, if beavers cultivated land, and built highly complex shelters and dams with sophisticated technology, that would be unnatural, just as it would be unnatural if extraterrestrials used interstellar probes to seed life.
4 One way to think about the value of naturalness is to say that natural entities are valuable because they are rare. On Earth, it is increasingly difficult to find areas with no or little human influence. But in the vastness of space naturalness is not really a scarce resource. However, one could argue that an unspoiled Martian environment is in danger of becoming rare in *our* solar system.

References

Attfield, R 1994, 'Rehabilitating nature and making nature habitable', *Royal Institute of Philosophy Supplements*, vol. 36, pp. 45–57.

Crick, FH & Orgel, LE 1973, 'Directed panspermia', *Icarus*, vol. 19, no. 3, pp. 341–346.

Elliot, R 1982, 'Faking nature', *Inquiry*, vol. 25, no. 1, pp. 81–93.

Graham, JM 2004, 'The biological terraforming of Mars: Planetary ecosynthesis as ecological succession on a global scale', *Astrobiology*, vol. 4, no. 2, pp. 168–195.

Greene, J 2014, 'Beyond point-and-shoot morality: Why cognitive (neuro)science matters for ethics', *Ethics*, vol. 124, no. 4, pp. 695–726.

Jakosky, BM & Edwards, CS 2018, 'Inventory of CO_2 available for terraforming Mars', *Nature Astronomy*, vol. 2, no. 8, pp. 634–639.

Katz, E 1991, 'Restoration and redesign: The ethical significance of human intervention in nature', *Restoration & Management Notes*, vol. 9, no. 2, pp. 90–96.

Katz, E 1992, 'The call of the wild: The struggle against domination and the technological fix of nature', *Environmental Ethics*, vol. 14, no. 3, pp. 265–273.

Katz, E 1993, 'Artefacts and functions: A note on the value of nature', *Environmental Values*, vol. 2, no. 3, pp. 223–232.

Katz, E 2012, 'Further adventures in the case against restoration', *Environmental Ethics*, vol. 34, no. 1, pp. 67–97.

Lee, K 1994, 'Awe and humility: Intrinsic value in nature. Beyond an earthbound environmental ethics', *Royal Institute of Philosophy Supplement*, vol. 36, pp. 89–101.

Lee, K 1999, *The Natural and the Artefactual: The Implications of Deep Science and Deep Technology for Environmental Philosophy*, Lexington books, Lanham.

Lindquist, MA 2022, 'Astroethics and the non-fungibility thesis', *Environmental Ethics*, vol. 44, no. 3, pp. 221–246.

McKay, CP 2009, 'Planetary ecosynthesis on Mars: Restoration ecology and environmental ethics', in CM Bertka (ed), *Exploring the Origin, Extent, and Future of Life*, Cambridge University Press, New York, pp. 245–260.

McKay, CP & Marinova, MM 2001, 'The physics, biology, and environmental ethics of making Mars habitable', *Astrobiology*, vol. 1, no. 1, pp. 89–109.

McKay, CP, Toon, OB & Kasting, JF 1991, 'Making Mars habitable', *Nature*, vol. 352, no. 6335, pp. 489–496.

Milligan, T 2014, *Nobody Owns the Moon: The Ethics of Space Exploitation*, McFarland & Company, Jefferson.

O'Neill, J, Holland, A & Light, A 2008, *Environmental Values*, Routledge, London.

Preston, CJ 2011, 'Re-thinking the unthinkable: Environmental ethics and the presumptive argument against geoengineering', *Environmental Values*, vol. 20, no. 4, pp. 457–479.

Schwartz, JSJ 2019, 'Space settlement: What's the Rush?', *Futures*, vol. 110, pp. 56–59.

Siipi, H 2004, 'Naturalness in biological conservation', *Journal of Agricultural and Environmental Ethics*, vol. 17, no. 6, pp. 457–477.

Siipi, H 2008, 'Dimensions of naturalness' *Ethics and the Environment*, vol. 13, no. 1, pp. 71–103.

Sivula, O 2022, 'The cosmic significance of directed panspermia: Should humanity spread life to other solar systems?', *Utilitas*, vol. 34, no. 2, pp. 178–194.

Streiffer, R 2003, 'In defense of the moral relevance of species boundaries', *American Journal of Bioethics*, vol. 3, no. 3, pp. 37–38.

Vogel, S 2003, 'The nature of artifacts', *Environmental Ethics*, vol. 25, no. 2, pp. 149–168.

14

IN SPACE THERE IS NO STATUS QUO

Space Communities as Social Experimentation Regarding Reproduction and Kinship

Evie Kendal

Introduction

Family-making is a culturally cherished and diverse human experience but one that is both influenced by socio-political agendas and often fraught with assumptions and hierarchical judgments. Even as broad social support for different family structures increases throughout the world, including for same-sex parents, mixed families, and single-parent households (Furstenberg et al., 2020), heteropatriarchal gender norms in reproduction and childrearing have proven highly resistant to change. As Linda Rae Bennett (2018) notes, "[r]eproductive desires are inextricably linked with both biological and social reproduction" with assisted reproductive technologies (ARTs) creating whole new "emergent biological possibilities" (p. 101). Nevertheless, ARTs have often been used to reinforce, rather than challenge, dominant cis- and heteronormative social structures through prioritizing (at least the appearance of) biogenetic relationships and patrilineal inheritance. New concepts of kinship and connectedness are certainly being actively explored and negotiated in many families using ARTs, but patterns of use, especially in the West, still demonstrate a bias toward the supposed ideal of the biologically related nuclear family model (Furstenberg et al., 2020). These biases manifest both in hetero- and homo-parental reproductive endeavors, and in single-parent and multiple co-parent arrangements (Delaunay, 2019). One possible reason for the pervasiveness of these cultural norms about family-making are historical assumptions about kinship, which assumes biological relatedness as the basis for familial relationships. Considering how a human space settlement might navigate the issue of family creation highlights a unique opportunity for reconceptualizing and legitimizing different models of reproduction and uses of ARTs outside of the existing status quo. As there currently are no families in space, any re-inscribing

DOI: 10.4324/9781003374381-14

of existing assumptions represents a choice. It is important to remember that we can make other choices.

This chapter will consider how a space community might arrange itself in terms of family units and childrearing, including the potential role of existing and emerging reproductive biotechnologies to support long-term human off-world habitation. The absence of existing expectations regarding reproduction in space communities means they can serve as experimental sites for new family organization systems. In so doing, they can also provide critical examinations of existing social and family paradigms on Earth. To explore this potential, this chapter will begin by considering where gametes might be sourced for off-world human reproduction, what genetic alterations to offspring might be justified in light of the extreme conditions of living in space, what methods of gestation might be suitable for an off-world settlement, and how resultant offspring could be socially cared for.

Sourcing Gametes and the Role of Biogenetic Relationships

In discussing what they label the "normative folk model of kinship" in America, Becker et al. (2005) claim immense significance is given to so-called "blood" relationships (p. 1301). This is often demonstrated through "resemblance talk," where evidence of biological relationships is sought through identifying shared physical traits believed to be the result of an assumed "genetic link between parent and child" and other members of the extended family (p. 1301). This resemblance supposedly legitimizes the child's place in the family and works to construct their identity with reference to their genetic ancestry. According to these authors, resemblance talk is "everyday talk," but its centering of biogenetic connections can be a source of anxiety for parents using ARTs involving donated gametes (p. 1306). In these cases, the lack of a genetic connection between the child and one or more of the commissioning parents can be stigmatizing and may motivate some prospective parents to select donors who share their phenotypic characteristics to obscure the presence of the third-party donor in the reproductive project. In many jurisdictions, matching of donors for appearance – e.g. skin, eye, and hair color – is encouraged or required, including in Portugal, France, Spain, Norway, Finland, and the USA (Delaunay, 2019, p. 385; Maung, 2018, p. 112; Nordqvist, 2010). It is noteworthy that in some jurisdictions this privileging of physical resemblance when selecting gametes for use in ARTs is being challenged. Hane Htut Maung (2018) relates that the UK's Human Fertilisation and Embryology Authority's (HFEA) *Code of Practice* (2003) required fertility clinics to attempt donor matching for physical characteristics and ethnic backgrounds, while its 2014 revision removed this requirement, allowing prospective parents to accept donors from different ethnic backgrounds, subject to the standard child welfare assessments involved in accessing ARTs (p. 112). He claims the practice of ethnic donor matching can promote problematic and stereotypical views of different groups, with

Pavone (2015) noting in Ecuador in particular, the "whitening" of the higher social classes has been facilitated by their enhanced access to ARTs and selection of "whiter" donors (p. 112). Thus, ARTs have allowed for the further concentration of certain phenotypic traits and their social capital among the more advantaged members of society, while also potentially feeding into the prejudices leading to discrimination against other groups. It has also been noted in the literature that ethnic matching for people of color is often limited, with "any form of non-whiteness" considered interchangeable in many fertility clinics (Newman, 2019, p. 713). This demonstrates that such policies and practices are not neutral or simply catering to isolated individuals and their personal preferences, but rather have the potential to significantly alter the phenotypic makeup of a population and exacerbate existing inequalities on the basis of racial appearance. For a new human habitation off-world, the impact of even small interventions into the available gene pool are likely to have substantial effects on the fledgling population.

Catarina Delaunay (2019) notes that in heterosexual couples, keeping a gamete donor anonymous allows for the "illusion that the social parents are the biological parents," (p. 390) – an illusion all the more readily supported when the donor resembles the non-biological parent. Alyssa M. Newman (2019) claims this kind of donor matching among heterosexual users of ARTs is intended to mask the presence of the donor gametes and allow offspring "to 'pass' as biogenetically related" (p. 712). This may be particularly desirable in a culture where blood relations are prioritized over social relationships. Maung (2018) claims a "great deal of value" is placed on physical resemblances between parents and children "as a mark of the 'normal' family," noting such a benchmark is "often uncritically assumed to be biologically grounded" despite there being many other ways a child may resemble their parents (p. 113). Sven Bergmann (2011) further claims the Euro-American kinship ideal is "first and foremost articulated by resemblance through blood lines or chromosomal information," leading to the creation of a "new gendered job market for migrants" to service the growing transnational fertility industry seeking donor matched gametes (pp. 285–286). Of resemblance talk he states: "addressing a newborn and commenting on his or her looks are guided by commonsense knowledge, through which everyone becomes an expert in applying Mendelian inheritance laws" (p. 286). Donor matching and anonymity thus both serve "a culture of disguise by substituting and simulating biogenetic inheritance and relatedness" (p. 286). Although beyond the scope of the current discussion, in many cultures, biogenetic inheritance is also directly related to a child's social, religious, and economic position in society, with ARTs having a potentially destabilizing effect among groups that privilege patrilineal kinship models, including many Middle Eastern cultural groups who Inhorn et al. (2017) note have traditionally viewed biological paternity as superior to social fatherhood (p. 47).

The primacy of biogenetic relationships is also evidenced among homosexual couples accessing ARTs, with Delaunay (2019) reporting that the lesbian couples in her study were most likely to pursue "both women getting pregnant, one at a time, from the same sperm donor," to create genetic links between the offspring and more secure legal parenthood for both mothers (pp. 390–391). In other words, the siblings will resemble each other due to their shared genetic father, while each mother retains a genetic relationship to at least one of their children, which is expected to protect them from certain legal challenges. Delaunay (2019) also relates: "Moreover, clinics in Spain match the physical characteristics of the sperm donor with those of the non-birth mother in order to create the semblance of a genetically related two-parent family" (pp. 390–391). Thus, even when the traditional biogenetic relationship is known to be absent, its simulacrum may be actively pursued.

When situated within existing Earth cultures, the traditional biogenetic relationship between parents and children – or its facsimile – has proven to be highly resistant to change. This has led to social impacts, such as racial discrimination, as well as population-based impacts, such as reducing the overall diversity of genetic mixes produced in human societies. While the impact of these individual and cultural choices may be obscured against the backdrop of accepted cultural norms, they can be foregrounded by considering how kinship structures can and should be constructed in future off-world communities that are not beholden to these existing expectations. When considering our future human off-world settlement, transporting a small number of grown humans alongside a large supply of embryos is likely to be the most cost-efficient and effective method of growing a genetically diverse space community. The extensive resources required to sustain human life during space exploration mean limiting the initial crew would be essential for mission feasibility. These adults would be responsible for setting up the facilities and raising the next generation of off-world inhabitants. However, this would require that this fledgling community abandon the privileging of biogenetic relationships in family creation, as most offspring would not be genetically related to the social parents who would raise them. Functionally, all families could thus be considered adoptive and blended. The possibility of phenotypic and ethnic matching would also likely be limited if the goal were preserving genetic diversity and avoiding a founder effect in the human settlement, where insufficient founding members lead to a loss of genetic variability in the population and increased risk of genetic disease inheritance due to inbreeding (Rotimi, 2023).

Despite the social shift this would involve away from heteropatriarchal models, there is no reason to assume a community whose family structures are not built on biogenetic relationships – either real or assumed – would materially suffer. Despite the pervasive role of the traditional biogenetic inheritance model in Earth-based use of ARTs, models for elevating social over biological ties in reproduction can also be found in many families on Earth, including in same-sex parent households, and mixed and adoptive families. These exceptions could furnish useful guidance for promoting alternative family structures in space. Furstenberg et al. (2020) note research on same-sex unions demonstrate "kinship is a malleable construct with exceptional capacity to encompass differences and deviations" (p. 1413). These authors also note that "[t]he literature suggests adoptive families have familial bonds as strong or stronger than those in nonadoptive families" (p. 1417). For our hypothetical space society, candidates could be selected based on their acceptance of diverse models of family connectedness or willingness to be educated and embrace such perspectives. Such selection processes are already used by many adoption agencies on Earth when screening prospective parents, to ensure children are placed with the families best suited to accept and support them. A couple that demonstrated they prioritized biological relationships (or their appearance) over other forms of kinship would likely be less attractive candidates. However, it's important to recognize where these preferences might come from. Petra Nordqvist (2010) claims that when lesbian couples engage in donor matching such that physical similarities help legitimize them as the "natural" parents, they are seeking access to the "cultural and social power that lies in a discourse of the 'natural' family" (p. 1140). However, this discourse is contextually bound and need not be reproduced in our off-world settlement. In other words, we can choose not to default to the status quo in Western society where the hierarchy of biogenetic relatedness would name a sperm donor the "real" father of a child he has had no social role in parenting (Wheatley, 2019, p. 142). Resemblance talk can either be rejected as a social practice in this new society or replaced with non-biological examples, such as gestures or mannerisms picked up through association with the social parents and family unit.

Another consideration is whether emulating the traditional nuclear family yields any benefits for an off-world society. Furstenberg et al. (2020) note this model of domestic organization only gained popularity in the West at the end of the 19th century and has never been the preferred configuration of the family unit in many low- and middle-income countries (p. 1405). These authors claim that despite "an ever-declining portion of the population resid[ing] in two-biological-parent households," the nuclear family still represents an ideal for many Western communities (p. 1405). However, they also note that stepfamilies, for example, can forge "a common identity" in much the same way as biologically related families, even if this often takes more conscious effort (p. 1409). The existence of diverse family models and other social changes are already challenging the supremacy of the nuclear family on Earth, but a space settlement is well positioned to expedite its dissolution by supporting wholly alternative family structures. Indeed, alternative models of kinship may lend themselves more readily to this context, including what Furstenberg et al. (2020) call *situational* kinship – the bonds that form when people share a particular setting. These authors separate these into marginalized settings, such as living on the streets; institutional settings, like prisons and schools; and organizational settings, such as workplaces (pp. 1419–1420). The harshness of living in space will incorporate characteristics of many of these settings, and to be successful, residents will need to arrange themselves into a functional social unit – a chosen family of sorts. Communal raising of the settlement's children might fit well within such a social structure, due to the general lack of resources expected in an early off-world setting, although it is possible some members will prefer a more traditional household arrangement. The additional considerations for gestating and raising a large number of biologically unrelated offspring will be considered in later sections of this chapter.

Genetic Engineering of Offspring for Adaptation to Space

Establishing a society where the majority of children are not conceived "naturally" also introduces the possibility of selecting or manipulating their genetic characteristics. This might be ethically justified on the grounds that humans are not evolutionarily adapted to live in space and this environment will be hostile to the survival of offspring (Szocik and Wójtowicz, 2019). Many of the ethical objections to genetic selection or engineering of human embryos lose at least some of their weight when applied to the off-world setting. For example, those debates that suggest selecting for desirable characteristics, such as height, mean a child is not unconditionally wanted and instead being reduced to a series of traits, are less convincing when the "desired trait" is survivability. While some degree of genetic essentialism may still be in play, selecting for radiation resistance, low oxygen and pressure tolerance, or higher bone and muscle density are best understood as minimally compensating for some of the natural disadvantage of being in the space environment, rather than as methods of conferring super-human abilities (Szocik and Wójtowicz, 2019). The common concern about shifting the bar for normal or average traits – the so-called genetic arms race – is also less prominent in the confined setting of the off-world community, where Szocik et al. (2019) state any "acquired advantages just might barely counteract comparable threats" (p. 73). Assuming a reality in which the significance of biogenetic relationships has already been diminished, ethical objections regarding the risk of genetic selection perpetuating racial stereotypes will also have reduced impact. For example, if "whiteness" cannot be passed down to one's offspring through genetic relatedness, and resemblance is not a factor when allocating children to prospective parents, the potential for skin tone to consolidate power in one family group over another is likely to deteriorate, the same with height, attractiveness, athleticism, and a host of other traits that currently confer social capital.

Another consideration that arises in the literature regarding gamete donation relates to the value of genetic information for offspring. It is generally assumed prospective parents have a duty to select a "healthy" donor, all other things being equal, but Newman (2019) notes there are also increasing social pressures to select one who will contribute to the "future child's identity and narrative of self," representing a "penetration of genetic knowledge into social life" (p. 712). This includes access to genetic medical histories, predispositions, and health risks and "using knowledge of personal genetics to inform connection, and a sense of responsibility to, a broader biosocial community" (p. 711). Newman

(2019) claims that the new biocitizenship favors those who have knowledge of their genetic makeup, and "[i]f being a 'good' parent entails taking advantage of every possible opportunity to ensure a child's success," securing this information for the child becomes a moral imperative (p. 714). In a context where genetic selection and/or engineering has been used to create a population better adapted to life in space, such information will be automatically available as it would have been documented during the selection process. This will also be important for maximizing genetic diversity in future generations of offspring by avoiding any consanguineous unions (e.g. genetic siblings raised in different families having biological children together and risking certain genetic diseases in their offspring).

Julian Savulescu's (2007) "procreative beneficence" argument assumes a duty to provide future children with the highest likelihood of a good life so resonates particularly well as a defense for genetically modifying offspring for survival advantage in space. Given that an off-world settlement is likely to be highly restrictive on children, any adaptation that can reduce this burden would be highly desirable, and by some arguments, morally obligatory. Genetic engineering could be seen to alleviate the suffering of future generations of space-faring humans by altering the genes responsible for thermal regulation, metabolic efficiency, musculoskeletal development, and organ function, to name a few (Kendal, 2020). This in turn would reduce the need for other protective measures, including external protective gear and pharmaceutical interventions. It would also reduce injuries and illnesses among the space community and thus contribute to the overall flourishing of the settlement.

Gestating the Offspring of the Space Settlement

Transporting a large number of embryos will be easier than transporting grown humans to populate our settlement. However, these embryos will still need to be gestated. If only a small number of adults are transported off-world for feasibility reasons, and only some of these are physiologically fertile cis-gendered women, there will be limited access to biological wombs to provide gestational services. Furthermore, the necessity for all original crewmembers to contribute to the establishment of the settlement means pregnancy and childbirth will represent a significant cost and an alternative for biological gestation may be needed. While it is likely some physiologically fertile settlers will want to gestate naturally, the additional risks and burdens of pregnancy in an off-world environment make this an ideal setting for the use of emerging artificial gestational technologies. There are also various ethical issues with any attempt to select *for* reproductive capacity and desire, as such methods are likely to be discriminatory and potentially coercive (e.g. excluding infertile people or pressuring candidates to go through with family plans they may no longer want) (Kendal, 2023). Nevertheless, as a practical concern, with a small initial crew pregnancy-related morbidity and mortality is likely to severely impact productivity, as well as carry significant risks to pregnant people and fetuses. As such, the acceptable risk threshold for attempting artificial gestation may be lower in space than it currently is on Earth, due to the unknown impacts of microgravity on fetal development and the increased radiation risks making biological gestation high-risk (Kendal, 2022). An artificial system for gestating fetuses off-world could be maintained in a protected environment with enhanced radiation shielding and thermal controls that might be difficult to achieve for an organic womb. At least in the early days, the risk profiles of organic versus artificial gestation may be sufficiently similar, or equally unknown, to achieve ethical equipoise, a.k.a. the genuine uncertainty regarding clinical outcomes that justifies the inherent risks of medical experimentation. Thus, some of the major objections to artificial gestation on Earth already do not apply to the space context, such as the fact that we have a proven safe method of growing fetuses and thus it would be unethical to replace this with an unproven technology. We currently lack clinical knowledge of off-world pregnancy safety, and it may well be that artificial gestation is the safer option.

Concerns about confused kinship are also less compelling in a scenario in which the biological and social aspects of parenthood are more clearly separated. ARTs are already challenging assumptions about biological motherhood, with Jenny Gunnarsson Payne (2016) noting they represent a threat to the traditional Roman legal principle *"mater semper certa est* (the mother is always certain),"* which previously assumed an unassailable parental right for birth mothers (p. 484). She continues: "it is no longer self-evident that the birth mother should be defined as a child's biological mother; in fact, it is no longer obvious what biological motherhood really *is*," suggesting options such as shared bloodstreams, the provision of nutrition, genetic relatedness, and "epigenetic influences taking place within the womb" (p. 484). Most of these candidates would be absent in the case of artificial gestation, where nutrition is provided intravenously and there is no placental blood exchange with the mother.

Even if there is initial resistance to artificial gestation, the history of ARTs suggests appeals to necessity and reproductive desire will smooth the way for this technology if it can be proven useful for establishing the human settlement. Bob Simpson (2013) notes that appeals to sympathy for the involuntarily childless have "ushered in wide and surprising levels of acceptance of new forms of intervention in reproductive processes as well as novel forms of substitution and artificiality" (p. S91). Artificial gestation merely represents one end of this spectrum. While current prototypes around the world are focused on saving prematurely born infants by allowing them to continue their fetal development in a fluid-filled environment (Kingma and Finn, 2020), advances in so-called partial ectogenesis have immediate relevance to the development of a fully extrauterine method of gestation for off-world use.

Other benefits of developing artificial gestation for our settlement include that it would remove the impetus to preferentially select physiologically and socially fertile settlers, therefore removing a source of discrimination and promoting diversity among the initial crew. This would allow room to select candidates based on a wider variety of more salient skills and traits. It would also allow for rapid population growth without loss of workers to pregnancy-related illness. If engaging a communal model of childrearing, the community could also raise a much larger number of children at one time than could be achieved using individual domestic units or if relying on biological gestation.

Social Parenting in the Off-World Setting

Becker et al. (2005) relate that for many parents using ARTs, they "want their families to be considered normal and their children to be viewed in light of their own uniqueness and not by whether they resemble other family members" (p. 1308). By establishing a cultural norm for our space settlement in which children are not expected to biologically resemble their parents, many different parenting options gain equal validity. In her study of homosexual couples, Delaunay (2019) found one of two responses when it came to gamete donors – detachment operations, where the donor was excluded from the family concept; and bonding efforts, where the donor was actively included in the "personal story" of the child's creation (p. 383). The genetic relationship is the same in both instances, but the social construction of parenthood is different. There is an opportunity in our off-world settlement to trial new models of parenthood and ways of incorporating third-party contributions into the resultant child's personal narrative. Just as some gay couples extend their child's kinship network to include a surrogate mother and her extended connections (Delaunay, 2019), so can we develop a community that is not bound by biogenetic assumptions and demands regarding biological gestation.

Eliza Garwood (2023) notes members of the LGBTIQ+ community are already adept at constructing new kinship narratives that incorporate both positive and negative aspects of their personal history, such as the prevalence of discrimination against the community and rejection by biological family (p. 36). In many cases there is a focus on emotional connectedness and intentionality that transcends any biogenetic relatedness. Furstenberg et al. (2020) note research on the children of such unions indicate they can successfully "deconstruct the normative centrality of biogenetic connections," and develop their own model of family (p. 1414). There is no reason to believe the genetically unrelated, artificially gestated children of our future space settlement will fail to achieve the same. When it comes to the parents in our space community, Chiaki Shirai (2019) notes that in studies of donor insemination in the US, the father's commitment to parenthood bore more relevance to the father–child relationship than any genetic relationship (p. 301). The same rationale must apply in our space context with intentional parenthood outstripping any biological connections. While ARTs have often served to promote conservative, heteronormative ideals of family, they can also radically destabilize kinship norms, gender roles, caring duties, and concepts of family (McKinnon, 2015; Taguchi and

Majumdar, 2021). These concepts often include assertions that "genetic links" are not essential to family formation, and that biological and social parents are equally important (Raes et al., 2014). This reconceptualization of existing reproductive norms also opens up the possibility of new co-parenting arrangements that go beyond the single or two-parent standard models. With the large potential number of children growing up together, it may very well take a space village to raise them all.

Further Considerations

While they fall beyond the scope of this chapter, there are various areas for future research that are necessary before the proposed space community can progress to achieve its goal of establishing desirable alternatives for kinship structures adapted to the contemporary off-world setting. One includes how to demonstrate respect for cultural diversity in family creation processes that are more firmly linked to biological relatedness. In other words, recognizing that abandoning biogenetic hierarchies may be more challenging – or some may even claim implausible – for some cultural groups. Kirsten Lovelock (2010) provides the example of Māori adoption practices in New Zealand, where biological kinship is considered of primary importance when placing a child (p. 130). Similarly, Bennett (2018) notes that in Indonesia, biological relatedness is a highly prized form of "kin-group capital," unlikely to be replaceable with other modes of family-making and connected to the cultural need to have children raised in the same religion they were "born into" (pp. 102, 110). Simpson (2013) also relates the unique multiple paternity systems protected under Sinhalese indigenous (Kandyan) law, which were displaced by colonialism and the introduction of "definitions of 'illegitimacy' derived from the ancient Roman concept of *patria potestas*" (pp. S88–S89). Such traditional views of kinship are reasserting themselves in the context of gamete donations, providing a "vernacular model for copaternity" not supported by previous Westernized models of anonymous donation (p. S89). Inhorn et al. (2017) also draw attention to different restrictions on the use of donated gametes impacting Muslim and Jewish communities, e.g. the preservation of patrilineal inheritance according to the teachings of the Qur'an, or the "transmission of the 'Cohen' or 'Levi' elevated ritual statuses" for orthodox Jewish men (p. 47). Thus, for some groups, gamete selection may be serving other valuable cultural purposes beyond promoting biological resemblance.

The Jewish community may also be disproportionately impacted by the advent of artificial womb technology, as Inhorn et al. (2017) note "[m]ost rabbis consider the womb to be the decisive factor in the transmission of Jewishness" (p. 47). While this has allowed a more permissive stance on egg donation for many Jewish couples, it poses a potential problem for artificial gestation. Yuri Hibino (2015) relates a similar challenge for Vietnamese society, which she describes as possessing "womb-centrism" as a dominant cultural notion (p.

113). Shirai (2019) notes the common practice of selecting gamete donors with matching blood types in Japan is related to the cultural idea of "parent–child blood type inheritance" that confer "naturalness" and "legitimacy" (pp. 306, 308). This belief is connected to the idea that mothers have a duty a nourish the developing fetus through their blood, with the gestational process providing the "biological tie," rather than genetics (p. 308).

A further consideration is how diversity in terms of disability might be preserved in the context of a society using ARTs and genetic engineering. Assumptions regarding the physical fitness required to be a parent often manifest in strict health screening rules for prospective adoptive parents, as well as gamete donors. On the other side of the equation, Alison Wheatley's (2019) study of sperm donors found many feared they would unwittingly father many children who would later seek them out, and that the mother of their genetic offspring would treat them poorly or otherwise be physically or financially unfit to raise them (pp. 143, 145). Implicit in this latter fear is a bias toward able-bodied future parents that warrants further examination.

Conclusion

Establishing an off-world human settlement will require new models of reproduction and family-making that can withstand the pressures of living in an artificial and often hostile environment. The feasibility of a long-term settlement would be greatly increased with a genetically diverse population in the next generation. One method of achieving this would be to transport large numbers of embryos and utilize artificial gestation and communal childrearing practices to build the new society. Such an approach would require a radical reconceptualization of heteronormative family structures and a commitment to prioritizing social over biological ties in parenting.

References

Becker, G., Butler, A., and Nachtigall, R.D. 2005, "Resemblance talk: A challenge for parents whose children were conceived with donor gametes in the US," *Social Science & Medicine*, vol. 61, pp. 1300–1309.

Bennett, L.R. 2018, "Infertility, adoption, and family formation in Indonesia," *Medical Anthropology*, vol. 37, no. 2, pp. 101–116.

Bergmann, S. 2010, "Fertility tourism: Circumventive routes that enable access to reproductive technologies and substances," *Signs: Journal of Women in Culture and Society*, vol. 36, no. 2, pp. 280–289.

Delaunay, C. 2019, "Dilemmatic tensions around parenthood: The ambiguous third-party role in assisted reproductive technologies and surrogacy in France and Portugal," *Política y Sociedad*, vol. 56, no. 2, pp. 381–404.

Furstenberg, F.F., Harris, L.E., Pesando, L.M., and Reed, M.N. 2020, "Kinship practices among alternative family forms in Western industrialized societies," *Journal of Marriage and Family*, vol. 82, pp. 1403–1430.

Garwood, E. 2023, "Queering the kinship story: Constructing connection through LGBTQ family narratives," *Feminist Theory*, vol. 24, no. 1, pp. 30–46.

Hibino, Y. 2015, "Implications of the legalization of noncommercial surrogacy for local kinship and motherhood in Vietnamese society," *Reproductive BioMedicine Online*, vol. 30, pp. 113–114.

Inhorn, M.C., Birenbaum-Carmeli, D., Tremayne, S., and Gürtin, Z.B. 2017, "Assisted reproduction and Middle East kinship: A regional and religious comparison," *Reproductive BioMedicine and Society Online*, vol. 4, pp. 41–51.

Kendal, E. 2020, "Biological modification as prophylaxis: How extreme environments challenge the treatment/enhancement divide," in K. Szocik (ed), *Human enhancements for space missions: Lunar, Martian, and future missions to the outer planets*, Springer, Switzerland, pp. 35–45.

Kendal, E. 2022, "Ectogenesis and the ethics of new reproductive technologies for space exploration," in E. Tumilty and M. Battle-Fisher (eds), *Transhumanism: Entering an era of bodyhacking and radical human modification*, Springer, Switzerland, pp. 211–226.

Kendal, E. 2023, "Desire, duty, and discrimination: Is there an ethical way to select humans for Noah's Ark?" in J.S.J. Schwartz, L. Billings, and E. Nesvold (eds) *Reclaiming space: Progressive and multicultural visions of space exploration*, Oxford University Press, Oxford, pp. 289–302.

Kingma, E. & Finn, S. 2020, "Neonatal incubator or artificial womb? Distinguishing ectogestation and ectogenesis using the metaphysics of pregnancy," *Bioethics*, vol. 34, no. 4, pp. 354–363.

Lovelock, K. 2010, "Conceiving reproduction: New reproductive technologies and the redefinition of the kinship narrative in New Zealand society," *Anthropological Forum*, vol. 20, no. 2, pp. 125–146.

Maung, H.H. 2018, "Ethical problems with ethnic matching in gamete donation," *Journal of Medical Ethics*, vol. 45, pp. 112–116.

McKinnon, S. 2015, "Productive paradoxes of the assisted reproductive technologies in the context of the new kinship studies," *Journal of Family Issues*, vol. 36, no. 4, pp. 461–479.

Newman, A.M. 2019, "Mixing and matching: Sperm donor selection for interracial lesbian couples," *Medical Anthropology*, vol. 38, no. 8, pp. 710–724.

Nordqvist, P. 2010, "Out of sight, out of mind: Family resemblances in lesbian donor conception," *Sociology*, vol. 44, no. 6, pp. 1128–1144.

Pavone, V. 2015, "IVF as a looking glass: Kinship, biology, technology and society through the lens of assisted reproductive technologies," *BioSocieties*, vol. 10, pp. 111–115.

Payne, J.G. 2016, "Grammars of kinship: Biological motherhood and assisted reproduction in the age of epigenetics," *Signs: Journal of Women in Culture and Society*, vol. 41, no. 3, pp. 483–506.

Raes, I., Van Parys, H., Provoost, V., Buysse, A., De Sutter, P., and Pennings, G. 2014, "Parental (in)equality and the genetic link in lesbian families," *Journal of Reproductive and Infant Psychology*, vol. 32, no. 5, pp. 457–468.

Rotimi, C. 2023, "Founder effect," *National Human Genome Research Institute*. Accessed April 30, 2023. https://www.genome.gov/genetics-glossary/Founder-Effect.

Savulescu, J. 2007, "In defence of procreative beneficence," *Journal of Medical Ethics*, vol. 33, pp. 284–288.

Shirai, C. 2019, "Genetic ties and affinity: Longitudinal interviews on two mothers' experiences of egg donation in Japan," *East Asian Science, Technology and Society: An International Journal*, vol. 13, no. 2, pp. 299–315.

Simpson, B. 2013, "Managing potential in assisted reproductive technologies: Reflections on gifts, kinship, and the process of vernacularisation," *Current Anthropology*, vol. 54, no. S7, pp. S87–S96.

Szocik, K., Campa, R., Boone Rappaport, M., and Corbally, C. 2019, "Changing the paradigm on human enhancements: The special case of modifications to counter bone loss for manned Mars missions," *Space Policy*, vol. 48, pp. 68–75.

Szocik, K. and Wójtowicz, T. 2019, "Human enhancement in space missions: From moral controversy to technological duty," *Technology in Society*, vol. 59, p. 101156.

Taguchi, Y. and Majumdar, A. 2021, "Kinship as fiction: Exploring the dynamism of intimate relationships in South Asia," *Contemporary South Asia*, vol. 29, no. 1, pp. 1–9.

Wheatley, A. 2019, "'We're not related in any way, only by blood': Danish sperm donors and (imagined) relationships," *Families, Relationships and Societies*, vol. 8, no. 1, pp. 137–152.

15

LONGTERMISM, SPACE COLONIZATION, AND HUMAN CONSCIOUSNESS

Émile P. Torres

What Is Longtermism?

Axiological longtermism is, roughly speaking, the thesis that the value of our actions in the present largely derives from their effects in the far future. Deontic longtermism is, also speaking roughly, the claim that what we ought to do is whatever makes the far future go best (Greaves and MacAskill 2021). This is based on considerations from (a) the field of physical eschatology, or the study of the future evolution of the cosmos, including our own solar system, and (b) modern cosmography, or "the science that describes and maps the general features of the universe" (Boeyens and Levendis 2008). According to (a) and (b), humanity or our posthuman descendants could survive on Earth for another ~1 billion years, and if we spread beyond our solar system, our lineage could persist for at least another ~10^{40} years, at which point protons are expected to decay (although we do not know for sure that this will happen) (Adams 2008).

Furthermore, given that there are upwards of 400 million stars in the Milky Way galaxy and up to 10^{23} stars within our future light cone – that is, the region of the universe that we could theoretically access if traveling at the speed of light – the future human population could be enormous (Ord 2021, 27). There are two possibilities here, depending on whether future people are biological or digital beings, the latter of whom would live almost entirely in virtual-reality computer simulations. On the standard account, these simulations would be run on planet-sized computers powered by Dyson swarms, thus enabling a greater population density than if our descendants were biological beings residing on terraformed exoplanets or in free-floating spacecraft like O'Neill cylinders. According to Toby Newberry, the Milky Way galaxy could contain some 10^{36} biological and 10^{45} digital people (Newberry 2021). On Nick Bostrom's count, there could be 10^{58} digital people in the universe as a

DOI: 10.4324/9781003374381-15

whole, although he adds that the number is probably much greater (Bostrom 2014). In an earlier paper, Bostrom estimated some 10^23 biological humans per century in the Virgo Supercluster alone, which could also house roughly 10^38 digital people per century (Bostrom 2003).

Hence, the longtermist thesis is based on the idea that if all the consequences of our actions count equally, then the potential bigness of the far future implies that these far-future effects will be the primary determinant of the value of our actions in the present. On a totalist utilitarian view, this means that the actions we ought to take are those that positively influence the far future rather than near term. "For the purposes of evaluating actions," Greaves and MacAskill write, "we can in the first instance often simply ignore all the effects contained in the first 100 (or even 1000) years, focusing primarily on the further-future effects. Short-run effects act as little more than tie-breakers" (Greaves and MacAskill 2019).

Overview of the Argument

In this chapter, I want to take a closer look at the longtermist vision of the far future and highlight several issues that, as far as I know, have not been taken seriously enough in the longtermist literature. My first claim is that colonizing the universe beyond our solar system will *almost certainly* require us to become or create digital beings, as interstellar travel looks to be impossible for biological humans. In other words, to produce "astronomical" amounts of "value" in the far future, we will need to colonize the universe, but to colonize the universe, we will need to create what I will call a "Digital World," i.e., a population of beings that are digital rather than biological in nature. This yields two potential challenges:

First, a Digital World would be, in ways that are not often appreciated, radically different from the world we are familiar with. For example, it is not clear that digital "beings" would be countable, as the calculations above assume: they would more likely take the form of hive minds, collective intelligences, distributed selves, and protean entities that continually share bits and pieces of themselves with other entities in their environment. This underlines the problem of "cluelessness," whereby judging the goodness or rightness of our actions in terms of their consequences is difficult or impossible because we are, in a deep and fundamental sense, unable to anticipate these consequences. Put differently, longtermists frequently defend their position using expected value calculations, which involve assigning probabilities to known outcomes having determinable values, and then taking the average of these probability-weighted values. But if we cannot even begin to imagine the outcomes that might obtain once a Digital World has been inaugurated, we cannot use expected value calculations to guide our actions. The Digital World, which is necessary for space colonization, would be so alien from our own world that we are clueless in a very profound way.

Second, the longtermist vision of the future doesn't just depend on the creation of a Digital World. It also (ostensibly) requires the digital "beings" that spread into the universe to be conscious. A universe without consciousness would be a valueless universe, or so many longtermists would argue. This yields two potential problems, one metaphysical and the other epistemological: (i) it might be that digital consciousness is not possible. It could very well be that functionalism in the philosophy of mind is false and the only type of matter that can give rise to conscious mental states is biological; (ii) even if a form of functionalism is true, it could be that the *particular* digital beings that we create are not, in fact, conscious – they could be philosophical zombies that, as such, behave intelligently but have no qualitative inner life. If we were to send such beings into the universe to colonize the 10^{23} stars within our future light cone, the longtermist project will have catastrophically failed. It thus matters *greatly* that we have robust tests for artificial consciousness to ensure that our digital progeny are actually conscious. One might expect longtermists to have addressed this issue at length, given what is at stake, but so far as I know they haven't. My tentative claim below will be that there may be no robust tests for consciousness in artificial systems – that is, no way to know with sufficient confidence that the colonization process, which may be irreversible once it is started, will in fact increase the total value in the universe. This places a giant question mark over the entire longtermist project: to colonize space, we need digital consciousness, but there may be no way to ever know if the digital beings created are genuinely conscious.

The rest of this chapter will elaborate on these claims. As the longtermist ideology increasingly shapes the world we live in, providing justificatory cover for billionaires like Elon Musk to pursue large projects to make humanity multi-planetary, it is crucial that longtermists address such issues. If there are flaws in the longtermist vision, then current projects guided by longtermism will have taken resources away from other cause areas like global poverty and animal welfare for nothing. In what follows, I will examine my three main theses, namely, that space colonization requires a Digital World, the Digital World would be profoundly different from our world, and confirming with a high degree of certainty that digital beings are conscious could be extremely difficult.

The Digital World

Let's begin by briefly looking at why creating a Digital World is almost certainly a necessary condition for space colonization beyond our solar system, if not within it. The main reason is simple: space travel poses serious psychological and physiological risks to biological human beings. The former concerns the fact that extended periods locked in the confines of incommodious spacecraft with a small number of companions could have detrimental psychological effects. As Campa et al. write, the "extreme, confined environments" of spacecraft "are likely to increase the incidence of potentially hazardous psychological effects due to confinement in a very unfamiliar environment and the loss of regular daily contact with the work and home environment on Earth" (Campa et al. 2019).

The latter arises from the effects of microgravity and space radiation, such as solar particle effects, solar wind, and galactic cosmic rays. On Earth, humans are protected from these hazards by our planet's atmosphere and magneto-sphere, beyond which radiation doses can be roughly 100 times more than ter-restrial exposure. This radiation can damage cells, cause cancer, and have deleterious cognitive effects (see Campa et al. 2019). With respect to micro-gravity, this has been linked to losses in muscle mass and bone mineral density, along with other forms of tissue atrophy (Li et al. 2018).

Technological advancements might enable us to devise new ways of protect-ing biological humans from these hazards. One can imagine such advancements making the colonization of our solar system possible. However, while the average distance between Earth and Mars is 140 million miles, the closest star to our Sun is roughly 25 trillion miles and the closest galaxy is 2.5 million light years, meaning that it would take 2.5 million years to reach it if one were tra-veling at the speed of light. The vastitude and inhospitable conditions of space make interstellar and intergalactic travel all but impossible for biological humans.

In contrast, these would not pose serious challenges for digital beings. As the longtermist Anders Sandberg writes, such beings would be:

> ideally suited for colonising space and many other environments where biological humans require extensive life support. … Besides existing in a substrate-independent manner where they could be run on computers hardened for local conditions, emulations could be transmitted digitally across interplanetary distances. One of the largest obstacles of space colonisation is the enormous cost in time, energy and reaction mass needed for space travel: emulation technology [a reference to uploaded minds] would reduce this.
>
> *(Sandberg 2014)*

Digital transmission would of course require that the destination had already been colonized, as transmission requires a transmitter and a receiver. But digital beings would also be ideally suited for traveling via spacecraft, perhaps propelled by solar sails, into deep space. Furthermore, they would be func-tionally immortal and hence able to travel for millions or billions of years to far-away galaxies.

Such considerations strongly imply that, to realize the longtermist aim of colonizing the accessible universe, we will need to create a Digital World. Even if biological humans figure out a way of reaching and living on Mars, it appears impossible that we could survive interstellar, much less intergalactic, distances as biology-based beings.

Beyond the Event Horizon

The creation of a Digital World, though, would mark a radical departure from the world in which we currently live. Verner Vinge's notion of the "technological Singularity" may be useful here, as the circumstances of existence in a Digital World may be hidden behind an "event horizon" that prevents us from knowing anything significant about them.[1] There are two aspects of this Digital World that make it inscrutable to us: one concerns the nature of the "beings" who would exist in it, while the other concerns the environments in which they are embedded. Focusing on the first, consider James Hughes' observation that digital beings would "be able to copy, share, and sell [their] memories, beliefs, skills, and experiences." They may have the ability to "selectively adopt personalities for specific purposes." Some might choose to publicly broadcast their inner thoughts and feelings, while "others will choose to spend a lot of time in someone else's life – like climbing into John Malkovich's head for weeks instead of 15 minutes at a time." The Digital World could thus inaugurate a radical new "post-individual" age, whereby bits and pieces of minds are duplicated, combined, modified, and discarded in an ever-fluctuating mosaic of ontological chaos. Hughes thus contends that "the most dramatic challenges to our social and philosophic world will probably come from hive minds and distributed selves," with collective intelligences arising from the merger of individuals and the boundaries between individuals coming to overlap in complicated, continually evolving ways (Hughes 2005).

This is one reason that calculations of future "people" are dubious: it is not at all clear that individuatable "people" would exist in a Digital World. Rather, such "beings" would more likely take the form of hive minds, collective intelligences, distributed selves, and protean entities whose boundaries are porous, thus enabling them to potentially redesign "themselves" from moment to moment. Perhaps each star would come to host a single "super-individual" around it, rather than trillions of individual people living in simulated worlds, thereby reducing the total number of "people" in the future by many orders of magnitude. If we can't begin to imagine what the Digital World might be like, then talk of the "expected value" of the far future is questionable. In other words, our decision-theoretic predicament is one of uncertainty rather than risk, where "uncertainty refers to situations under which either the outcomes and/or their probabilities of occurrences are unknown to the decision-maker," while "risk refers to decision-making situations under which all potential outcomes and their likelihood of occurrences are known to the decision-maker" (Park and Shapira 2017). Since we cannot imagine potential outcomes of a Digital World, we cannot assign probabilities to them. Our ignorance of the future is much deeper and more fundamental than longtermists seem to assume.

Digital Consciousness

Let's be clear about what the longtermist vision would entail, given the above considerations: longtermists imagine our descendants colonizing space and building planet-sized computers on which to run virtual-reality worlds full of trillions of digital people. But since colonizing space requires digital beings, we can recognize two stages of the Digital World unfolding: in the first, digital beings would interact with the physical universe, control spaceships, and eventually build giant computers powered by Dyson swarms. In the second, the resulting simulations would be populated by digital beings with simulated bodies, interacting with each other in these virtual-reality environments. The first stage is necessary for the second, while the second is what would enable "astronomical" amounts of "value" to be generated.

None of this would matter, though, if the resulting digital beings – especially those populating these vast computer simulations – were not conscious. Consider Hilary Greaves and William MacAskill's conception of "human," which they take "to refer both to *Homo sapiens* and to whatever descendants with at least comparable moral status we may have, even if those descendants are of a different species, and even if they are non-biological" (Greaves and MacAskill 2021). Since possessing a comparable moral status as such almost certainly requires such descendants to be conscious, the desideratum of consciousness is built-into their definition of "humanity." Put differently, if our descendants were to lack consciousness (and hence comparable moral status), then "humanity" would no longer exist, which is just to say that we will have undergone extinction – a type of extinction that I call "normative extinction" (Torres 2023).[2] Or consider a scenario from Nick Bostrom:

> in which machine intelligence replaces biological intelligence but the machines are constructed in such a way that they lack consciousness (in the sense of phenomenal experience) ... The future might then be very wealthy and capable, yet in a relevant sense uninhabited: There would (arguably) be no morally relevant beings there to enjoy the wealth.
>
> *(Bostrom 2013)*

Hence, it matters greatly that our digital descendants are capable of conscious experience – that there is "something it is like to be" them.

How, then, can we be sure that the digital beings that we become or create will in fact be conscious? Given that the entire longtermist vision of the far future hangs on this question, one might assume that a considerable amount of ink has been spilled reflecting on it. Yet, so far as I know, no longtermist has systematically examined it to date. The issue's importance is underlined by the claim that once a colonization explosion has commenced, there may be no do-overs, which means that we will need a robust method of identifying consciousness in artificial systems before the *very first* generation of digital beings is launched into space. The stakes could not be higher, since if this initial generation of beings is not conscious, and if they proceed to replicate throughout space, an existential catastrophe will have occurred. By "existential catastrophe," longtermists mean any failure to fulfill our "longterm potential" in the universe. Since fulfilling this "potential" requires flooding the universe with value, and hence consciousness, the avoidance of an existential catastrophe crucially depends on our ability to detect consciousness in non-biological entities before colonization begins.

One response could be to say that if the digital beings that colonize space are brain emulations that replicate the functional organization of one or more actual human brains, then they would almost certainly be conscious. There are several problems with this. First, we do not know if consciousness is an "organizational invariant," that is, a property that emerges from systems with the right functional organization, independent of their material substrate (Chalmers 2011). Some form of "biological naturalism" could be true instead, which would mean that emulated brains would not be conscious, even if they were to convincingly reproduce human-level intelligent behaviors (see Pigliucci 2014). Second, even if the digital beings that initiate space colonization begin as brain emulations, it is entirely possible that they would quickly morph into new, alien minds as a result of the phenomena discussed in the previous section. If such beings have access to their code, they might also recursively self-improve, resulting in minds that are radically different than ours. We may, therefore, be much less confident that the resulting beings are conscious, even if they were conscious at some point in their earlier history. Third, whether or not the digital beings that colonize space are conscious, how sure can we be that the digital beings who end up populating the virtual-reality environments envisaged by longtermists will be conscious? Would these also be brain emulations? Again, this is unlikely because of the "post-individual" phenomena explored by Hughes, the possibility of self-improvement, and so on.

Hence, we would need a "consciousness test" that could enable us, with an extremely high degree of certitude, to affirm that the beings who populate the Digital World are in fact conscious. Have any such tests been proposed? In her book *Artificial You: AI and the Future of Your Mind*, Susan Schneider explores three potential tests for consciousness: the chip test, the AI Consciousness Test (or ACT), and a test based on Integrated Information Theory (ITT). I cannot dwell on the details of each test here; suffice it to say that, while these are probably the best tests thus far delineated, all have serious limitations. Consider the ACT, for instance. This is based on the idea that making sense of certain ideas or scenarios requires one to have had conscious experiences. Imagine that a digital system is asked about the possibility of an out-of-body experience, life after death, switching bodies with another system, or whether it would prefer being shut off for 300 years in the future or having been shut off for 300 years in the past (a time bias). Making sense of such questions would, Schneider argues, require the system to have experienced conscious states. In her words, "these scenarios would be exceedingly difficult to comprehend for an entity that had no conscious experience whatsoever." Yet, she adds that, while passing this test may be sufficient for a digital system to be considered conscious, it is not necessary, as one can imagine systems that fail but are nonetheless conscious

(Schneider 2019, 57). Furthermore, this test might not apply to digital beings that achieve superintelligence, as they could find ways to cheat that we might not be able to detect. The ACT is thus limited to "some kinds of AIs, not all AIs" (Schneider 2019; for further criticisms, see Udell 2021).

The point is that we have no good way to determine whether the digital systems that we create are conscious. This problem is even more acute when we consider the possibility of hive minds, collective intelligences, distributed selves, and the protean entities mentioned earlier. Yet the entire longtermist project depends on us being overwhelmingly confident that digital beings would in fact be conscious – indeed, it requires not just that we have a test for the first generation of digital beings, but that these digital beings have tests of their own to ensure that the entities populating the computer simulations they build throughout the accessible universe are also conscious. The lack of a robust test for artificial consciousness thus places a giant question mark over the entire longtermist project.

Conclusion

In conclusion, fulfilling the longtermist project requires the colonization of space beyond our solar system, which in turn requires the creation of a Digital World. This Digital World will likely be so different from our current world that we are in a position of decision-theoretic uncertainty rather than risk. Furthermore, since the entire longtermist vision depends on the possibility of digital consciousness, if non-functionalist theories like biological naturalism are true –and they might be – then this vision cannot be fulfilled. But even if functionalism were true, we would still encounter the epistemological problem of being able to determine with a very high degree of certainty that the particular digital beings that we create are in fact conscious, and that the digital beings that they create in giant computer simulations are also conscious, and so on. The challenges that such considerations pose to the longtermist project are, I believe, much more formidable than longtermists have previously recognized.

Notes

1 See Yudkowsky (2007).
2 Normative extinction would occur if *Homo sapiens* has successors, but these successors have lost some normatively important capacity that excludes them from the extension of "humanity," meaning that "humanity" no longer exists. It contrasts with demographic, phyletic, terminal, final, and premature extinction, all of which have their own unique ethical and evaluative implications. See Torres 2023.

Bibliography

Adams, Fred C. "Long-Term Astrophysical." *Global Catastrophic Risks*, 2008, 33.
Boeyens, Jan CA, and Demetrius C Levendis. "Elements of Cosmography." *Number Theory and the Periodicity of Matter*, 2008, 183–208.

Bostrom, Nick. "Astronomical Waste: The Opportunity Cost of Delayed Technological Development." *Utilitas* 15, no. 3 (2003): 308–314.

Bostrom, Nick. "Existential Risk Prevention as Global Priority." *Global Policy* 4, no. 1 (2013): 15–31.

Bostrom, Nick. *Superintelligence*. Oxford University Press, 2014.

Campa, Riccardo, Konrad Szocik, and Martin Braddock. "Why Space Colonization Will Be Fully Automated." *Technological Forecasting and Social Change* 143 (2019): 162–171.

Chalmers, David J. "A Computational Foundation for the Study of Cognition." *Journal of Cognitive Science* 12, no. 4 (2011): 325–359.

Greaves, Hilary, and William MacAskill. "The Case for Strong Longtermism." *GPI Working*, 2019.

Greaves, Hilary, and William MacAskill. "The Case for Strong Longtermism." *GPI Working*, 2021.

Hughes, James. "The Illusiveness of Immortality." *Death and Anti-Death* 3 (2005).

Li, Kai, Chao Yang, Hongyu Zhang, Feng Wu, Hailong Wang, Hongqing Cao, Zihan Xu, Bai Ding, Yinghui Li, and Zhongquan Dai. "Screening and Identification of Novel Mechanoresponsive MicroRNAs in Rat Femur under Simulated Microgravity." *Acta Astronautica* 153 (2018): 166–173.

Newberry, Toby. "How Many Lives Does the Future Hold." *Global Priorities Institute Technical Report*, 2021.

Ord, Toby. "The Edges of Our Universe." *ArXiv Preprint ArXiv:2104.01191*, 2021.

Park, K. Francis, and Zur Shapira. "Risk and Uncertainty." *The Palgrave Encyclopedia of Strategic Management*, 2017.

Pigliucci, Massimo. "Mind Uploading: A Philosophical Counter-Analysis." *Intelligence Unbound: The Future of Uploaded and Machine Minds*, 2014, 119–130.

Sandberg, Anders. "Ethics of Brain Emulations." *Journal of Experimental & Theoretical Artificial Intelligence* 26, no. 3 (2014): 439–457.

Schneider, Susan. *Artificial You: AI and the Future of Your Mind*. Princeton University Press, 2019.

Torres, Émile P. *Human Extinction: A History of the Science and Ethics of Annihilation*. Routledge, 2023.

Udell, David B. "Susan Schneider's Proposed Tests for AI Consciousness: Promising but Flawed." *Journal of Consciousness Studies* 28, no. 5–6 (2021): 121–144.

Yudkowsky, Eliezer. 2007. *Three Major Singularity Schools*. Machine Intelligence Research Institute. https://intelligence.org/2007/09/30/three-major-singularity-schools/.

INDEX

Printed in the United States
by Baker & Taylor Publisher Services